W9-CBA-430

PS
3525   MICHENER   19505
.I 19   Sel.
A6   A12900 387002

ILLINOIS CENTRAL COLLEGE
PS3525.I19A6
STACKS
Selected writings,

A12900 387002

WITHDRAWN

Illinois Central College
Learning Resource Center

THE MODERN LIBRARY
OF THE WORLD'S BEST BOOKS

Selected Writings of James A. Michener

The publishers will be pleased to send, upon request, an illustrated folder setting forth the purpose and scope of THE MODERN LIBRARY, *and listing each volume in the series. Every reader of books will find titles he has been looking for, handsomely printed, in definitive editions, and at an unusually low price.*

SELECTED
WRITINGS
OF
JAMES A.
MICHENER

With a special Foreword by the Author

Illinois Central College
Learning Resource Center

THE MODERN
LIBRARY
NEW YORK

19505

© Copyright, 1957, by Random House, Inc.
Copyright, 1947, 1951, 1953, by James A. Michener
Copyright, 1950, 1951, by The Curtis Publishing Company
All rights reserved under International
and Pan-American Copyright Conventions
Library of Congress Catalog Card Number: 57–6493

PS
3525
.I 19
A6

Random House IS THE PUBLISHER OF *The Modern Library*

BENNETT CERF • DONALD S. KLOPFER

MANUFACTURED IN THE UNITED STATES OF AMERICA BY H. WOLFF

To Helen Strauss
Friend of Writers

FOREWORD

This is the book of a very lucky guy.

Consider the problem of age. There is a saying among writers: "If you've always wanted to write a book and don't do so before the age of thirty-five, you never will."

I published my first book, *Tales of the South Pacific*, when I was forty.

Then consider what happened to that book. Have you ever seen the first edition? It shows how little the publisher and I thought of its prospects. We knew it didn't have a chance, so we published it on the cheapest paper available, with the poorest binding, and in order to save a few cents we didn't even start new chapters at the tops of new pages. For example, on page 134 begins the story "Fo' Dolla'," which was to inspire one of the generation's best musical comedies. It begins six lines from the bottom of the page, in order to scrimp a little paper.

The book was published in complete secrecy, but in the offices of the *New York Times* a perceptive, excellent, learned, hard-working, incorruptible and brilliant reviewer, Orville Prescott, happened upon it and wrote a dazzling report. (He subsequently panned some of my work, but the above adjectives still stand. He got me started.)

Contrary to general belief, the book was never a best seller and would have died unspectacularly, except that the Pulitzer Prize judges waived many rules—it was not a novel, it was not laid in the United States, it did not necessarily represent American values—and awarded it a prize. Again, this caused no great stir and the book would once more have died a genteel death except for the fact that a Hollywood reader tried to sell it to his studio, was told, "You could never make a picture out of this," and in order to prove his own judgment, took it to Rodgers and Hammerstein. Two nights before their show opened, these men telephoned me. In addition to my royalty, which they were required to pay, they voluntarily gave me a part of the ownership, which they were not required to do and which I did not request. As a result, I was free to travel and to write as I pleased.

I saw clearly that I could make a good living for the rest of my life writing and rewriting South Seas fiction, but I did not want to do that. I felt that with the security of *South Pacific* behind me I ought to experiment. I hope I have used my freedom courageously.

First I constructed a kind of book that had never been tried before, *Return to Paradise,* half fiction, half hard reporting. Then I did a political book in an entirely new vein, *Voices of Asia.* Then I tried an intense, bitterly controlled novel, *The Bridges at Toko-ri.* Then I tried a novella in an antique style, *Sayonara.* Then I laid off for two years and wrote a philosophical essay on Japanese art, *The Floating World.* To my amazement, these diverse efforts prospered.

But the luckiest aspect of my life as a writer has been the opportunity it has given me to live part of each year in Asia. It has been my good fortune to know Asia in a time of great flux. My sojourns have covered the Korean War, the gaining of Japanese independence, the creation of new states in Indonesia, India, Burma, Ceylon, Pakistan and in the former Indo-China. I have watched the awakening of Afghanistan and the arousing of the Muslim world. I have numbered among my friends the poor people of Asia and their appointed leaders.

I was extremely lucky that my consuming interest in Asia coincided with America's belated discovery of that part of the world, and if the genius of Rodgers and Hammerstein had accomplished nothing more than my mission to Asia, I would be eternally grateful to them.

For the average American is at heart a European. He springs from European stock, wears a European name, speaks a European language, adheres to a religion he acquired by way of Europe, thinks in philosophical and logical patterns developed in Europe, and clings to a system of government whose foundations were laid there.

When he has saved enough money for an overseas vacation, he hurries to Europe, where he studies European art, European music and European history. In fact, he becomes so deeply imbued with European criteria that when he encounters anything from Asia he feels instinctively, as in the case of Asiatic music, that "there is something wrong with it."

This preoccupation with Europe is understandable, and I am neither surprised nor discouraged when I find little Asiatic influence on American life. A possible exception might be the Christian religion, which did undergo some Asiatic modifications and whose leader, Jesus, was an Asian with a dark, semi-Asiatic complexion. But in the main, before we Americans received Christianity it had been pretty well cleansed of Asian strains. Most Americans are quite convinced that Jesus was a white man, as proved by the paintings of Italy.

Therefore, our difficulty in knowing Asia is understandable. Few Americans are descended from Asian ancestors, few bear Asian names, even fewer speak an

Asian tongue. Our college students rarely spend their summers in Asia, and as adults they read no Asian books, see no Asian plays, listen to no Asian music and rarely see Asian art. Up to now, there has really been no reason, other than cultural curiosity, why Americans should be interested in Asia.

But in recent years our nation has entered its last two wars through the Asian gateway, and the probability is great that if future wars come, they will come through that same gateway. Our major peacetime involvements will also include Asia. Therefore, whether we have the background or not, we are compelled to deal with this part of the world. My recent life has been largely pre-occupied with this problem, and this book summarizes the steps whereby I reached my present concern.

It includes the most widely read single piece of writing I have done, "The New Mem-sahibs," which touches the core of our problem in Asia—one that will probably never be solved—namely: How can a sweet and gentle American wife from Ottumwa, Iowa, move into a big house in Singapore or Bombay and promptly blossom out as the inheritor of every fatal arrogance that destroyed the British in Asia? Many American corporations that operate in Asia have pondered this problem and have included my essay in their booklet of instructions to new employees. Like most writing, it has accomplished little.

I am happy that this collection includes *The Bridges at Toko-ri*, the purest writing I have done so far. It sprang from my experiences in the Korean War but, with artistic license, suppressed the fact that each time I fly in a combat jet I become violently airsick. I have been a willing warrior but never a very competent one.

One important change has been made in the text here

offered, and another of equal importance has been evaded. When I first wrote about Asia I was not aware that citizens of that continent, because of long humiliation by white men, had grown to despise and resent the word *Asiatic* when used to describe themselves. I have changed this word to *Asian.* Nor did I know that citizens of China resent with perhaps even greater fervor the word *Chinaman.* After my first several books appeared I formed close friendships with many Chinese and learned what I had not known before. In various places in this reissue of my work I have corrected this offensive word to *Chinese;* but in certain stories in which local idiom is employed in narrating a story, I have retained the original term. If I were rewriting these stories today, I would not use the word except where dialogue required.

I hope that these pages reflect something of the personal excitement I have found in the Pacific Ocean and in Asia. In the wild beauty of the sea, in the human tenderness of the atolls, and in the violent wonder of Asia I have known a deeply satisfying life.

In addition, I have tried to report one truth: America and Asia, from here on out, are indissolubly linked insofar as interest, development and history are concerned. That the people of these lands are so easy to know and to love makes our job easier. That the world has grown so small makes the work imperative.

A few hours from now I shall board the morning plane at New York. It leaves just after breakfast and I shall have lunch tomorrow in Tokyo.

As I said before, I'm a lucky guy.

Tinicum, Pennsylvania   JAMES A. MICHENER
September 5, 1956

CONTENTS

from

TALES
OF THE
SOUTH
PACIFIC

Our Heroine

Two weeks after Nurse Nellie Forbush proposed to Lieutenant Harbison she received a newspaper clipping from Little Rock, Arkansas. In the section devoted to rural news was a large and pretty picture of her in formal uniform. The caption read: "Our Heroine. Otolousa Girl Arrives in New Hebrides to Help Wounded Americans."

Nellie looked at the photograph smiling at her from the newspaper. She was younger then, and much more sure of herself. She hadn't been seasick for eight days. When that photograph was taken she hadn't lived in mud, on poor food, under a stinking mosquito net. Nor did she have a lonely feeling about her heart, so that days and nights were the same.

No, she was a happy girl when she posed for that picture. She had gone into Little Rock with her mother and Charlie Benedict. They were both proud of her, her mother because she looked so fine and patriotic in her new uniform. Charlie because he hoped to marry her.

Charlie had been unexpectedly glum when the pictures were delivered to Otolousa. "You're beautiful!" he said. "You'll never come back to a 4-F."

"I want to see the world, Charlie," she had replied. "I want to meet other people. I want to see what the world's like. Then, when the war's over, I'll come back." Neither she nor Charlie believed that she would.

In the New Hebrides she was seeing plenty of people. Too many! She was often the only girl among a hundred men. Most of them wanted to make love to her. But that isn't what Nellie Forbush meant when she said she wanted to see the world. She had meant that she wanted to talk with strange people, to find out how they lived and what they dreamed about, interesting little things that she could treasure as experience.

Hers was the heart hunger that has sent people of all ages in search of new thoughts and deeper perceptions. Yet at the end of a year in Navy life Nellie had found only one person who shared her longing for ideas and experiences. It was Dinah Culbert. She and Dinah had a lust for sensations, ideas and the web of experience. She and Dinah were realists, but of that high order which includes symbolism and some things just beyond the reach of pure intelligence.

She was sorry, therefore, when Dinah was ordered north to help set up a new hospital. They were talking together the night before Dinah left. Together they were laughing at poor, handsome Bill Harbison. They heard that he was drinking a good deal. Nellie had already told Dinah of how she had proposed to Bill and been refused. Dinah recalled that one night recently Bill had been slightly drunk at a party and had greeted her affectionately with a lurch and a loud, "Hi, Grandmom!"

The two nurses were talking when they heard a commotion by the guardhouse. An Army officer was helping a nurse out of a jeep. A doctor was running over. Soon heads popped out of all the windows. They saw another doctor come up and start to attend the officer. Like fire, news spread through the dormitories.

It was that quiet nurse who liked the Army captain. The one stationed in Vila. He was driving her home. They had stopped for a while. Near the airfield. No, she didn't neck with him much. They were watching the planes. Three men jumped out of the bushes at them. They had clubs. They knocked the captain down and started to pull the nurse out of the jeep. When she screamed and fought, one of them tried to hit her with a club. He missed her and broke one of the assailants' arms. The wounded man bellowed. Then they got mad and grabbed her by one arm and one leg. She held onto the steering wheel, and the captain started to fight again. They hit him once more, and then . . .

A car came by. The three assailants saw it coming and fled. Two Army enlisted men were in the jeep and gave chase to the culprits. But by that time the would-be rapists were gone. One of the enlisted men drove the captain's jeep to the hospital. The captain was badly beaten around the head. The nurse was shivering from shock, but was not hurt.

All night cars whizzed by. They stopped all vehicles. At 0300 all hands at all stations were mustered in dark, sleepy lines. Officers checked enlisted men and other officers. Finally, toward morning, a man was found with a broken arm. He had slipped on a coconut log. Why hadn't he reported it? Just got in. What was he doing out? Hunting flying foxes. What with? A gun. Where was it? His friend took it. Who was his friend? He didn't know. How could he be a friend if he didn't know his name? He didn't know. Where did the friend live? He didn't know. Did anybody see him go hunting flying foxes? No. Was anyone along whom he did know?

Nobody. Just him and the friend? Yes. Was his friend in the Army or Navy? He didn't know.

They locked up the suspect in a hospital ward. He knew nothing and the police were never able to establish that he was a rapist. If he was, his accomplices were not detected.

From then on nurses rarely went out at night unless their dates carried loaded revolvers. In the hot mornings Lieutenant Harbison and his friends practiced target shooting so that in the cool nights they could protect their girls from enlisted men. Of course, the Army captain who had defended his nurse so well supplanted Harbison as the local hero. The captain became a greater hero when he proposed to his nurse and was accepted. They used to sit in the corner of the hospital club and talk. She would drink root beer and he usually had a coke. Lieutenant Harbison was now going with a scatterbrained floozy. They used to spend a good deal of their time in the bushes. After she was sent home he took up with a divorced nurse who knew he was married. They worked out some kind of arrangement. Nellie used to nod at them whenever she saw them. She noticed that Bill was getting fat.

There were many other attacks or near attacks on nurses in the islands. They were grim, hushed-up affairs. Nobody ever knew exactly what had happened. Just rumor and surmises. But in time every nurse knew she lived in danger. She could see in the baleful looks of enlisted men that they considered her little more than a plaything brought out to amuse the officers. With thousands of men for every white woman, with enlisted men forbidden to date the nurses, it was to be expected that vague and terrible things would occur.

In spite of this, Nellie found herself watching men
with a deeper interest. The good men seemed better
when there was trouble. The armed enlisted man who
drove the hospital car when she went riding with
officers seemed more willing to protect her. And every
man who was apprehended as a rapist was obviously
degenerate in some way or other. Back home they
would have been evil, too.

"Men seem even nicer now than they did before,"
she said one day as Dinah was packing. "I thought it
would be the other way around."

"Men are always nice," Dinah laughed.

"I was thinking the other night, Dinah. Out here
good people seem to get better and bad people get
worse."

"That's true back home, too, Fuzzy brain. Wait till
you know some small town really well, Nellie."

"But this is the first time I knew that everybody
lives in danger all his life. We do, really. It's just that
bit by bit we make arrangements that cancel the
dangers. We have certain girls to take care of certain
men. If a man wants to become a crook or a gangster,
we have . . . Well, we seem to have certain areas more
or less staked out for him. Is that true?"

"I don't know, Nellie," Dinah said as she packed her
duffle bags. "All I know for sure is that so far as I have
been able to determine, nothing you can possibly imagine is impossible. Somebody's doing it or is going to do
it. That goes for the good as well as the bad."

Shortly after Dinah's departure, shocking word was
received at the hospital. Bill Harbison and some men
from LARU-8 were flying down to Nouméa for fresh
vegetables. The plane caught fire. Radioed its position

east of Nouméa. It went into the rough ocean and all hands were lost.

Nellie could not work and had to be excused from her duties. She lay down, and against her will, she cried. It was horrible to think of a man so young and able dying so uselessly. In that moment Nellie found that war itself is understandable. It's the things that go along with it, things that happen to people you know, that are incomprehensible, and have been in all ages. She was physically ill for three days.

Then, in a flash, word came that all but one of the men had been found on a life raft. They were knocked about, but they would be all right. Harbison was saved. Again Nellie stayed in her room. She found that she did not want to see Bill, but that she was very glad he was alive. She realized that Bill carried part of her with him, and she was happy when that part lived again. Yet when the handsome young lieutenant appeared in the hospital with his indefinite nurse trailing along, Nellie felt sorry she had seen him again. He was sunburned from his exposure, handsomer than ever. Every night for a week he sat at one table or another with his nurse, telling about the days on the raft. They must have been horrible.

Nellie was rescued from her emotional impasse by thoughtful Dinah, who asked for her to be sent north. Gleefully she packed and waited for the plane. She had never ridden on an airplane before. She watched it come in from Nouméa, carefully noted the busywork that accompanies any landing or take-off, and gasped when she saw how exquisite Efate and Vanicoro were from the air. The pilot purposely flew east a bit so his passengers could see the volcanoes. The landing was perfect, and Nellie stepped out of the plane in much the same manner that Cinderella must have stepped from the pumpkin. This was living!

Dinah met her at the airfield. That night she met Emile De Becque. It was at a dinner given in a French plantation home in honor of the new nurses. Nellie, Dinah, three other nurses and some doctors were seated in an open-air, roofed-in pavilion by the ocean. Candles provided flickering light. Screens kept moths away, and a small Tonkinese boy went around periodically with a mosquito bomb which he delighted to make fizz. Young Tonk men served the food, which was very good.

At another table sat two Frenchmen having their dinner. One was short and fat, the proprietor of the plantation. Nellie had met him earlier in the evening. The other was a remarkable fellow. He was in his middle forties, slim, a bit stoop-shouldered. His eyes were black and deep-set. His eyebrows were bushy. He had long arms and wrists, and although he used his hands constantly in making conversation, they were relaxed and delicate in their movements.

Nellie tried not to stare at the Frenchman, but while waiting for the lobster and rice, she was detected by the proprietor studying his guest. The fat Frenchman rose and approached one of the doctors. "Ah, docteur!" he cried in bonhomie. "May I present my very good friend, Emile De Becque? He is our foremost De Gaullist!" At this recommendation everyone at the table looked up.

De Becque nodded slightly and rose. As he stepped toward the hospital dinner party, the rotund plantation owner continued his introduction: "M. De Becque was our first and bravest De Gaullist. He rounded up much support for the general. And when the Japanese threatened, M. De Becque and a young sea captain went to all the islands and arrested all suspicious persons. If the Japs had landed, he would have been our resistance leader."

M. De Becque nodded again and smiled in turn at each nurse as he was introduced. He had a gold tooth in front, but it did not detract from his strong features. Nellie noticed that he looked particularly French because his hair came so far down on his forehead. He wore it short, and the neatness of his head offset the inevitable sloppiness of tropical clothes.

"M. De Becque arranged the details for our flight to the hills," the plantation owner went on. "Did you know we were going to hide out until you came? M. De Becque arranged for many natives to act as guides. All women were armed."

Nellie was later to discover that in all the New Hebrides, if you could believe what you were told, there was not one Pétainist. And yet, as she looked at the fat proprietor and many others like him, she had a strange feeling that of them all only Emile De Becque acted from conviction. She felt he would have continued to act so had Pétain himself occupied the islands.

She saw a good deal of De Becque in the ensuing weeks. The tall Frenchman was eager for someone to talk to, and although he could not express himself perfectly in English, he could make himself understood. De Becque never called on Nellie. The doctors, always an interested group of men, asked De Becque to their dinners from time to time. After dinner was over, Nellie and Dinah and one or two other nurses usually joined the party and argued politics or when the war in Europe would end. The Frenchman was an able arguer, and not even the handicap of language prevented him from impressing on all present the fundamental soundness of his reasoning. Soon he was the only Frenchman attending the informal arguments at the hospital; for whereas any plantation owner was interesting once or twice as the product of an exotic world, De Becque was of himself interesting. He was as good a man as his interrogators.

"I suppose," he once said, "that men were either De Gaullists or Pétainists a long time ago. I think they grew up that way. Of course," he added slyly, "some never grew up, and it was those we had to play with."

"But why," a doctor asked, "did you elect to follow De Gaulle in particular?"

"De Gaulle?" the Frenchman asked contemptuously. "What's De Gaulle? Who cares what De Gaulle is? He looks puffed up to me. I don't like him." He snorted and waved his hands. "Ah!" he added. "But what De Gaulle stands for! What decent man could do otherwise?"

After De Becque had been a guest at the hospital several times he proposed that he act as host one night at his plantation. The doctors were delighted. "The nurses, too?" the Frenchman suggested, lifting his shoulders and stretching the word *too* into three syllables.

"Why not?" the doctors asked, and a few nights later a small party of Americans chugged up the hill to De Becque's plantation. It was situated upon an extensive plateau overlooking islands and the sea. Most Englishmen and Frenchmen in the islands like their houses abutting on the ocean, but not De Becque. He favored the grand view! And from his veranda there was such a view.

His house was built in an octagon with one side twice as long as the others. In that side he lived, had a few books, a radio, and an old gramophone. In the other seven sides he had a dining room, a warehouse, a store, a series of bedrooms, and a completely furnished room for guests. In the latter one might expect to find a missionary, a Tonkinese family, a government official, or a trader. On the night of his dinner the room was empty.

In the center of the octagon was placed the kitchen, a small, low, sooty building into which only the Tonkinese cooks went. From it came a series of fine dishes. Around the one-storied house clustered an odd collection of buildings whose original purposes were long since lost. Tonkinese and natives lived in them and followed their mysterious ways.

A Buddhist temple crouched on the edge of the jungle. It gave visiting missionaries much concern, for natives found its tinkling bells and rhythmic drums much more fun than Methodism or provincial Catholicism.

The long room with its deep veranda faced south, and from it one could see four lovely things: the channel where the great ships lay; the volcanoes of Vanicoro; the vast Pacific; and an old Tonk's flower garden.

Nellie thought she had never before seen so florid a garden. There were flowers of all kinds, azaleas, single and double hibiscus, hydrangeas, pale yellow roses and types she did not know. About the garden were flamboyants and bougainvilleas, red flaming bushes. And everywhere there were capriciously placed frangipani trees. De Becque pulled half a dozen branches for his guests and showed them how native men wear the four-leafed, white and yellow flowers in their hair. The nurses smelled the flowers their host gave them and were delighted. The frangipani was the odor of jungle. It was sweet, distant and permeating. In addition it had a slightly aphrodisiac quality, a fact which natives learned long ago.

De Becque's dinner put to shame any the doctors had ever offered him. It started with soup, grilled fresh-water shrimp, lobster and rice, and endive salad. Next came in succession three courses: filet of porterhouse, lamb chop, and a delicious concoction of rice, onions, string beans and black meat of wild chicken. Then De Becque served the "millionaire's salad" consisting of tender shoot of coconut palm sliced wafer-thin and pressed in olive oil, vinegar, salt and pepper. Cup custard with rum, small cakes, coffee and a choice of six liqueurs ended the meal. And all this was on the edge of the jungle, 550 miles from Guadalcanal!

To say that the hospital staff was astounded would be an underestimate of their reactions.

"Where did you get lobster?" a doctor inquired.

"We catch them here by various means. Out in the deep water."

"How about the wild chicken?"

"Those black men you saw by the gate when you came in. They shoot them with arrows or with .22's. They are wonderful shots, I think."

"I think so, too," the doctor replied. "But where do you get such big shrimp?"

"Far up the island rivers. You see, my friends, we don't eat this way every day. That's obvious. Not more than once every two weeks. You see, for lobster I must tell the men five days in advance. For shrimp a week. For wild chicken, two days."

"How did you train the natives to serve so well?" Dinah asked. "They actually seemed to enjoy it."

"I am patient with them," the Frenchman answered. "They make their mistakes on me, and when they serve you they are prepared to do a good job. Isn't it that way at the hospital?"

"Tell me, M. De Becque," an inquisitive doctor asked, "how long did it take you to organize and build this plantation?"

"Twenty-six years," De Becque said. "I came here as a young man."

"You chop it out of the jungle yourself?"

"With some natives and a family of Javanese workers."

"The yellow people I saw outside. They're not Javanese, are they?"

"No," De Becque replied. "They're Tonkinese. Very fine workers. We bring them over from Tonkin China."

"Twenty-six years!" an older doctor said. "Wonder what I'll have to show for my life at the end of twenty-six years?"

"You were willing to throw all this away in the event that Pétain won?" Dinah inquired. The Frenchman smiled at her.

"I thought this was the war to prove that Pétain could never win," he said graciously. "You Americans worry about De Gaulle and De Gaullists, and yet every one of you acts as if he were a De Gaullist. Your speeches and your actions don't coincide."

After dinner the guests sat in the screened-in veranda. A doctor had brought along two mosquito bombs to keep the pests away. Their host served whiskey, beer, coke, ginger ale, root beer and rum. As the evening wore on and a fine crescent moon rose into the midnight sky, talk turned to the islands.

"How can a man have stayed so healthy here?" one doctor inquired.

"Hard work and temperate living," the Frenchman replied. "I serve a great deal of alcohol but use it sparingly myself. I have tried to do all things in moderation."

The nurses wondered what "all things" covered. "Do you think other white people could live in the tropics, too?" one asked. "That is, as well as you have?"

"They do," he said. "I think will power has a lot to do with it. You take the island of Malaita in the Solomons. Oh, what a place! Yet a man I know well, fellow named Anderson—he found life there quite successful."

"Tell me, M. De Becque," a nurse asked, "is it true that most white men in the tropics are running away from something?"

The Frenchman turned in his chair to face his impertinent questioner. She was a young girl, so he smiled. "Yes," he said. "I believe that is true. Suppose that I was running away from something. Where could I find a lovelier spot than this?" He swept his hand across the front of the veranda and pointed toward the silent peaks of Vanicoro. "As a matter of fact," he said in a quiet voice, "is not each of you running away from something? You were not married yet, your lovers were at war, or your wives were beginning to bore you. I don't think it wise to inquire too closely into reasons why anybody is anywhere!" He smiled at the embarrassed nurse.

"Oh, M. De Becque!" she said. "I didn't mean it that way!"

"I know you didn't, my dear! But that's the way I understand the question. It's no good to think that all the men in Marseilles are normal and happy without secrets and everyone out here is a fugitive! That sort of thinking is foolish in today's world. I wonder how many men and women in Marseilles envy me right now?"

It was after midnight, and the nurses had to return. They were reluctant to leave the plantation. At the gateway where the jeeps were parked M. De Becque detached Nellie from the group. She had stood so that he could if he were so minded. "Ensign Forbush," he said. "You have shown great interest in my home. I would like to have you visit the plantation again."

"I should like to," Nellie replied frankly.

"With your permission I shall stop by for you one afternoon. You would enjoy my cacao grove."

Three days later, in the cacao grove, Nellie admitted that she had never seen anything which so impressed her with its natural, unexploited beauty. Within that grove she was to spend many of the happiest hours she would ever know, and one of the bitterest.

Plantation owners in the tropics usually plant their coconut trees in stately rows along the ocean front and inland for a mile or two. Grass is kept closely cropped beneath the trees so that fallen nuts can be gathered without difficulty. Most coconut groves look very neat. The tall palms appear like thin ballet dancers with fantastic headdresses. But a cacao grove grows haphazardly. It usually forms the boundary between plantation and jungle. Trees spring up helter-skelter from year to year, and around them jungle brush proliferates. At times it is difficult to tell where cacao trees end and violent jungle begins.

At the point where his cacao and coconut met, De Becque had long ago built himself a pavilion big enough for two or three people. Its base was teak wood in eighteen-inch planks, its half-sides of woven coconut palm and its roof of heavy thatch. Two benches of mahogany and two massive, comfortable chairs of teak were the only pieces of furniture. Four grotesque rootoos, native masks carved of coconut log, decorated the four corners. Two were incredibly long-nosed jungle gods and two were native views of white women, with red lips. The masks gave color to what might otherwise have been a barren pavilion.

It is doubtful, however, if anything could be barren within a cacao grove. As Nellie waited in the pavilion while De Becque talked with his natives, she could hardly believe that what she had thought of as the monotonous jungle could be so varied. Above her flew an endless variety of birds. White, green, red, purple and yellow lorikeets more beautiful than any bird except the quetzal swirled and eddied through the grove. Their harsh cries were modified by the delicate chirping of a graceful swallowlike bird that flew in great profusion among the cacao trees. This gracious bird was sooty black except for a white breast and belly. Gliding and twisting through the shadows it looked like a shadow itself. Then, bursting into the sunlight, its white body shone brilliantly. At times sea birds flew as far inland as the cacao grove, and occasionally a gaunt hawk from the distant hills would settle there for a day and drive the darting swallows away.

But it was the cacao tree that won Nellie's admiration. The cacao is small, hardly more than a bush, reaching at most twenty feet in height. It has a sturdy trunk, thick branches about five feet from the ground, and grows symmetrically. Its leaves are brilliantly glistened, like poison ivy only more shimmering. And they are of myriad color. Some are pale green, others darkest green, some purple, some almost blue, or gray, or bright yellow. And on most trees at least fifty leaves are brilliant vermilion, shading off to scarlet and deep red. Each leaf is iridescent, and dead leaves drop immediately from the tree.

A cacao grove, in rainy weather, is a mournful and lovely place. In bright sunlight it is a hall of mirrors, and at dusk it has a quality of deep jungle quiet and mysteriousness that is equaled nowhere else in the tropics. In large measure these attributes are aided by the beauty of the cacao pods themselves. They grow in fairy-tale manner. In late January and February the cacao puts out buds that will later grow into pods. They appear without reason at the strangest places! Two inches from the ground on a barren, stiff trunk, a pod will suddenly appear. On one branch there may be a dozen pods. On another, none. In the crevice formed where a branch leaves the trunk a cluster of pods may appear and the branch itself may be bare. A mature cacao in full season looks as if someone had stood at a distance and flung a huge handful of random pods upon it.

At first the miniature pods are light purple. Then as they grow to full size, they become a weird greenish purple, like the paintings of Georges Bracque. Next they are all green, and from then on they become the chameleons of the jungle. On one tree mature pods, which now look like elongated cantaloupes seven and eight inches long, will be bright green, golden yellow, reddish yellow, red, purple and greenish purple. And on each tree a few will be dead, charred, black, ugly, with small holes where rats have eaten out the sweet seeds, which, when toasted and ground, become cocoa.

While Nellie waited for De Becque to finish the work he was doing, she studied the grove and mused upon the perverseness of people whereby *cacao* in French become *cocoa* in English. The multicolored lorikeets, the iridescent leaves, and the flaming cacao pods formed a superb picture for a hot afternoon. Later, when her host appeared, tall, stooped and breathing hard, she asked him to sit by her.

"Why did you build this pavilion?" she asked.

"I like to be near the jungle," he said, remaining in the doorway.

"Do you come here on rainy days? Is it nice then, too?"

"It's best on rainy days," he said. "But it's strange. The place serves no purpose. It's too far from the kitchen to eat here. There's no bed, and it isn't screened in. Yet I think I like it better than any place on my plantation."

"I was looking at the cacaos," Nellie said in a singsong kind of voice. To herself she was saying, "I shall marry this man. This shall be my life from now on. This hillside shall be my home. And in the afternoons he and I will sit here." Aloud she continued, "They are beautiful, aren't they?"

"A rugged tree," he said. "Not like coconuts. But they don't pay as well."

"Mr. De Becque," she began. "That sounds silly, doesn't it? I meant M. De Becque."

"Why don't you call me Emile?"

"I should like to," she said, half laughing in self-consciousness.

To himself De Becque said, "This is what I have been waiting for. All the long years. Who ever thought a fresh, smiling girl like this would climb up my hill? It was worth waiting for. I wonder . . ."

"Emile?" Nellie began. "May I ask you a question?"

"Of course you may," he replied, smiling.

"Why did you leave France?"

There was a long pause. Nellie and Emile studied one another across the little distance of the pavilion. Outside swallows darted through the cacao trees and lorikeets screamed at them for trespass. It was a jungle day, warm, heavy, thick with sunlight.

"It was not to my discredit," the Frenchman replied.

"I know that," Nellie assured him.

"I killed a man," Emile went on dreamily, his voice blending into the heavy silence of the cacao grove.

"Why?" Nellie asked, not the least disturbed. It seemed as natural a mode of behavior for Emile De Becque as writing a letter. He had said, "I killed a man," and she was relieved that it was not something serious.

"A town bully. A town cheat. It was in a little place near Marseilles. Everyone was glad to see him die, and the fault was his. But they thought I should leave. The police investigated for three days, giving me time to get away. I could not make up my mind and an old man who had been a sailor told me, 'I was on an island once. The men wore pig's teeth and the women wore nothing. Anything you planted would grow on that island. With a little money a daring man could make a fine living there and become rich.' I listened to him, my mind in revolt. Then he said something that decided me: 'And opposite the island is another island with two volcanoes. You can see them all the time.' That did it. My mother had always wanted to see Naples. She read a book about Pompeii and wanted to see Naples. She never did. Lived all her life right near Marseilles. I clapped the old sailor on the back and shouted, 'You have a good idea, old man! I'll see *two* volcanoes!' I left that night, and the next day the police came to my home. 'Where is Emile De Becque?' they demanded. 'He is wanted for murder.' The old people in the house said, 'He ran away!' 'The scoundrel!' said the police. 'If he comes back, we'll arrest him. Mark our words, we'll get him!' They were furious, and all the time I was sitting in a café in Marseilles, waiting four days for a ship. They knew it and were afraid to send news to Marseilles, because they knew that sometimes ships lay over three or four days. Finally they sent a young fellow in to spy me out. He found that I was gone, and posters soon appeared in Marseilles. But I have never gone back."

"How did you kill him?" Nellie asked, surprised at her courage.

"With a knife," Emile said, showing some satisfaction, even at that distance.

"You've never regretted being out here, have you?" she asked.

"Never!" he said emphatically and simply. Then he added a peculiar comment. "This plantation is worth more than a hundred thousand dollars."

In the cacao pavilion the two strangers looked at one another. Each had a half smile. De Becque's gold tooth showed. Nellie's infectious grin fought for possession of her full lips. She thought that he was not an old man, and yet not a young man, either. He was a respected man, wealthy, a man with deep ideas. He was one who killed with a knife, came out for De Gaulle, and was to have led resistance against the Japs.

"Nellie," he said quietly, scarcely audible above the lorikeets. "In the hottest months you could go to Australia." Nellie made no reply. She merely watched De Becque as he rose, crossed the silent pavilion, and bent over her. She raised her lips. Although he merely brushed her lips with his, she had the distinct impression that she had been kissed by a man, a whole man, a man worthy to be loved.

He sat upon the arm of her teakwood chair for several minutes. "I must go soon," she said quietly. As she rose, standing beside him, she noticed that her nose came to his shoulder. Standing there, with it pressed against his moist shirt, she asked, "Are you married, Emile?"

"No," he replied.

"I'm so glad," she murmured, pressing her funny nose deep into his shoulder. He patted her on the head and led the way down the long path that wound among the coconuts.

"You have dinner?" the Tonkinese cook asked.

"Just for me," De Becque replied. "I'll be back soon."

"Emile," Nellie said as he stopped his Australian car by the guarded wire gate. "Let me think for a few days. I'll tell you then."

"All right," he said.

That evening Nellie confided the news to Dinah. "I think I'll marry him," she said.

"It's hot on this island," Dinah replied.

"It's hot in Arkansas, too," Nellie said laughingly.

"But you can get out of Arkansas."

"And I can go to Australia, too. Many women do in these islands. During the hot season."

"I don't suppose it's up to me to tell you that you hardly know the man," Dinah said, looking at the pretty young nurse.

"I don't want you to say that, Dinah," Nellie said. "But when I was in love with Bill Harbison you said that you knew I was heading for trouble. Do you feel that way now? Do you, Dinah?"

The older woman thought a moment. "No," she said. "As a matter of fact, I envy you. That is, if you have the courage to do it. This isn't an easy life."

"But it's a life, Dinah! We can get books here, too. Emile reads a lot in French. We can talk about things."

"Nellie," Dinah said seriously, "why don't you write a long letter to your mother?"

When the airmail answer arrived from Mrs. Forbush it was filled with pocket knowledge accumulated from a long life. It read in part: "Marriages of older men and young girls work for a while. But you must think of the future. Will you be happy there if he dies before you do? . . . The women of the place, if they are mostly French, will not like it having you there. Have you thought of that? . . . Love can make almost any marriage work, and if he has money, as you say, that is all so much the better . . . What do you really know about him? Why did he leave France? . . . He is probably a Catholic, too . . . Nellie, I always thought you might marry Charlie Benedict. He has a good job now . . . If your Pop was alive, he would probably say, 'Go ahead. Three square meals a day is as good there as here!' But life ought to have more than three square meals a day. You ought to have friends and old places to help you along . . ."

Mrs. Forbush rattled on, casting merits against demerits, and came to the tentative conclusion that it was Nellie's life and she would have to lie in it. Mrs. Forbush had her metaphors mixed, but her conclusions were sound. Nellie showed the letter to Dinah. "Your mother has good sense," the older nurse said.

"She'd have to have to raise four of us," Nellie laughed. "But I want something more in life than she had. Mom didn't have much."

"She had enough to raise four pretty good kids," Dinah laughed. "And she didn't learn good sense out of a book."

"I think I'll marry him," Nellie said. Dinah had no comment. She wondered to herself what she could have done, and like Mrs. Forbush could come to no conclusion.

When De Becque called for Nellie next day she suggested they spend the afternoon in the pavilion. When they reached it, they were warm and breathing hard. Again the sun was hot upon the cacaos, and the lorikeets were wild in protest over some imagined slight. Suddenly they grew quiet.

"Look!" Nellie cried. "Look!"

A great hawk of the islands was sweeping overhead in long circles. It had come down from the mountains. No swallows were to be seen. With a delicacy foreign to his intent, the hawk sailed quietly by, moving a wing slightly now and then. Soon he was gone, and the brave lorikeets were out once more with furious chatter.

"I've thought as best I can, Emile," the young nurse said. "I want to marry you!"

"Fine!" Emile said with much restraint. They kissed twice. Then they sat in massive chairs and watched the life and beauty of the cacao grove.

"It will be a good life, Nellie," the Frenchman said. "You will like it. There is a good hospital on the other island. And if you like, you can go to Australia to have your children. The boat comes once every three months, and there are many people here. I have my own small boat, and two plantation owners have a large power launch. I shall teach you to read French, too. I have many books. And we can get English books, too. I have not told you, but I have a lot of money saved."

At the thought of having saved things over the years Emile grew pensive. Outside the birds called to one another and the golden cacaos reflected sunlight from their myriad facets. "I will die before you, Nellie, since I am older," he said in a reflective manner. "But if you like the islands then, you will have no need to fear hunger or poverty. And if you have children, they will be growing up. By that time there will be an American base here. Your little girls will have fine American young men to choose as husbands. And if you don't like the islands, you can then return to America. You will have enough to live on."

Nellie could say nothing at this comment on eventual death. The hawk was idling in the dark sky and the lorikeets, like Nellie, were silent. They, too, were thinking of death.

Before De Becque left Nellie at the wire gate of the nurses' quarters, he told her that he would be gone for a few days. He had to deliver some beef to the island on which the French government had sequestered all young girls and unmarried women. It was a small island some sixteen miles distant, and there white, yellow, and black girls lived protected from the inroads of American troops far from home and inhibitions. De Becque and other planters kept the island supplied with food. For the first time, Nellie kissed him good-by at the gate. She winked at the guard. "We're getting married!" she said.

While De Becque was gone, she visited the Navy captain who commanded her hospital. She told him that she intended to marry De Becque and asked what arrangements could be made.

"It's a long process," the captain warned her. "I don't understand it myself. The Army has charge of details in this area. But I'll take you to see the general, Ensign Forbush."

He did, and Nellie found the general a kindly old man who had daughters about her age. "I don't approve," he said half severely, "but I know how it is when girls make up their minds. One thing, Ensign Forbush: Have you or your friends made inquiries into M. De Becque's past? You have. Then we'll start the papers through the mill. But he'll have to appear in person. Bring him in when he gets back."

Nellie sighed and smiled at her commanding officer. The step was taken! She was surprised at the interest a captain and a general took in her affairs. She felt happy and important.

At dinner that night Dinah Culbert asked Nellie if, seeing that De Becque was away, she might like to sit at a table where an entertaining naval aviator was a guest. He was back from a tour of the islands and had some witty stories. At dinner Nellie sat next to the guest, a Lieutenant Bus Adams. As the meal progressed he told one fascinating story after another. He made himself the butt of most of the humor, but as the evening wore on he finally asked for another drink and said, "I've never told this story before to a mixed group. It's really a man's story, but women might enjoy it, too. It's the only story I've run upon that fulfills the promise of these islands. I call it 'The Frenchman's Daughter.' It took place on Luana Pori, and I know it's true. I know the Frenchman's daughter. She's a magnificent woman, about twenty-three. Half French, half Javanese!" Adams continued with a rambling narrative that captivated his listeners.

Doctors and nurses alike were following him with intense interest as he finished. "There!" he said. "Didn't I tell you it was a tropical story?"

"That is!" one of the doctors agreed. "You ought to write that down, Lieutenant."

"No, no!" Bus said, wagging his finger. "I've found that these stories don't sound half so good when told in daylight. It's the wine, and the night, and the moon out there. That's what turns the trick."

"I suppose all these islands are loaded with unbelievable happenings," a doctor suggested. "As strangers, we don't hear about them."

"That's interesting!" Adams said. "Because if I understand correctly, the Frenchman in this story lives on your island. Quite a character, I'm told. Raised hell when they wanted to go Pétain some years ago."

Before anyone could stop him, Adams had blurted out the news. The Frenchman's notorious daughter was De Becque's daughter. Her mother was a Javanese.

The Frenchman's three other daughters who lived on Luana Pori were half-Javanese, too, but by a different mother. And somewhere near Vanicoro, on a small island, he had four other daughters, more beautiful than their sisters. The mothers of these girls were Polynesian and Tonkinese.

"He never married," Adams concluded. "Women were crazy about him, and he treated them fine."

Nellie Forbush sat very straight and smiled at the aviator as he spoke. Later on he refused to believe what the doctors whispered to him. "Jesus!" he said.

Nellie smiled at the doctors and the other nurses. Taking Dinah's hand, she excused herself. The two nurses went out the long corridor leading to their own quarters.

It was strange, but Nellie found no cause to cry. De Becque was a man of the islands. He had lived here for twenty-six years. He was a powerful man, and women were plentiful. Through him they saw a chance of rearing fine daughters, half white, and they eagerly took that chance. To judge from Bus Adams' story, the De Becque girls were fine and beautiful. Latouche, the eldest, was apparently wild, but she was smart and lovely.

"I'll not make up my mind about anything," Nellie said to Dinah when they were alone.

"What's past is past, Nellie," Dinah reasoned. "I told you less than a week ago that I wasn't worried about De Becque. I'm not now. This is a rough life out here. He's lived it. And kept everyone's respect. Only fighters do that, Nellie!"

"I'm not going to make up my mind," Nellie repeated. "Mom had a funny idea about that. Once she wanted a hat very much and had saved enough money to buy one. She went in to Little Rock with all the money in her hand. 'I won't make up my mind,' she kept saying to herself. Finally she was in front of the department store. There was exactly the hat she wanted. She looked at it for a moment and then started crying. Because that ornery store had put new baby carriages in the next window. She had to have a baby carriage. It was for me. Mom always said it was best to live right and make up your mind on the spot."

The two women talked late into the night. Other nurses, catching the story by grapevine, spent the night telling one another what a rotten break it was that Nellie . . . They were somewhat disappointed when she appeared at breakfast bright and chipper. She hadn't yet made up her mind to be heartbroken.

Two days passed, and finally De Becque called her on the hospital telephone. Mustering up her courage, she smiled at the girls on her hall and hurried down to meet him. She noticed with apprehension that he was morose, too. In strained silence the two lovers drove along the coral roads and up the hill to his plantation. They parked his car by the gate and walked slowly between the coconut palms. De Becque was silent, as if worried. Nellie's heart was pounding harder than her lungs. As they neared the end of the coconuts and the beginning of the cacaos, De Becque stopped impulsively and kissed his bride-to-be tenderly. "You are my hope," he whispered.

Nellie consciously placed her hand in his and walked with him toward the pavilion. She felt him trembling, and thought it was she. They paused a moment to watch the dipping black and white swallows. Then they stepped into the cool pavilion.

"Aloo, Nellie!" cried four young voices.

Nellie looked in astonishment at four little girls who stood behind one of the teakwood chairs. "Allo, Nellie!" they cried again. Then they came forth, in gingham frocks, pigtails, and curtsies.

Two were Tonkinese, that is, they were half Tonkinese, and they were beautiful as only Eurasian girls can be. They were seven and nine. Their almond eyes were black. Their foreheads were clean and high. They had very white teeth and golden complexions.

The two other girls were half Polynesian, daughters of that strange and proud race. They were round of face and darker than their sisters. Their eyes were black as pools at night, their hair the same, long and straight even in pigtails. They had rich mouths and splendidly proportioned bodies. They were ten and eleven.

At the end of their curtsy they said once more, "Allo, Nellie!"

"They're my daughters," De Becque said proudly. "I have four others. They all live in Luana Pori. One of them is married. I have their pictures here." From an envelope he produced a well-thumbed photograph of four tall, thin, sharp-eyed girls. The first and third were exquisite beauties, lovelier than Bus Adams had painted them in his story. The second and fourth were handsome girls, and only their sisters' storybook charm made them seem plain. It was noticeable that each had a quizzical smile on her lips.

"My family!" De Becque said. He put his hand on Nellie's shoulder. "I had to tell you first," he said.

Nellie Forbush, of Otolousa, Arkansas, could not speak. She was glad that her mother had taught her never to make up her mind beforehand. Beside her was a strong, tough man. It was someone like him she had in mind when she said long ago, "I want to get out and meet people." It was not old ladies in white lace sitting by the fireside that Nellie wanted to meet. It was men and women who had courage. She looked at the picture of Latouche, De Becque's eldest daughter, and saw in her Emile's fire and determination. Yes, Latouche could kill a man and fight the entire American Army. The aviator's story was believable. Nellie thought that she would like Latouche.

But before her were other indisputable facts! Two of them! Emile De Becque, not satisfied with Javanese and Tonkinese women, had also lived with a Polynesian. A nigger! To Nellie's tutored mind any person living or dead who was not white or yellow was a nigger. And beyond that no words could go! Her entire Arkansas upbringing made it impossible for her to deny the teachings of her youth. Emile De Becque had lived with the nigger. He had nigger children. If she married him, they would be her stepdaughters.

She suffered a revulsion which her lover could never understand. Watching her shiver, he motioned to the little girls and they left the pavilion. "Nellie," he said, pulling her into a chair and standing over it, "I have no apologies. I came out here as a young man. There were no white women in this area. I lived as I could. No women ever hated me or tried to hurt me. You must believe me, Nellie. I loved those women and was kind to them. But I never married because I knew that some day you would come to this island."

He stood before her in considerable dignity. He was not crawling, and yet by every word and gesture he was fighting to have her believe in him.

"Oh! Look at that big one!" the little girls cried in French. Their soft voices drifted through the pavilion like the sound of distant music. Nellie looked at them running among the cacaos. The little Polynesians were dark, she thought. Almost black.

She swallowed hard. The pounding in her chest was still strong. "Where are their mothers?" she asked.

De Becque clasped his hands and looked away. "The Javanese are back in Java. They went a long time ago. I don't know where the Tonkinese is. She was no good. The Polynesian girl is dead."

Nellie was ashamed of herself, but a surge of joy ran through her entire body when she heard that the nigger was dead. Yet even as she entertained that thought the oldest Polynesian girl looked in at the window and cried in softest tones, *"Papa! Voilà une petite souris dans ce cacao!"* Nellie's hands went toward the window. The child had in her eager face and soft voice the qualities that made De Becque a man to love.

"Va-t-en jouer!" Emile said quietly.

"Oui, papa," the golden little girl replied.

"I don't know what to say, Emile," Nellie mumbled. "You don't understand."

"I know it's a surprise, Nellie. And a rude one. I know that."

"No!" Nellie cried in real anguish, stamping her foot. "It isn't that! It's something you don't know."

De Becque, defeated by tears, stood aside. Why Nellie thought he was incapable of understanding, it would be difficult to say. He had read of America. He knew something of its mores and shibboleths. And yet Nellie was correct in assuming that no Frenchman could understand why, to an Arkansas girl, a man who had openly lived with a nigger was beyond the pale. Utterly beyond the bounds of decency!

"I can't . . ." She stopped in her explanation. It was no use. The inescapable fact remained. She buried her head in her hands, and in the torment of conflicting thoughts and ideals started to cry.

"Please take me home," she said.

At the foot of the hill the Tonkinese cook expressed his astonishment that she was leaving. He held up his hands in horror. "Dinner all fine. He cooked. He good!" the cook protested. Moved by his appeal, Nellie agreed to have dinner and then go immediately. At a separate table the four little girls, obviously great favorites of the cook, had their dinners. They babbled quietly in French, displayed exquisite manners, and excused themselves when they went to bed. They, too, like the nigger wife, were indisputable facts. Nellie caught herself whispering, "I would be happy if my children were like that!"

Emile drove down the hill in silence, but at the turn onto the coral road four thugs were waiting for the car. They had been planning this assault for some time, four crazy young Americans, their minds addled by wild emotions. As they leaped at the car, Emile sped the motor and whipped out a brass pipe on the end of a knotted chain. It cut across the face of one assailant and hit another on the head. The swerving car wiped the remaining two loose against a tree. De Becque drove furiously until he met some enlisted men coming the other way in a truck. Wheeling around in a spire of dust, he led them back to where the assault had taken place. One rapist had been unable to run away, his leg bashed in by the car. The enlisted men jumped on him and started beating the bushes for the others. They found one, dazed, his face and head bleeding. The others were gone.

"Take them to the police, if you please," De Becque said quietly.

"You bet we will, mister!" an Army man said.

The truck pulled away. De Becque slumped over the wheel for a moment. Then he carefully rewound his lethal weapon and stowed it where it could be most easily grabbed in a hurry. Nellie was afraid to talk. She rested her head on his shoulder. De Becque drove very slowly.

"The world is not pretty," he said. "It's only the hard work of some people that makes it so. Remember that, Nellie. This could be your island. Your home. You'd make it that!"

"You don't understand," she whispered. At the barred gate she made up her mind.

"What is it, Nellie?"

"I can't marry you," she said. "I could never marry you!"

De Becque kissed her good-by. The guards smiled. They knew she was going to be married soon. She was a damned nice girl, too. If they were all like her. One guard made a circle with his forefinger and thumb. He winked at De Becque.

"Hey!" he whispered to his pal when Nellie had gone. "The guy had tears in his eyes! What the hell goes on here?"

In her room Nellie undressed and lay upon the bed. She was excited and nervous. She could still see the ugly, hungry looks of the men who had tried to pull her out of the car. She thought, "Maybe they're the men who have to drive cars while officers and nurses neck in the back seat." She flung her arms over her head. "This whole thing is so rotten. Oh, I never should have come out here at all. It's all wrong!"

She thought of Emile De Becque and the little brown girls in the cacao grove. Her thoughts were as chaotic and tormented as those of the men who had attacked the car. "This place does something to you," she groaned. "I just can't think!"

And then she knew what she wanted. Her mind was made up. She rose, pulled a dressing gown from a nail over her head, and started to write a feverish letter. It was to Charlie Benedict in Otolousa, Arkansas. She told him something he had been waiting years to hear. She would marry him. She wanted more than anything in the world to marry Charlie Benedict. Right away. Now! She yearned for the safety and security of knowing what was happening and what had happened. She wanted Otolousa and its familiar streets. She didn't give a damn if she never saw another strange place the rest of her life.

At that moment Dinah Culbert entered the room. "Made up your mind?"

"Yep! I'm going to get married!"

"Good! Nellie, that's a fine decision!" Dinah's enthusiasm upset Nellie a bit.

"But to Charlie Benedict back home!" She bit her lip and laid the pen down. "Oh, Dinah!" she cried. "I couldn't marry a man who had lived with a nigger!"

"Of course not," Dinah said dryly. She didn't live in Arkansas and wouldn't understand. "Hell! What's this?" She picked up from Nellie's desk a picture from an Arkansas newspaper. "Why, Nellie!" she cried. "This is you!" Dinah looked at the picture approvingly. Then she read the caption, "Our heroine!" She repeated the words, "Our heroine!" Then she looked at Nellie, tears in her eyes, nose red, mouth drooping. "Our heroine!" she shouted, waving the picture in Nellie's wet face.

Nurse Forbush caught a fleeting glimpse of herself in the clipping. She thought of the afternoon the picture arrived in Otolousa. *I want to see the world, Charlie. I want to live with people!* The ridiculousness of her situation amused her. She started laughing at Dinah. Then she laughed at herself. The two nurses caught one another by the arms and started dancing.

"Our little heroine!" Dinah repeated over and over again until her chuckling became uncontrolled. Then she sat in Nellie's chair. In doing so, she knocked the letter to Charlie Benedict on the floor. With a grand sweep Nellie picked it up and crumpled it into a little ball.

"So long, Charlie!" she cried, tossing the ball into a corner.

"Nellie!" Dinah cried. "Where did you get this?"

"What?" the now half-hysterical Nellie answered.

"This picture. It was on the floor by your jacket." It was the picture of the four De Becque girls.

"Oh!" Nellie cried in astonishment. "Emile must have . . ."

"What lovely girls!" Dinah said.

Nellie stopped laughing. She looked over Dinah's shoulder. They were lovely girls. Look at Latouche! Winsome and confident. Her three sisters, too. Calm, happy, cocky young girls. They seemed to be afraid of nothing. They seemed like their father.

"They *are* like De Becque!" Nellie said in a whisper.

"What did you say?" Dinah asked.

"Look, Dinah! Look at them! How much fun they seem to have!"

"You'd never have a bored moment around them," Dinah replied sagaciously.

"And the four little girls! Dinah, they're sweet. And so well behaved. Oh, damn it all!" Nurse Forbush walked up and down. She saw her letter to Charlie in the corner. "Damn it all!" she cried again, kicking at the letter.

"Very reasonable behavior!" Dinah laughed. "For a little heroine!"

"What's the use of bluffing, Dinah?" Nellie confessed. She ran over to the older nurse. "Now I *have* made up my mind. I want to marry him . . . so very much!" She started crying and sank her head on Dinah's shoulder. Dinah thereupon consoled her by crying, too. In mutual happiness they blubbered for a while.

"I think your mind is made up the right way this time," Dinah whispered.

"Quick!" Nellie cried. "See if you can get a jeep! We've got to get one right away! I've got to tell him, tonight!" She hurried about the room getting her clothes together. "Oh, Dinah!" she chortled. "Think what it will be like! A big family in a big house! Eight daughters, and they're darlings. I don't care who he's lived with. I got me a man! My mind's made up. Mom was right. Wait till the last minute!"

In great joy she dressed and hurried downstairs with Dinah. While they waited for the jeep the guard asked, "Changed your mind, Ensign?"

"Yep!" she laughed. "I did!" He made a circle with his thumb and finger and winked at her. "Good hunting!" he said.

Dinah urged their driver to hurry. "Can't do but twenty-five," he growled.

"But it's an emergency!" Dinah protested.

"It's always an emergency," the driver replied. "This is an awful island!"

"But this is a real emergency!" Dinah insisted.

"Oh! Well! Why didn't you say so?" the driver asked in a most co-operative spirit. "In a real emergency I always do twenty-six."

Nellie winced as they passed the place where four men had jumped on the car earlier that night. As they reached the plantation, she directed Dinah and the driver to wait. Hurrying across the garden she went to the veranda. It was empty. The dining room was empty, too. Then she heard sounds from one of the bedrooms.

She hurried along the walk and found the source of the sounds. There it was. The little girls' bedroom. She opened the door. The four girls were in nightgowns, standing about a bed on which De Becque sat. They were singing "Au clair de la lune" in childish voices. Emile rose, smiled at Nellie, and hummed along with his daughters. Nellie added her uncertain treble to the chorus, and before long they were singing the old song so loudly that Dinah and the driver could join in from the jeep.

A Boar's Tooth

LUTHER BILLIS and Tony Fry were a pair! Luther was what we call in the Navy a "big dealer." Ten minutes after he arrived at a station he knew where to buy illicit beer, how to finagle extra desserts, what would be playing at the movies three weeks hence, and how to avoid night duty.

Luther was one of the best. When his unit was staging in the Hebrides before they built the airstrip at Konora he took one fleeting glance at the officers nearby and selected Tony Fry. "That's my man!" he said. Big dealers knew that the best way for an enlisted man to get ahead was to leech on to an officer. Do things for him. Butter him up. Kid him along. Because then you had a friend at court. Maybe you could even borrow his jeep!

Tony was aware of what was happening. The trick had been pulled on him before. But he liked Billis. The fat SeaBee was energetic and imaginative. He looked like something out of *Treasure Island*. He had a sagging belly that ran over his belt by three flabby inches. He rarely wore a shirt and was tanned a dark brown. His hair was long, and in his left ear he wore a thin golden ring. The custom was prevalent in the South Pacific and was a throwback to pirate days.

He was liberally tattooed. On each breast was a fine dove, flying toward his heart. His left arm contained a python curled around his muscles and biting savagely at

39

his thumb. His right arm had two designs: *Death Rather Than Dishonor* and *Thinking of Home and Mother*. Like the natives, Luther wore a sprig of frangipani in his hair.

It was Luther's jewelry, however, that surprised Tony. On his left arm Billis wore an aluminum watch band, a heavy silver slave bracelet with his name engraved, and a superb wire circlet made of woven airplane wire welded and hammered flat. On his right wrist he had a shining copper bracelet on which his social security and service numbers were engraved. And he wore a fine boar's tusk.

"What's that?" Tony asked him one day.

"A boar's tusk," Billis replied.

"What in the world is a boar's tusk?" Fry asked.

"You got a jeep, Mr. Fry?"

"Yes."

"Then why don't we go see the old chief?" Billis leaned his fat belly forward and sort of hunched up the two doves on his breast.

"Put a shirt on," Tony said. "We'll take a spin."

In the jeep Billis sat back, his right foot on the dash, and gave directions. "Out past the farm, down the hill, past 105 Hospital—say, Mr. Fry, have you seen them new nurses out there?—down to Tonk village, and I'll take over from there."

Tony followed the instructions. When he reached the two *séchoirs* where copra and cacao were dying, Billis said, "Drive down that grass road." Tony did so, and soon he was at the seaside. Before him, around the edges of a little bay, a host of native canoes and small trading vessels lay beached. Beside the prows of the ships, colored men from all the Hebridean islands had pitched their tents. This was the native market of Espiritu Santo.

Most of the natives knew Billis. "Allo, Billis!" they cried.

"Got any cigarettes, Mr. Fry?"

"No, I don't."

"Shouldn't ever come down here without cigarettes." Billis spoke to the men in beach-la-Mar and explained to them that this time he had no smokes.

"That's OK, Billis!" an old man said.

"Got any boar's tusks?" Billis inquired.

"We got some," the old trader replied.

"Let's see."

"In ship."

"Well, go get from ship!" Billis cried, slapping the old man on the back. The natives laughed. The old fellow went to the shore, waded in and started swimming toward a ship anchored in the bay. Tony surveyed the market. Chickens were selling at two dollars each. Eggs were a dollar a dozen, and plentiful. Grass skirts were two dollars, shells were a dollar a handful. Watermelons, grown from American seed, were abundant. Eight kinds of bananas were on sale, war clubs, lava-lavas, toy canoes, papayas, and the fragrant pineapples which grew on Vanicoro.

Soldiers and sailors moved about among the native tents. From time to time thin native men and boys would stagger into camp under mammoth loads of junk. By an island order natives were permitted to strip any junk pile before it was set afire. So they came to Santo from miles around in every kind of canoe. They took home with them old tables, rusty knives, bits of tin, ends of copper wire and all the refuse of a modern army.

"Looks like he's got a pretty good one, Mr. Fry," Billis said as the old man swam back to shore, holding in his teeth a boar's tusk. The trader came ashore, shook himself like a dog and sat on his haunches before a small fire on the beach.

"All same too good!" he said, offering Billis the tusk.

Luther handed it to Fry, who twirled the ugly thing in his hands. "Grim-looking thing, isn't it?" he asked. The tusk was rude, ugly, just as it had been ripped from the underjaw of a sacrificial wild pig. It was dirty white in color and formed an almost perfect circle about five inches across. At its widest the tusk itself was about a quarter of an inch thick, so that it formed a natural bracelet. Tony slipped it over his right hand. It hung dull and heavy from his wrist.

"You got one cleaned up?" Billis asked the old man.

"He got," the trader replied, pointing to a native friend.

"Let's see," Billis suggested.

"You buy? You look? You look?" the doubtful Melanesian asked.

"I look, I look, I knock your block off," Billis shouted.

This delighted the Negro, who produced a tusk slightly smaller than the first and beautifully polished. Whereas the first was dirty and crude, this one was a pale golden ivory, soft to the eye and lustrous. It curled in a circle and seemed one of the finest bracelets Tony had ever seen. It was solid ivory.

"This comes from this?" Tony asked, indicating the two tusks.

"That's right. The dirty one has the enamel on yet. The ivory is all hidden on that one. Them natives has a secret way of getting the enamel off. I figured out a way of knocking it off with an emery wheel. I do it for them at a buck a tusk. They finish up the polishing."

Tony surveyed the tusks. They were like something from Greek legend. The shimmering, golden jewel and the rude barbaric thing from which it sprang. "What's a tusk like this one worth?" Tony asked, indicating the polished bracelet.

Billis spoke in beach-la-Mar to the natives. "He says fifteen dollars."

"Whew! Is that a good buy, Billis?" Luther took the tusk and studied it. Like the tusks of all pigs, it was composed of three triangular pieces of ivory welded together by nature. Light played delicately upon the irregular faces. Fry was entranced at the jungle jewel as Billis twirled it around his thumb.

"It's worth fifteen dollars, Mr. Fry," he said. But then a happy thought struck him. "Of course, I know where you can get a better one."

"Where?"

"On Vanicoro."

"Where's that?"

"That island over there."

"Way over there?"

"It's not so far."

"No, Billis. You just want the ride. I know you big dealers. Besides, I get seasick."

"You don't have to go, Mr. Fry. You send me. I'll go."

"What do you have cooking over there, Billis? You have a big deal on?"

"The sacred ceremonial, sir. I've been invited. You

know the damned Navy. Can't see its way clear to letting me go."

"What's all this about, Billis? A sacred ceremonial?"

"He'll tell you," Billis said, indicating a young native.

By this time Fry knew he was hooked. When an officer gets in the clutches of a big dealer it's one thing after another. Tony knew he ought to stop right where he was. "I'll take this one," he said. He gave the second trader fifteen dollars and put the tusk in his pocket.

But the young native, dressed in brief shorts, was beside him. "Fine ceremonial," he said in good English. "My uncle kill all his pigs. He got more pigs than any other man on Vanicoro. You like to come, my uncle be very proud. He maybe kill one pig for you. He gonna kill one pig for Billis."

"What's this killing pigs, Billis?" Fry asked.

"Well, they're holy pigs, sir."

"Holy?"

"Yes," Billis replied. The young native shook his head in agreement. "But you see, sir, they aren't really holy till they're dead."

"Wait a minute, Billis! You're getting me all mixed up."

Luther smiled. That's what he was trying to do. He'd been wanting to go to Vanicoro for a long time. This looked like his chance. If he could get his officer sufficiently mixed up and interested, well . . .

"It's simple, sir," he said with mock honesty. "Pigs is their religion. They keep pigs the way we keep churches. The rounder the pig's tusks is, the better the church. Sort of the way it is back home. The Baptists got to have a higher steeple than the Methodists."

"Are you kidding me, Billis?"

"Oh, no! Lenato here will tell you, won't you, Lenato?"

The young native smiled and nodded his head. "Billis, he see pigs. He go back jungle one day 'long me."

"So that's where you were? Don't you ever work, Billis?"

"Well, when you're just sitting around waiting . . ."

"What's this about a chief killing a pig for you?"

"Billis one fine man," Lenato said. "He give many presents."

"Oh!" Fry said knowingly. He looked at Billis, who glared at Lenato. "I suppose you'd be happy if I didn't ask what presents."

"That would be very good of you," Billis replied.

"Much stuff!" Lenato said eagerly. "Sheets. Calico. One hammer. Some wire. One carbine." Billis blew air up his fat nostrils and looked out to sea.

"Much stuff?" Fry repeated. "For that you get a pig." Tony looked at the fat SeaBee. "Billis," he said, "I think we ought to go over to Vanicoro. I'd like to see that chief's hut. I'll bet it's wired with Mazda lamps and has an electric icebox!"

On the way back to camp Billis explained more about the tusks to Tony. "When them pigs is young," he said, "they're staked out to a tree on a short length of jungle rope. All their lives they live in that little circle, tied to the tree. The old Maries of the village feed the pigs. Chew the food up first and spit it out. So the pig won't hurt his tusks muzzlin' hard food."

"That's a lot of trouble for a pig," Tony observed.

"But the pigs is sacred. I'm tellin' you, the whole religion is pigs. Nothin' more."

"Billis? Where do you find these things out?"

"Oh," the SeaBee replied, "I'm sort of like you. I like to know things."

Fry looked at him sideways. He wondered if the fat fellow were pulling his leg. Billis continued, "For example, if you was to look under my shirt now you'd see a little extra tattoo. They done that up in the jungle. I joined the tribe. They like me pretty much up there. I helped them to kill the last ceremonial pigs."

"Why did you join the tribe?" Fry asked.

"Oh, some fellows out here read and some carve boats, and some go nuts. Me? I sort of like to fool around with people."

"What did you do in civilian life?"

"Sold cars."

"Pretty successful, I guess."

"Made a very good livin'. Say, Mr. Fry, would you like to see the two tusks I got when I joined the tribe?"

"Yes, I would," Tony said.

"Let's pull in up the road a bit."

Billis led Tony to a small shack which had been fitted up by the SeaBees as a recreation hut. It had every known kind of machine or gadget that could be stolen, borrowed, or ripped off a crashed plane. "Where'd you get all this junk?" Tony asked.

"One place and another," Billis replied truthfully. Fry laughed. The room was a monument to the spirit that made America great. "I wouldn't change a splinter of it," Tony said to himself.

From a corner Billis produced a grisly object. It was the lower jawbone of a wild boar. Jungle ants had eaten away the flesh, leaving only the whitened bones, teeth, and the two curving, circular tusks. They protruded upward from where the lower eyeteeth would naturally have been. But they were not teeth. No, cased in enamel they were pure ivory, like the tusks of elephants.

Fry looked at the jawbone for several minutes. Then he asked a cautious question. "Billis? If this is the lower jawbone, as you say—look at those tusks. They grow right back into the jawbone. That one over there makes a complete circle and grows back through its own root."

"That's the most valuable kind. Of the one-circle tusks, that is."

"But how does it do that?"

"Grows back through the pig's face," Billis said nonchalantly.

"That's barbarous!"

"Very difficult to do. Most pigs die when the tusk starts growing back into their face. Most of those that live die when it starts to grow back into the jawbone. The natives have eight or nine different prayers to a pig to beg him to keep living until the tusk makes a perfect circle. Would you like to hear one?"

Billis grabbed the jawbone and started a weird incantation to the dead pig. "Put it down," Fry said. "The damned pig must live in agony."

"Oh, the pig!" Billis said. "I was thinkin' of the Maries. You see, men don't raise the pig. The Mary raises the pig. If she lets it die, she gets a beating. Yes, the pig. It must hurt him pretty bad. The last four years must be real painful."

"Four years?"

"Yeah, it takes about seven years to grow a good tusk. It begins to enter the face about the fourth year.

This here pig lived about five years after the tusks started through the bone."

"How horrible!" Fry said.

"Seems funny to me," Billis said. "But everyone I show this to always thinks about the pig. What about the people? They was mighty proud of this porker. It was the best pig in the area. It was sacred. Men came from all the villages around to see it and worship it. Two tusks right through the face. One of them right through the root of the tusk itself. That's mighty sacred as pigs go!"

"You have an interesting time out here, don't you?" Fry asked, somewhat sick at his stomach.

"Yeah, I do. Uncle Sam says I got to stay out here. But he don't say I got to be bored!"

"I'll tell you, Billis. You see about that trip to Vanicoro. I'd like to check into this."

"Maybe we can get a boat somewhere."

"If you can't, nobody can."

"I may have to use your name. That OK?"

"Get the boat. You know how it's done." Fry smiled at his fat friend.

"Mind if I ride down to the mess hall with you, sir?"

"Come ahead, big dealer."

Tony was unprepared for what happened that night at dinner. He showed the polished tusk to his fellow officers at mess and Dr. Benoway gasped. "Oh! I'd like to buy that from you, Fry!" he cried.

"It cost fifteen bucks," Tony replied.

"I don't care. Will you sell it?"

"What do you want it for?"

"I'd like to send it to my wife," Benoway replied.

"Good idea. Sold!"

"What would a woman want with a thing like that?" an acidulous, sallow-faced officer asked.

"I don't know," Benoway replied. "She might like to see it. See what things are like out here."

"What are you doing? Dressing her up like a savage?" the officer persisted.

"I'm not doing anything. I'm sending her a present."

"It's a hell of a present, if you ask me."

"Nobody asked you," Fry broke in. "These tusks are strange things," he continued. "Have you heard how they grow them?" He repeated what Billis had told him.

"That's absolutely grotesque!" the same officer persisted. He was an unhappy, indifferent fellow.

"Perhaps so," Fry agreed. "A friend tells me they're the center of all native religion."

"They would be!" the sallow officer said grudgingly. "This godforsaken place."

"If it's their religion, it's their religion," Fry said, not wanting to be drawn into an argument, yet not wanting to miss a good fight if one were available. "Sort of like Episcopalians and Buddhists. You can't throw out the whole religion because it's not logical!"

"But this filthy stuff! The pain! The misery!"

"Now look, friend. I'm not defending the damned pigs," Fry said. "But for heaven's sake, be consistent. I suppose you're a religious man. You probably believe in something. No, don't tell me what it is. But if it's Christianity, the central fact of your religion is that a living man endured hours of untold agony so that you might be saved." The argumentative officer gasped. "So that you might be ennobled."

"Fry," the officer said, "I always thought there was something wrong with you."

"Wait a minute! I'm not in this. Leave me out. But you made some statements that needed challenging!"

"All that misery. Yes, even torture!"

"I know," Fry said patiently. "Pain is at the center of all religions. Almost all beauty, too. Fine things, like human beings, for example, are born of pain. Of great suffering. Of intense, in-driving horror. Fine things never come cheaply. Suppose the hog had run wild, ground down his tusks? Done what he had damned pleased? Who would have been richer, or wiser, or better? Only the hog and the guy that finally ate him. But as it was! Well, that boar ennobled the life of an entire village."

"And the boar himself?" the sallow officer asked.

"Friend," Tony said. "I'm going to say a pretty harsh thing. Now please don't get mad at me. But here goes. You seem like a funny man to ask such a question. Really you do. No one in this room ought to ask a question like that. Because you are the wild boar. You are staked out unwillingly to your own little troubles. Your tusks are growing in upon you. From the way you look I think you are feeling the misery." Tony looked at the officer and grinned that silly grin of his.

"Just what do you mean?" the officer asked, leaning forward.

"Oh, damn it all," Tony said. "Who started this anyway?"

"You did," the officer replied.

"Well, what I mean is this. I'm arguing from analogy. Here you are, staked out on a jungle island. God knows you didn't elect to come here. Most of you fellows are naval officers because the draft was hot on your necks, and you know it. Each month you are here you grow older and most of you grow poorer. Take Doc Benoway. If he was back home he could be making a thousand dollars a month, or twice that. Yet he's out here. His wife is growing older. He begins to worry about things. The next push. He may be the one that doesn't make it. What holds you fellows here? A three-foot chain to the stake of custom? An idea of patriotism? I don't know why I act the way I do. But if you're interested . . ."

"Go ahead."

"I think there must be something ennobling in this vast and timeless waste. Not to me, but to somebody who follows me. Look, the boar that raised that tusk is dead. He may have been dead fifty years. Yet here we sit admiring it. Well, fifty years from now some-where . . . let's say in Des Moines, Iowa—some high-school girl will suddenly catch a faint intimation of what we accomplished out here." Tony lifted a glass of water and held it against his face. It was cool.

"Filthy!" the sallow officer cried. "It's rotten, the whole business! You're nothing but a dirty bunch of communists. That's what you are, communists!" Saying this he banged out of the door and disappeared in the black night.

"Holy cow!" Fry cried. "Who in the world is that guy?"

"He's having wife trouble. Back home. Poor guy is almost going nuts."

"Why in the world didn't somebody tell me?" Tony asked.

"His performance tonight was merely routine. Last

night he wanted to fight a man who said Los Angeles was bigger than Philadelphia."

"I sure pick the dillies to argue with," Fry laughed. "What happens to a guy like that?"

"We send them home, mostly. Sometimes they snap out of it when real trouble begins on a beachhead. A couple of them have shot themselves. It all works out all right. But if there was ever a wild boar staked out to a three-foot circle, that's the guy."

"I should follow the advice of my uncle," Fry mused. "He says a gentleman never argues except on one question: 'Who picks up the check?' Then it's perfectly legitimate for you to argue that it's the other fellow's turn. Sage advice, that."

On the following Thursday Billis appeared at Pallikulo landing with a crash boat. Naked to the waist, a frangipani in his hair, the doves flying in stately formation toward his heart, and his bracelets jangling, he was a proper figure of a tropical sailor. He was giving the coxswain orders at the rate of six a minute.

Fry and Benoway met him at the pier. "All aboard!" Billis cried. "Anybody else coming?"

"No," Fry replied. He had invited the sallow officer, but that sick man had replied, "No! You and your damned wild pigs." "OK," Fry had said. He could never stay angry at anyone. "Would you like us to bring you back some pineapples?" The officer had looked up warmly, clutching at even the straws of friendship. "Would you?" he asked eagerly. "I don't want to take the ride. I get seasick." "Boy," Tony laughed. "You should see me get seasick!"

Aboard the crash boat Tony and Benoway met the officers and crew and a ruddy little man who wore the

cross of the Chaplains' Corps. "This is Chappy Jones,"
Billis said. "From our outfit. I was tellin' him about the
new religion I found. Even promised him I'd get him
tattooed if he wished!" Billis laughed and the little
chaplain beamed.

"Ah, yes!" he said. "And I presume you are the
doctor?"

"Yes," Benoway nodded.

"Do you think there might really be an epidemic?"
the chaplain asked.

"What?"

"That epidemic you have to go over to investigate,"
Billis interrupted.

"Merely normal precautions," Fry interposed, glar-
ing at Luther.

"What's this . . ." Benoway began.

"It's a rare opportunity for me!" the chaplain said.
"You know, I teach comparative religion at the semi-
nary. Vanicoro is the taboo island in these parts. It's
also the lepers' island. Interesting, almost a parallel to
our medieval belief that the very sick were special wards
of God."

The crash boat was gathering speed through the blue
waters of Pallikulo Bay. Overhead the early morning
planes set out for Guadal and Nouméa. Far up the bay
the great floating drydock was being assembled, and
to the west the daily halo of cloud was gathering upon
the gaunt mountains of Espiritu Santo.

"Lovely day for a trip to a sacred island," Benoway
said.

"Wonderful opportunity for all of us," the chaplain
said. "I don't know of anything in the world quite like
this pig worship. It gives us a unique opportunity to

see the mind of primitive man at work calling forth
his gods."

"What do you mean, chaplain?"

"Here we see a religion spring full blown from the
mind of man. We see it flower in answer to man's expressed needs."

"Then Billis was telling the truth when he said the
pigs were the religion?"

"Ab-so-lute-ly," the ruddy chaplain replied. "The
religion is well known in sociological circles. Well
known. Well documented. As I said, it's unique in this
small circle of islands. From an airplane you can see
with a glance the entire region in which it flourishes."

"What's the religion like?" Benoway asked.

"Primarily it's a monument to man's perversity.
There is no place on earth where living is so easy as on
these islands. They are rich, laden with food, and before
the white man came, inordinately healthy. No one
had to work, for the world was full of fruit and vegetables, and in the woods there was enough wild boar
for everyone. You would have to call it a paradise, even
though most of you may never want to see it again.

"But there was one flaw. Amid all this luxury there
was no reason for living. That may sound like a silly
statement, but it is literally true. There was no reason
for living. Men fought bravely, but they didn't collect
heads to prove it. They ate one another, but when the
meal was done, it was done. They traveled nowhere.
They built nothing. But most of all they worshiped
no gods. There was nothing in life bigger than they
were. Like all people, they had some vague idea of life
after death, but their conceptions were not what we
call codified. All they had were some rough rules of

behavior. Don't kill women. Truce in battle. Things
like that. But up here," the chaplain said, tapping his
temple, "there was a void. There was no reason for
doing anything."

"Are you making this up?" Fry asked in a whimsical
manner.

"Oh, no!" the chaplain assured him. "All a matter of
record. What do you suppose these people living in
their earthly paradise did? Believe it or not, they
decided to make life more difficult for themselves.
They created, at one swoop, something to live for.
Now believe me when I tell you that they took one
of the commonest things in their acquaintance, one of
the dirtiest: a jungle pig. And they made that pig the
center of their aspirations. In one shot they built
themselves a god. And the important thing about it is
this: When the pig was dead and had some eating value,
it was no longer of any merit. Then it wasn't a god any
more. Only when the pig lived in his filthy misery, and
grew tusks back into his own face, and ate your crops,
and took your time, and frightened you when he got
sick, only then was the pig a god! In other words, the
most carefree people on earth consciously made their
lives more difficult, more unhappy, and much more
complex." The chaplain stopped and stared eastward
at Vanicoro. The sacred island was dim and symmetri-
cal in the morning light. Clouds hung over the top-
most volcano where the sacred lake was hidden.

"Are you getting seasick?" the chaplain asked.

"I feel pretty good so far," Benoway replied.

"That's quite a story, Chaplain," Tony said.

"The interesting part is still to come," the slightly
green chaplain said. "I think I'd better stand over here

by the rail. Not only did the natives say that their god had spiritual value only so long as he was a burden. They also say that no pig has social value until it is given away to a friend. If you eat your own pig, you are a glutton and a miser. If you give your pig to somebody else to eat, you're a great man."

"Somewhat like the old Christian religions," Tony mused.

"Very similar," the chaplain agreed. "True spirituality has usually seen that man is happier giving than getting."

"What changed that in our civilization?" Fry asked.

"Some sort of compromise with progress. If you give away all the time, you lose the incentive to gain more, and the incentive to gain is the incentive to create. American civilization has grown too far toward the creating and too far away from the giving. It'll adjust later on. It'll have to. Men will go mad from too much getting. They always have in the past."

"On the other hand," Fry argued, "you'll have to admit that the Melanesian ideal of all giving hasn't produced much."

The chaplain nodded and swept his hand about the horizon. "In these islands you have the lowest ebb of civilization in the world. I don't think mankind can sink much lower than these people. Of course, *sink* is an unfair word. They never reached a point any higher than they are now. Even the Solomon Islanders are ahead of these people."

The crash boat rolled in the swelling sea. Spray came over the prow. The chaplain's face had completely lost its ruddy appearance. "Keep talkin', Chappy!" Billis called encouragingly from his vantage point on the bridge.

"Interesting man, Billis," the chaplain said wanly. "He took me into the jungle a few weeks ago to see a ceremonial. We may see one today. They're unbelievable. A family raises a pig for nine or ten years. It has value only in the fraction of a minute when you stand over it with the sacred club, ready to kill it. Then everybody says, 'Look at the wonderful pig he is going to kill! He must be a very fine man to kill such a pig!' After the pig is dead and the meat given to friends they say, 'The owner of this pig is a wonderful man. Look at all the meat he gave away to his friends.'" The chaplain laughed as he acted out the speeches. It was like being in a pulpit again. Somewhat shaky, but a pulpit all the same.

"Billis tells me we are going to see a truly sacred pig today," he continued. "One whose tusks have made two complete circles! They have burrowed twice through the pig's face and once through the jawbone. I understand men from other villages come from miles about just to see the holy tusker. The chief is going to kill the pig soon. He must. For if that pig were to die, or if it were to break one of its tusks, he would be a scorned man. Everyone would say, 'He was unwilling to give the holy pig away. Now see! It is nothing. It did him no good! A man with only a little pig is better than the chieftain. For the man with the little pig can give it away!' That's exactly what they'd say."

The crash boat rolled and turned. Fry was making bets with himself that the chaplain would heave before the lee of Vanicoro was reached. But the game little fellow stuck it out. "You're lookin' better, Chappy!" irreverent Billis called down from the bridge.

"I feel better!" the chaplain said. The boat was heading for the bay of Bali-ha'i, a tiny island with rocky cliffs facing the sea. "Looks good to see land again," he said.

As soon as the boat was anchored off the white sands of Bali-ha'i, Billis was fighting a rubber dory over the side, giving the coxswain all sorts of help and trouble. Fry, Benoway and the chaplain climbed in. Billis shoved off and rowed energetically toward Banicoro across the channel. As soon as the bumpy little boat hit land, Billis took charge of the expedition.

A group of small boys had gathered to greet the Americans. Billis talked with them briefly and selected a lad of ten to lead him to the high country near the volcanoes. Billis and the boy walked in front, followed by Fry. The chaplain and Benoway brought up the rear.

The party traveled through dense jungle, across small streams and up steep hillsides. At the end of the first mile everyone was sweating freely. The little chaplain dripped perspiration from his thumbs. Fry grunted and swore as the stuff ran off his eyebrows. Billis, surprisingly enough, seemed never to tire. Once he passed a native and his Mary. "Hiya, Joe! Whaddaya know?" he called out in breezy fashion.

The grinning native had been across the sea to Espiritu. He called back, "Good duty, boss!"

"So long, Joe!"

A little while later a chief and his three Maries came along the narrow trail. Billis stopped and talked with them briefly in beach-la-Mar. Then he grinned at the officers. "He says there's a pig killing, all right. Up in the hills."

The narrow trails now became mere threads through the immense jungle. It was difficult to believe that these frail communications had served men and women for more than five hundred years. And they were still the only trails between the hill villages and the sea.

At last the men came to a native village. It was a sight new and strange to Benoway. It was not at all what he had been led to expect. Only by grace of custom could it be called a village. It was more correctly a homestead. Only one family lived there, and they were absent on a visit. Off to a sing-sing somewhere deeper in the jungle. Or maybe to the pig killing higher up the mountainside.

Benoway and the chaplain were tired, so the party rested. The little boy looked on in open disgust while the white men panted and sweated and took off their hot shirts. The kraal in which they had stopped was about forty yards in diameter. Within the fence, made of trees bound together by lianas, not a blade of grass grew. The earth was reddish and packed hard. A few scrawny trees struggled through the earth, all at odd angles from having been bent in youth. Probably the kraal had been there for three hundred years or more.

Within the circle a collection of huts had grown up. Billis explained their uses. "This one for sleepin'. That one for cookin'. That one for chiefs' sons. That one for wives. That one reserved for any special pigs. Over there the hut for Maries goin' to give birth. That far one for Maries menstruatin'."

The total effect of the kraal was planned orderliness.

It looked almost neat. Benoway commented on this fact to Billis. "Why not?" the latter asked. "They got nothin' else to do!"

The men were breathing more easily now. Throwing their completely wet shirts over their shoulders, they climbed upward toward the hill village where the ceremonial killings were to be held. As they neared that high place, weird screams penetrated the jungle.

"Them's the pigs!" Billis explained. His eyes were dancing with expectation. "Them pigs always seem to know." The absorbent jungle muffled the unearthly screams, and there were no echoes. Even though the ritual was holy, the doomed pigs screamed.

The kraal which the men entered was bigger than the earlier one. It was more pretentious, as befitted a chief who had lived in glory and who had a boar with double-circle tusks. The old man came forward to greet the Americans. He jabbered in some strange language with Gillis. There was much solemn shaking of hands.

The chief's long beard hung in two points like a massive W. His face was heavily wrinkled. His teeth were good. Like most natives, he was very thin. He wore a string of shells about his neck. Around his middle he wore a thick belt of palm fronds. In front a woven lap-lap was suspended; behind, a tuft of leaves bobbed up and down. He looked like a rooster when he walked.

In spite of this, he maintained a solemn dignity. He motioned the Americans to a place in the circle of his guests. Seven chiefs were present. Each had brought his sons. In odd corners of the kraal the Maries of the chieftains were gathered, each group on a spot separated from the rest. There was no visiting among the

Maries. But children and dogs raced about the huts. They knew a holiday when they saw one.

In the center of the kraal an altar had been built. It consisted simply of a circle of sanctified palm fronds with room for the old chieftain to stand in the center.

Now from a hut other chiefs brought a sacred frond from a tree growing near the edge of the ancient lake high up among the volcanoes. They blessed it as they gave it to their friend. They likewise blessed the heavy, brutal sacrificial club. It was made of ironwood, that unbelievable jungle wood that rusts in water. The old chief grasped the club, waved it in the air and cried ritualistic phrases.

Blessed by his friends, possessed of the sacred palm frond and the ironwood club, the chief was ready. His six Maries came forward from their recesses along the matted wall. Each led by a jungle rope the boars she had nurtured. If need arose, old men beat the reluctant sacrifices forward. There was infinite screaming. The hot jungle was filled with sound. Relentlessly, with faces unmoved, the women staked their pigs in a semi-circle before the altar. Their chief touched each pig with the ceremonial frond.

The Maries then stood silent. They were naked except for a single strand of fiber about their waists and an even thinner strand in front. "Old superstition!" Billis whispered. "If she moves that strand aside of her own will, it ain't rape."

From the altar the chief presented his oldest Mary with a long, ancient ironwood spear. As she held it aloft, he blessed it. Then the old woman placed the spear upon the testicles of the boar she had reared. As she did so, the other wives in turn solemnly placed

their hands upon the long spear. Then they moved to
the next pig. They were seeking the blessing of fertil-
ity.

Now from the huts came a terrible screaming. The
chief's favorite Mary was bringing forth the pig whose
tusks made two complete circles. It was a small pig,
grown wizened in misery. When it was tied, protesting,
to its stake, the proud woman who had coaxed it to
maturity signified that all barren women in the kraal
were free to share the blessing of its magic testicles. This
they did, reverently, proud to participate in their
friend's good fortune.

The women retired. Within his circle of palm fronds
the old chief waited. "This is his wonderful moment!"
the chaplain whispered. "Watch."

Slowly the other chiefs moved forward. Their tail
feathers bobbed in the hot sunlight. They chanted a
song of praise in honor of the man who was truly rich
because he had so much to give away. Half-doleful at
first, they later burst into violent shouting. At the
height of their song, one suddenly grabbed a pig that
screamed horribly. Even Fry, who knew what to expect, gasped.

Swiftly the old chief raised his massive ironwood club
and smashed it down upon the pig's snout. He then
thundered twenty blows upon the pig's skull. With
great passion he crushed every bone in the pig's head.
Then, with delicate precision, he gave two ceremonial
blows that ended the sacrifice. He completely caved
in all the bones surrounding each eye. Yet in all his
apparently wild smashing, he never touched either of
the tusks. Stained in deep blood, they fulfilled their
function. They brought a fleeting immortality to the

man who gave them away and to the woman who had reared them. Now they dug at the bloody earth into which they were tossed by excited chiefs who chanted new songs and hauled new pigs to the slaughter.

After the fifth pig was killed in this shuddery manner, Benoway found that he had to look away. In doing so he noticed that all other eyes were straining intently at the savage ceremonial. "It must have been like this when Aztecs killed their human sacrifices," he thought. But he, too, looked back when one pig in death throes broke loose and destroyed the circle of palm branches. Drenched in blood, the graceful branches trailed through the red dirt. "How different the significance we place on palm branches," Benoway thought.

"You'll notice," the chaplain was whispering to Fry, "that these people use palm branches, too. I understand the ancient druids did, also. Or something like palm branches."

Fry turned to relay this information to Benoway, but he saw that the doctor was sick at the stomach. "Sorry, old man," he said.

There was a new rain of crunching blows when the pig was recovered. The animal screamed madly, died horribly, and the ceremony drew to a close. Then a hush fell over the packed kraal. The pig of them all was finally hauled forward. For the last twenty minutes he had heard his fellows die protestingly, but he had made no sound. He remained quiet while the chiefs grabbed him. He allowed them to drag him before his ancient master. He cried out only slightly when the first terrible, face-smashing blow fell. By the time his eyes were beaten in there was no more than a dull murmur over the kraal. Benoway had to get up and leave. No one smiled.

The sacred ceremonial branch was broken by the chief. He threw it to the ground and made a short speech in which he divided the dead pigs among his friends. Then, with a rush, the chiefs and their sons fell upon the carcasses and began to dress the meat. They used long knives. With one slash they cut away the pig's head. Then they gutted him and threw the entrails to the Maries, who salvaged edible portions. Dogs dragged the remainders to the corners of the kraal. Finally the carcass was slashed into eight or ten pieces. Deftly the jungle butchers passed tough loops of fiber through the tendons to make handles. These they handed to their wives.

The Americans were offered the four choice chunks. The chaplain started to decline for all, but Billis nudged him. "Hey, Chappy!" he whispered. "Take a couple. We can trade 'em down at the shore. They're mad for hog meat!" So the Americans took two large pieces. Billis breathed more easily. "Hell," he whispered to Fry. "You could get maybe a dozen pineapples for them!"

Young men and women now left the kraal to gather branches for the great fires that would be built. The chiefs talked among themselves for a moment and then deftly cut out the lower jaws from the heads of the dead pigs. From each jawbone two tusks, of varying quality, protruded. Some were mere circles. Others had grown back into the jawbones. All were dirty white against the dark red of the bloody bones.

The old men discussed long and ardently the attributes of each tusk. Never, they agreed, had any chief in their lifetime given away such fine boars. Lovingly the tusks were appraised, but when the double-circle ones were reached the men sat in silent admiration. Such tusks might never again be seen in their declining lifetimes.

Delicately the chief who had dispensed this largess picked up the jawbone with the sacred tusks. He deftly knocked at it with his knife. Then he grasped the tusks firmly and with a harsh, wrenching motion, tore them loose from their long tomb of misery. One he gave to Fry, one to the chaplain. He smiled at them and then nodded. They must go. Soon there would be dancing and feasting and lovemaking. That was a private affair.

Down the long trail to the ocean they went. The chaplain, after carrying his messy tusk for a short distance, said, "Benoway, do you want this?" The doctor leaped for it. Chappy smiled. "The appurtenances of the religion are slightly revolting."

"I feel that way myself, sometimes, on Sunday in Connecticut," Fry laughed.

"You're right, Lieutenant," the chaplain said. "But it takes strong ritual to affect some sinners."

Luther Billis swung along the jungle trails, pushing lianas from his face, shifting the heavy bundle of pork from time to time. He was singing snatches from an old South Seas song he had picked up from a Burns Philp trader:

> *Right above her kidney*
> *Was tattooed the "View of Sydney."*

He was terribly pleased with the day's expedition. Close behind him followed the little native boy, dreaming his heart out as he watched the pork slapping Billis on the back.

19505

from

RETURN
TO
PARADISE

Mr. Morgan

The atolls are beautiful. . . . Not
even the wild hurricanes . . . or
the bitterness of a life slipped past
can subtract one portion of the
crystal beauty of these miraculous
circles in the sea.

WHEN I was a boy we lived in this manner. At six each morning the church bell summoned us to prayer and wardens stood by the entrance checking our names. If a man were missing other wardens were sent running to find him, and if a man and girl were both missing we trembled until they were found, for we knew what the penalty would be if they had been together.

After church we were allowed to go about our duties, except that wardens could summon us to jail at any time if we had broken rules. One day a week we had to work on church land making copra or we fished for pearl shell in the lagoon, turning over all we found to the pastor. We had also to keep careful records of any money we made from schooners, for of this the wardens collected one share in ten, as the Bible directs.

At sunset the bell rang again, and we gathered for prayer. After that we could eat when we wished, but in the evening began the most troublesome of our rules. All young men and all unmarried girls had to

carry lighted lanterns wherever they went. This was
to help the wardens keep track of what was happening
on the island, and if two lanterns were seen heading
toward the bush in back of Matareva, the wardens ran
there to see that no indecencies took place. Of course,
some young men were smart enough to put out their
lights and wait for girls, but if they were caught the
wardens beat them. The girl was further humiliated
next morning in church, after which both the offenders
were sent to jail.

At nine each night the church bell rang again and
everyone had to be indoors. Sometimes it was very
beautiful at that hour. The moon would shine down
upon the lagoon and through the village of Matareva
pale lights would move mysteriously from house to
house. Those were the wardens, checking up to see that
all families were behaving themselves properly. The
wardens had a right to enter any house at any time for
an accounting of what each person inside had been
doing for the past day, but on week nights the wardens
did not abuse this privilege, unless one of them became
attracted to some girl, and then he would break into
her house almost every night, whether she wished him
to or not. It was useless to protest, for the pastor knew
that his control of Matareva depended upon the absolute loyalty of his wardens, whom he excused of even
the most brutal behavior.

On Saturday nights the wardens became especially
active, for no frivolity was allowed from then until
Monday at daybreak. No husband must sleep with his
wife. There must be no kissing, no singing, no reading
of books. The rules were strictly observed in most
homes because on these nights the wardens gave no

warning. There was a rush at the door, a clatter of clubs and people moaning from cracked heads.

On Sunday we prayed three times and had a procession led by the wardens. We marched from the lagoon to the church and stood at solemn attention while the pastor, in a black suit, walked slowly from his house to the church. Then we entered behind him. This took place only at the eleven-o'clock service, but even if it was pouring rain we marched as usual, the wardens with umbrellas, the pastor under a canopy held by four boys.

One Sunday, at the end of an unprecedented spell when fish deserted our lagoon, a school of tunny dashed in through the channel, driven by sharks. They arrived just as the procession started and fishermen who had been without food for days looked passionately at the leaping fish, but wardens dashed up and down striking the men with clubs to keep them from breaking line. On Monday the tunny were gone.

Our law, our parliament, our judge and our business dictator were all one man: the pastor. His name was Thomas Cobbett and he came from some unidentified rural village, perhaps in New Zealand or Northern England. In appearance he was ordinary, a small man with watery blue eyes. Actually he was an inspired prophet right from the latter pages of the Old Testament, with a penetrating voice and a sure faith that God personally guided him in the government of our atoll. He appeared always in a black suit and, when surrounded by his burly wardens, was a terrifying symbol of God's wrath in Matareva.

Often we puzzled why the government permitted him to usurp its powers, but many years later an official

explained that there had been so much clamor about
Christianizing the islands that it was decided to leave
one forgotten atoll exclusively to missionaries so as to
test what they could accomplish.

Pastor Cobbett accomplished miracles. Even today
many people will say there was never a finer island than
Matareva in the old days. We were forced to bathe
each afternoon. We had to kill the land crabs that
burrowed in our gardens, buy screens for our kitchens
and nail tin around our coconut trees to keep rats from
eating the young nuts. We had to burn coral to make
lime for painting our houses, and our walks had to be
lined with white shells. Every woman worked one day
a week at the church, so that the gardens there were
the most beautiful in the Pacific.

The pastor was equally relentless regarding our
spiritual lives. The old music, which everyone knows to
have been lascivious, was forbidden and replaced by
church hymns. Dancing was completely taboo and
wardens could arrest anyone who dared to start the
lewd old hulas. Everyone had to get married, widows
must not talk with men except in the presence of
other women and the number of illegitimate babies—a
phrase never used on our island before Pastor Cobbett's
time—was much reduced. There were some, of course,
for in the old days girls had babies before they were
married as proof that they would make good wives, but
Pastor Cobbett raved against the practice and the
penalties were brutally severe except when the father
proved to be a warden. If the warden was unmarried,
he had to marry the girl right away. If he already had a
wife, he was reprimanded in private and the girl was
publicly humiliated before the entire village on Sunday

morning. She had to march from the rear of the big church up to the altar, fall upon the floor, put a black cloth over her head and walk back past all of us. It was always surprising to me that any girl would have the courage to risk such public shame, but many did and it was found that old women of the village supported them in their behavior, but as the old women died off, the girls found no consolation and some of them committed suicide, a thing never before heard of in our village.

Did no one revolt against this tyranny? As I said, some old women tried, because not even the wardens were cowardly enough to beat an old woman. Nor was the pastor able to quell them, for when he preached against them they stared back with implacable hatred. He solved the impasse by having his wardens spy on the family of the offending woman until a son or husband was detected breaking some trivial rule. Then the old women learned that no one could get the better of Pastor Cobbett. Once a man tried, but he was thrashed so often and spent so much time in jail that he fled to Tongareva, but his canoe was fragile. It capsized and he was eaten by sharks. After that Pastor Cobbett ruled our lives inflexibly.

But in 1919 a small schooner from Suva put into our lagoon and landed a man who was to revolutionize Matareva. He was a tall thin man with stooped shoulders and a dark complexion. He wore a dirty shirt, unbuttoned, and white cotton pants that seemed always about to slip off his hips. He had no shoes, a battered hat, a small suitcase. He stood on the wharf and stared at our village. Then he hitched up his pants with his wrists and said, "Just what I expected. "I'll stop here."

The pastor hurried up and said, "There are no houses."

"I'll build one," the stranger replied.

"We have no materials. None."

"Those leaf huts look OK to me," the man said.

The pastor grew red in the face and said bluntly, "We don't want white men on this island."

So the stranger dropped his suitcase, planted his hands on his hips and growled, "You sound like a sergeant."

The pastor shouted for his wardens, who ran up with clubs, but the barefooted stranger sidestepped them, searching for some weapon of his own. An old woman kicked him a board, and with it he fairly flew at the astonished wardens, who were accustomed to punishing men afraid to strike back.

The stranger fought with such fury as we had not seen before, and soon the fat bullies retreated with bad bruises, leaving the amazed pastor alone by the wharf. The visitor walked up to him and said, "The name's Morgan. I'll build my house over here."

That night he stayed with my father, and at great risk to themselves, four men of the village crept into our house after midnight. "Morgan Tane," they whispered, "that was a good fight you did!"

"We were proud to see the wardens run," another whispered.

"Morgan Tane," said the spokesman, "you were brave to challenge the pastor. No one has ever been so brave before." There was a long silence and then the spokesman said in a hushed voice, "We have been waiting for a man like you. Will you help us to fight against the wardens?"

The stranger answered promptly. "Me? I didn't come down here to fight. I had enough of that."

"But Morgan Tane," the spokesman whispered, "here you will find no peace. The wardens will never let you spend one night in peace."

The stranger lit a cigarette, puffed on it several times and said, "Then I'll have to do something about it."

"Good!" the men cried. "We'll have a great rebellion."

"You don't understand," Mr. Morgan corrected them. "I'm not interested in trouble. I'm not going to be your leader. I'm not going to fight the wardens. I came down here for rest and quiet."

"But if the wardens . . ."

"It looks to me as if each man has got to handle them his own way. I'm going to bed."

He started building his house next day, and by Sunday he was completely involved in our struggle against the pastor, for as we prepared for the customary procession, it was noticed with hushed surprise that Mr. Morgan, bare to the waist, was hammering on his rooftree. Two wardens were sent to haul him into church, but they retreated in dismay when he produced a shotgun and said, "This thing is loaded."

They rushed off to report the crisis to the pastor, who came out into the road and studied the infidel from a safe distance. Then he wiped his face and waited for the congregation to reach the church. When the procession passed the uncompleted house, Mr. Morgan stopped his hammering and sat cross-legged on a barrel, weaving pandanus during the service. After the closing hymn he went back to the rooftree.

Pastor Cobbett knew that if he let this insult go unpunished, his hold upon Matareva was doomed, so when church was over he gathered his wardens and strode to the place where the white man was working.

"Mr. Morgan!" the pastor cried in his sepulchral voice. "Do you intend to desecrate the Sabbath?"

"Go away!" Mr. Morgan growled.

"You have spoken," Pastor Cobbett cried in terrible tones. "Now God shall destroy this sacrilege."

The pastor stepped up to the nearest pole and began to shake it as Samson shook the pillars of the temple. "Don't be a damned fool," Mr. Morgan called down from the rooftree.

"Come! Wardens! Everybody! Pull down the house of evil." The wardens, who knew of the shotgun, refused, but there were many natives who believed that Cobbett's voice was the voice of God, and these sprang into action, pulling down one of the posts so that a corner of the new house collapsed, tossing Mr. Morgan into the dust.

There was a moment of fateful silence as he slowly picked himself up, brushed off his pants and stood with his feet apart in the dust, studying the pastor. Finally he asked, "Reverend, are you crazy?"

"God has spoken," the missionary cried in his Old Testament voice. "Men, destroy the blasphemy!"

The hypnotized natives rushed to the remaining poles and ripped them from the ground. Mr. Morgan remained with his head cocked to one side, staring with amazement at the impassioned scene. Still he did nothing and Pastor Cobbett exulted in victory, crying, "The devil in our midst has been cast out."

That was enough. Mr. Morgan looked at the pastor

with disgust and said, "They shouldn't of let you out of the booby hatch." He rummaged among the ruins of his house and then walked doggedly to a spot some thirty feet away. There he raised his shotgun and with six cold, deliberate blasts destroyed each of the stained-glass windows in the church. They had been the glory of Matareva, and as they crashed an anguished sob arose from the watchers.

Pastor Cobbett stood like a man who has seen death striding across the motus. When he finally found strength to speak, a last fragment of window fell into the dust. He threw his hands over his face and gave an animal-like wail: "Sodom and Gomorrah have come! Surely God will strike this island with pestilence and evil." So powerful was his cry that true believers started to quake as if the day of judgment were at hand.

Mr. Morgan stalked back through the trembling crowd and hitched up his dirty pants. "Pastor," he said firmly, "if you want to hold prayer meeting, do it on your own land. Get off mine." He flourished the empty gun and the fearful natives drew back in horror as if he were truly cursed. Pastor Cobbett, still staring at the mutilated windows, made incoherent sounds and licked his parched lips.

"All right," Mr. Morgan said. "Who's going to help put these poles back in place?" No one moved. "Well, come on! You knocked them down."

Pastor Cobbett shrieked, "If anyone dares aid the infidel, God will strike him dead!"

"Please!" Mr. Morgan cried. "Shut up! Now you, Teofilo. Grab the pole." There was a deep silence. Many men must have wanted to aid the stranger, but they knew that when he left Matareva, Pastor Cobbett and the wardens would remain behind. No one would help.

"God be praised!" the pastor exulted.

Then a most memorable thing happened. In Matareva there was a girl named Maeva. Even on our island of beautiful girls she was handsome. She had very long hair that was envied by our women, strong arms and good teeth, but although she was already past twenty no man had married her because Pastor Cobbett said she was cursed of the devil because she refused to carry a lighted lantern at night.

Now she left the huddled crowd and crossed to where Mr. Morgan was waiting. "I will help you," she said.

"Wardens!" shouted the pastor. "Take that evil girl!"

"Reverend," the stranger said patiently. "For the last time, go home."

"Wardens! Wardens! Seize her!"

Mr. Morgan waved the empty shotgun at the crowd and said, "If you don't want to work, get out!"

Slowly the wardens withdrew. Now Pastor Cobbett stood alone, facing Mr. Morgan and the girl. "Maeva!" he cried in an ashen voice, both commanding and pleading. "Your soul will rest in hell."

Mr. Morgan turned his back on the lonely, apocalyptic figure and said to the girl, "You? What's your name?"

"Maeva," she said.

"That's an odd name. Bring me the hammer."

That night in my father's kitchen a group of Matareva men assembled secretly. They said, "The wardens are afraid of this man. Even the pastor can do nothing.

It's time for us to drive our persecutors from the island."

My father said, "It would be fatal to start a rebellion that didn't succeed."

"With Mr. Morgan it will have to succeed," another whispered.

A warden came to the door and the men hid under the porch. "Everybody here?" the warden asked.

"Yes," my father replied. Then he crept across the yard where my mother plants the crotons and hibiscus and in a few minutes he was back with Mr. Morgan.

"Morgan Tane," our oldest man said, "you are at war with the pastor. Good! May we join you?"

"Look, old man!" Mr. Morgan replied. "I'm at war with nobody. Now don't bother me any more."

He left us, but on Saturday he discovered that he had been wrong. He was at war. It began this way. Maeva, who had been working with Mr. Morgan, had slept each night at her brother's, but on Friday the wardens waited for her and had beaten her severely.

Next morning she limped up to the new house and sat upon the porch, her nose dripping blood. Some old women who hated the pastor gathered in bitter groups along the road. No one spoke. A warden went past and took the names of all who were watching.

Mr. Morgan rose late that day, for he had been working hard all week. The old women saw him stretch, sluice his head with a bucket of cold water and look at his tongue in a mirror. Then he came onto the front porch.

He looked with cold fury at Maeva's handsome face, all smeared with blood. Next he looked at the crowd of old women. It was a long time before he did anything. Then he fetched a basin of water and there on the front porch fixed Maeva's nose. It had been broken. After that he took her inside.

All that day there was whispered bitterness across Matareva. Word passed that any plans for rebellion must be stopped, for again the wardens had triumphed. It was said that what had happened to Maeva had finally convinced Mr. Morgan that resistance was useless.

On Saturday night, therefore, the wardens raided my father's home with new brutality and beat him for some minutes, adding, "We know you were talking with the white man. We know everything."

On Sunday we gathered as usual at the lagoon and lined up as the wardens directed. The bell rang strangely through the shattered windows and our procession started toward the imposing door.

At this moment Mr. Morgan appeared barefooted on the porch of his new house. Behind him stood the girl Maeva, her face bandaged. With long, careless steps, his toes kicking dust, the stranger walked along the dusty road and right up to the line of wardens. "Which one of them was it, Maeva?"

The handsome girl, her hair down to her waist, stepped from behind Mr. Morgan and pointed fearlessly at one of the worst wardens. "That one," she said.

The white man lifted his shotgun and there was a terrified gasp from the crowd, but he handed it to the girl and said, "I showed you how to use this. If anyone— a warden, the pastor, anyone comes at me, kill him."

Then slowly, like a wave about to crash upon the reef, he went to the warden who had beaten Maeva and with a sudden grab pulled the hulking man out of line. In silence, and in fearful efficiency, he beat the man until it seemed as if his small right hand could drive no more. The warden was fat, cowardly. Twice Mr. Morgan hauled him to his feet and waited until the bully got set. Then with merciless blows he knocked him down again. Blood was spattered across the white uniform.

So awesome was this cruel scene that no one in the procession moved, but we could see the beating from where we stood, and when it became apparent that Mr. Morgan was willing to fight the entire force of wardens, one after the other, a murmuring restlessness agitated the crowd and it appeared there might be a general uprising, but this was forestalled by the appearance of Pastor Cobbett.

"No one must move!" he cried in his great prophetic voice, but when he saw the ruined face of his leading warden he turned pale. Mr. Morgan, tired and breathless, stood back on his heels, blood across his dirty, sagging pants.

He spoke first. "The wardens told you I'd run away. Well, I like it here. I'll probably stay the rest of my life." He grabbed the shotgun from Maeva and walked slowly back to his house alone, and as we watched him go, barefooted and bent forward, we knew that even though he would not lead our rebellion, he was from that day on an atoll man.

We never called him by any name but Mr. Morgan. He received twelve letters a year, no more, no less, each from the United States Government. Once when he cashed a batch of his pension checks with a passing trader he said, "It's good money. I earned it. Got shot up in France while the rich kids in our block stayed home." His only other reference to America came one night when the ocean hammered the reef in great violence, making thunder. "Sounds like the Third Avenue El," he said.

We were much surprised that after the fight he did not take the girl Maeva home with him. It was obvious that he could have any girl he wanted. He was brave and he had a regular income. At night pretty wahines began to drift by his house, but he took no notice of them. When curfew rang he usually went right to bed, and twice when girls braver than the rest snuffed out their lanterns and hid upon his porch, he put on his sagging pants and led them boldly to their homes, where he delivered them to their mothers.

It may seem strange to people not of the islands, but we were all offended, men and women alike, that a stranger should have come among us and found our girls undesirable. My mother was commissioned to talk this over with Mr. Morgan, and she asked, "Are they not beautiful?"

"They're all right," Mr. Morgan said, his hands in his pockets.

"Then why don't you take one into your house? To mend your clothes? To cook?"

"Look," said the man gruffly. "I don't want any women around."

Yet it was he who finally ended the foolishness of the lanterns. It happened this way. My mother is not easily put off. She knew that every man needs a woman for cleaning up, if for nothing more. So she went to see Maeva, whose nose had now healed. She said, "Maeva, you must not let Morgan Tane live alone. It is no good." But Maeva replied that when she looked in the mirror she was ashamed. The wardens had beaten her so that she thought herself no longer pretty. But Mother knows well how love works and she said, "He will look at the hurts you received for him and he will let you stay."

So Maeva combed her hair, made a wreath of frangipani for her head and washed her feet. Then she went to the new house with her bed mats. She arrived when Mr. Morgan was on the reef and by the time he returned at sunset a fine meal was ready.

"That looks good," he said, and they ate together. Maeva had a face that men enjoyed to look at, so they spent a long time eating and finally Mr. Morgan stood up and ran his finger along her nose. "It's not much of a nose," he apologized.

"You fixed it well," she insisted.

"It's all right," he said. "Now you must go home."

Maeva allowed tears to come into her eyes and said, "Morgan Tane, it is no good for you to live alone. See, I have brought my things." With her brown foot she pushed open the door to the small room and there on the floor beside his large bed lay her sleeping mats.

Mr. Morgan studied them for a while and then stooped down and rolled them into a heap. He tossed them over his shoulder and started out the door. "Please, Morgan Tane!" the girl cried. "Not while it is still light. The village will laugh at me."

He dropped the mats and sat with Maeva while darkness crept over the lagoon. "Have you a wife?" she whispered. "In America?"

"Me? No."

"I am sorry," she said. "I am sorry you do not know

that it is good for each man to have his wahine." She moved very close to him and that night he did not make her leave.

Of course the wardens noticed this, and early next morning, when Mr. Morgan was out to buy some canned beef from the Chinaman, they descended on the house and arrested her, being very careful not to hurt her in any way, for they wished this affair to be completely legal.

At the jail Pastor Cobbett listened to the evidence and promptly sentenced her to three weeks at hard labor. The jail doors were locked and Maeva went to work.

When Mr. Morgan returned with the meat, he assumed that Maeva had gone back to her own home for a while, but when noon passed he felt a little relieved that he was not going to be bothered with a woman about the house. He preferred not to be bothered, so at dusk he carried Maeva's bed mats back to her mother. Within a few minutes he learned what had happened.

In a blind rage he stormed up to the jail and demanded that Maeva be released. The jailer said Pastor Cobbett had the keys, so Mr. Morgan grabbed a chair and knocked the door down. Then he set Maeva free and when the girl stepped into the street she was surrounded by other girls, each with a lighted lantern. Angrily Mr. Morgan took a big stick and broke every lantern. The wardens, seeing that he had no shotgun with him, started to close in on him all together, but he shouted for the men of Matareva, and at last the great rebellion was on.

We burned down the jail, ripped the handsome doors off the church and chased the wardens all across the island. Whenever we caught one we threw him back to the women, who did many funny things to the fat men, I can tell you.

Under Mr. Morgan's direction all the wardens were finally herded together by the lagoon. Their uniforms were disgraced in the mud. Their heads were sore from women's fists. "You'll leave the island forever," Mr. Morgan said.

The men of Matareva then cried, "Where is the pastor?"

The mob rushed to his house, but he was waiting for us. He had been waiting since midnight, a small, watery-eyed man in a black suit. He appeared on the porch and slowly the rebellion stood at attention. Pastor Cobbett raised his eyes and moaned, "God will condemn the island of Matareva forever!" The men nearest the porch moved back.

Now Mr. Morgan came up and said, "Go on back to bed, Pastor."

"God will bring all the curses of Babylon upon you!" the prophetic voice cried.

"What do you know about God?" Mr. Morgan asked impatiently, jumping onto the porch and shoving the little missionary back into the safety of the house.

Then there was a shout at the lagoon, and Mr. Morgan had to hurry down there, for some women had got hold of the worst warden and were beating him up all over again. Mr. Morgan made my father's house the new jail and put three men to protect the wardens until a schooner could be sent to Tahiti.

The long night ended with everyone singing and shouting. Then suddenly there was a profound silence, for to the east, behind the church spire, the sun began to rise. It flooded Matareva with wonderful light, and it was a great majesty to all of us, for in my lifetime the people of my village had never before stayed up all night. An old woman began a few nimble steps, and soon the entire population was chanting the fine dirty songs of long ago. "Wahine! Tane!" The music grew louder and we danced.

In the soberness of daylight my father and the village leaders met with Mr. Morgan to discuss what must be done next. "Done?" he asked. "I guess we'll have to build a new jail."

"What we mean is, about the pastor?"

"Why do anything about him?" Mr. Morgan asked.

"We'll need a new government. We must report what has happened."

"We don't need a new government," Mr. Morgan said.

"But the pastor?"

"There's nothing wrong with him. You've just got to stand up to him, that's all."

"But Morgan Tane, now that you have led us . . . We would like it if you agreed . . ."

"Don't take things too seriously," he said sleepily. "It's just like in France. We had a rotten sergeant. We argued with him. Then we beat the living hell out of him. After that things were all right."

"You mean you're willing to have Pastor Cobbett stay here?" my father asked in astonishment.

"Why not?" the tired man asked, and with that he went off to bed.

The effect of these events on Pastor Cobbett was unbelievable. When the wardens were banished we expected him to flee also. Instead, he became more active than ever. Shorn of his temporal power, he increased his spiritual dominion over us. We would see him night and day tirelessly tramping our atoll, exhorting people to mind the ways of God. He had no pride, no shame. He would burst upon unmarried lovers and stand there in the midst of their confusion, pleading with them to marry like decent Christians.

He was now in his sixties, a little man with a mass of white hair. He continued to wear black suits and his voice was more booming than ever. We were no longer required to attend church but most of us did, for he changed the service to make it more inviting. He introduced twice as many songs and even fitted his own religious words to robust island tunes. I think he knew that our women mumbled the original verses about lovemaking by the lagoon, but he seemed not to care so long as they came to church. And always there was that small figure, thinner now, probing into every corner of island life.

For example, he went boldly to Mr. Morgan's house and said, "Morgan, you and Maeva ought to get married."

"Have a chair," Mr. Morgan said gruffly.

"I don't suppose you've ever thought about it," Pastor Cobbett said, "but Maeva would like it."

"I don't think she'd care," Mr. Morgan replied.

"Why not let her decide?" the pastor suggested.

"Hasn't she had enough of your religion? Broken nose? Public shame?"

"Mr. Morgan," the pastor cried as if he were in church, "where God is concerned things like that don't matter."

"You'd better go, Pastor. Such talk makes me sick."

"I'll call Maeva." Without waiting for permission the little man went to the door and shouted for the girl to come in. She was pregnant at the time and seemed one great, placid ball of humanity.

"Pull up a chair," Mr. Morgan said.

"Maeva," Pastor Cobbett began, "I've come here to ask Morgan Tane to marry you. In the church. Would that please you?"

The black-haired native girl looked at the two men, the one who had broken her nose, the one who had mended it with his own hands, and although she knew that she was offending the latter she said quietly, "Yes."

Pastor Cobbett rose dramatically and said, "You're right, Maeva. Any decent Christian woman wants to be married." With that he left.

There was a long discussion between Maeva and Mr. Morgan, but he finally said, "I understand how you feel, but I don't think I'll get married."

Nor did Pastor Cobbett content himself merely with religious matters. He performed all his old governmental functions, aided now by a council of native men, including my father, and he evolved the new plan whereby we made a better grade of copra for sale direct to Belgium.

Once, after a long meeting about health rules, he excused himself and went back to see Mr. Morgan, who never attended any discussions.

"I'm not going to argue with you, Morgan," he said bluntly. "I just want to tell you that I've seen lots of white men in the tropics. They all face three inevitable tests. One, have they the courage to marry the girl? Two, are they proud of her when she is pregnant for the first time? Three, and when the boat arrives from their own country—it always arrives, Morgan—do they introduce the woman and her dark children to their countrymen?"

That was all he said, and he must have known a great deal about Mr. Morgan, for the white men failed each test. He never married Maeva. Furthermore, he was ashamed and perplexed while she was pregnant, indifferent when the girl was born. And when schooners put into the atoll, Maeva and the baby were forbidden to appear in the front part of the house.

Once an American yacht sought refuge in our lagoon, but Mr. Morgan avoided the crew. Finally three of them forced their society upon him with loud cries of, "They say you're a real Yankee beachcomber!" He did not invite them into his house, but they came anyway with three cases of beer. When they were brave with drink one asked, "Is it true you're married to a beautiful native girl?"

"That's right," Mr. Morgan replied, his shoulders bent forward and his hands in the pockets of his sagging white pants.

We never understood what he did with his time. He didn't write. He never read books. He didn't like to fish nor did he sit and yarn with people about the old times. He was a man who lived entirely within himself. He did not even take pleasure in his glowing wahine, who always walked five steps behind him when they went to the beach for a swim.

And yet we knew that here was a brave man, perhaps the bravest we had ever known. Because of this knowledge, our disappointment in him was trebled, for we had hoped that he might lead us to a better way of life, one with more purpose and happiness. He was not concerned with this, and painfully we discovered that he stood for nothing. He was a moral zero and we knew that such a man could never show us how to govern Matareva.

When I became the schoolteacher I understood why my father and the other old men returned at last to the pastor. He stood for something. Of course, when he ranted, "It's God's will!" we were no longer fooled. We knew that no man can say what God's will is, but we also knew it was important that we be led by someone who was at least concerned about what that will might be. We had hoped for a better man than the pastor to lead us, but failing that we had to make do with what was at hand.

The years passed and we forgot Mr. Morgan. Life passed him by and he walked the beach, a man of no consequence, a man loved by no one except perhaps Maeva. Then suddenly he was catapulted tragically back into the orbits of our village as he had been years before. Now the women of Matareva gathered before the white man's house and wept, saying to one another, "At least he's human, like the rest of us."

Maeva was deeply stricken with our most dreaded illness, tuberculosis. I am told that elsewhere this disease lingers in the patient's lungs for many years. It is not so with us. There is the racking cough, the pallor under our brown skins and the chest all caved away. There is nothing we can do against tuberculosis, nothing except die.

I often saw Maeva in the last stages of her illness. It was terrifying. Here was a strong woman who had fished off the reef in her own canoe, yet now she was thin as a ghost, her face fallen in. Here was a girl so beautiful that sailors from schooners would walk like schoolboys to her house, bringing gifts, yet now even her lovely lips were sunk into the gasping mouth. She lay on the floor where she had always slept, and no one could look at her without knowing that death must already be sailing his canoe at the reef's edge.

The effect on Mr. Morgan was something nobody could have predicted. He seemed to us never to have loved his wife, yet now he sat day after day with her, his unlighted pipe between his teeth. He had sent his daughter to a family down the beach while he sat in the silent house caring for the dying girl.

Once when Pastor Cobbett came to talk with Maeva, Mr. Morgan could bear no longer the sight of that vanished face and he burst from the house like a madman. He came rushing down to see my father and cried, "God! God! She just lies there!" My father took him for a walk along the lagoon, but the pounding waves that roared upon the reef reminded the shivering man of Maeva fishing. The stars coming out were like the candles she had burned in his house. He walked mechanically until my father had to leave him, and all that night Pastor Cobbett stayed with Maeva. In the morning Mr. Morgan returned, apparently reconciled to what must happen. When the pastor had trudged off, the white man said, "The lagoon with stars upon it is beautiful, Maeva." So far as we knew, he had never before commented in any way about the atoll he had shared for many years. Now he walked endlessly among us, hurrying back to Maeva to tell her how we looked, what we were doing that day. Once he stopped me and grabbed me by the arm. "Have you ever seen heron crashing down on a fish?" It was a common sight, the great black bill snipping the water, but he stood there transfixed.

The next day Pastor Cobbett asked Mr. Morgan if Maeva would like to have a few prayers. Mr. Morgan said he didn't think so, but Pastor Cobbett said he would come in anyway. He was there when Maeva died, quietly, as if not knowing that this sleep was different. For a moment Mr. Morgan would not believe that she was dead, and then he stood by the bed crying, "No! No!"

All night he stood there by the wasted figure on the mat. Our old women came to dress the body and they thought it improper that he should watch them, but he would not leave. When the village keeners came to wail their penetrating lament for the dead soul on its vast journey, he fell into a chair and kept his hands over his ears. The weird cry of the mourners drove him mad and he shouted that they must stop, but they could no more forsake the dead than they could stop the sun from climbing at last above the trees of Matareva.

At the funeral Pastor Cobbett stood by the grave and preached great moving words so that we all wept for this good woman who was dead, but before the pastor ended Mr. Morgan left the graveyard and returned to the lagoon beach, where he walked for many hours. Finally the pastor said to me, "You must talk with him. He would be offended if I did."

I followed him until he turned and saw me unexpectedly. Again he grabbed my arm imploringly and asked in a hushed voice, "Have you ever seen a star like that? Casting a shadow across the lagoon?"

I said that at Matareva we often saw that star and he threw his hands across his face and cried, "There

was so much Maeva could have shown me!" He walked
off in agony and I watched him for a long time.
Finally I went up to him and said, "Morgan Tane, I
think we should go to the Chinaman's and have a
beer."

"That's a good idea," he said.

We went to Ah Kim's and opened two bottles, but
after drinking only part of his Mr. Morgan said, "I
think I'll go to bed."

We expected this upheaval of his world to bring Mr.
Morgan at last into the heart of our village, but instead
it drove him further from us. He did not even bother to
recover his daughter from the house along the beach,
and the family living there were very happy to keep
the girl as their own, for they prized a white man's
child.

So once more we forgot Mr. Morgan. He caused no
trouble, spent his money cautiously. Sometimes from
my school window I would see him shuffling barefooted
along the beach, his shirt open, his pants hanging low
upon his hips. Often he did not shave and for days on
end we might not see him. His daughter Turia was
growing up, a bright, fine-limbed girl like her mother.
Once Pastor Cobbett, now seventy-six, found her with
a sailor off an Australian ship and punished her on the
spot. Mr. Morgan, when he heard of this, said she
probably deserved it.

That is how things were in 1941, and then one day a
schooner called to say that Honolulu had been
bombed. We had an old radio on Matareva and under
Pastor Cobbett's excited urgings a man from the
schooner got it working. For days on end the pastor sat
transfixed before it, piecing together the news of war

in our ocean. He borrowed a map from my school and
called the head men of the village together. He proved
it inevitable that Japan would invade Matareva and to
prevent this organized a complete lookout system, a
line of fighters for the beaches and a hiding place for
the radio.

Early in his operations the frenzied little missionary
approached Mr. Morgan, who said, "The Japs'll never
bother with this dump."

"But in war we must be prepared!" the pastor argued.

"I fought my war," Mr. Morgan replied.

"But it's your nation that is threatened!" Cobbett
cried angrily.

"They're tough. They can look out for themselves."

He would take no part in the wild plans evolved by
the pastor, but when the government destroyer put into
our lagoon and reviewed what Cobbett had done the
defense minister said, "Remarkable! Remarkable! All
we need give you chaps is a radio for sending as well
as receiving." Later the government had to impose
strict rules about this radio, for Pastor Cobbett reported voluminously every four hours.

Yet it was this radio which finally brought Matareva
full into the war. Pastor Cobbett was listening one
rainy, wind-swept afternoon when he heard the lonely
signal of an American plane, lost in a violent storm.
He rushed into the road crying, "Plane trying to find
Bora Bora!" We hurried to the radio and heard a plea
for any kind of help.

I was handed the microphone, and for twenty minutes I repeated over and over, "C-47. C-47. This is
Matareva. Bad storm outside the reef, but you can land

in the lagoon." It was weird and haunting to be sending words that might never be heard. Then finally came the crackling whisper: "Matareva. Matareva. We cannot land on water. Have you level ground?" The men about me argued for a moment and I reported, "C-47. C-47. There is no land. Crash on calm water a hundred yards from shore. Our canoes will save you." I said this fifteen times and at last we heard the bewildered pilot: "I cannot get there before dark. Matareva. Matareva."

A tall figure stepped beside me, barefooted, stoop-shouldered, no shirt. Mr. Morgan said, "We'll put lights on the motus. Lights around the lagoon."

"C-47," I cried in the flat voice that betrays no hope, no fear. "We will light the lagoon as follows." I started to explain but the pilot broke in: "How will we know where the shore is?"

Mr. Morgan grabbed the microphone. "Come in, you damned fools," he snapped. "You've nowhere else to go. Head between the green lights. Land short of the red ones." And as I sat there, encouraging the pilot, Mr. Morgan dashed out into the rain and shouted for everyone on Matareva either to get into his canoe or take a light and stand along the reef. When the first lights blew out he cried above the storm, "Pastor! Didn't you have some extra lanterns in the church?" When a man near the lagoon cried, "No plane can land in this storm," Mr. Morgan snapped, "If we don't save them, they're too dumb to save themselves."

He took a motorboat and a dozen lanterns wrapped in whatever green cloth the women could provide. He called for volunteers and set out across the lagoon to where the great waves thundered on the reef. Night came, and about the entire lagoon you could see the

thin ring of lights, green clusters to the west, a red
cluster marking the landing course.

"C-47. C-47," I called. "Everything is ready. The
canoes will be at your side within a minute after you
land."

The pilot called back in an ashen voice, "The lights?
All set?"

"Come in between the green. Finish at the red."

And then Pastor Cobbett took the microphone and
said in a low, powerful voice, "Pilot! God will bring
your plane in. God is riding with you."

The wind howled but above it we heard the droning
of a crippled motor. We had never seen an airplane at
Matareva, and everyone along the lagoon, those with
beacons and those who tensely clutched their paddles,
stared into the sky. A wavering light appeared and an
astonished cry rose from all Matareva. The plane was
so big. It was so low.

It came roaring in between the green lights. Its wing
dipped perilously toward the water, then straightened.
There was a long hiss, a flash of spray and gas tanks
exploding in the night.

Instantly our canoes dashed in among the flames and
our pearl divers leaped into the crackling waters. Not
one American was lost.

We had a night of wild celebration. Each man of
Matareva thought himself a true hero. We spoke endlessly of what we had done, whose canoe had been first
among the flames, which man had stood knee deep
among the sharks, waving his green lantern.

There were six Americans and we were amazed at
how young they were. Their navigator, no more than a
boy, blubbered when he saw Mr. Morgan. "We had a

million dollars' worth of medicine and radio in that plane. We lost it all."

"There's plenty more where that came from," Mr. Morgan said. He took the six men to his house and for the next three weeks Matareva knew such excitement as we had never experienced before. The talk was all of America, and slowly Mr. Morgan became involved. He said, "Forget Pearl Harbor. We lose lots of battles. But we win lots of wars." He stared pointedly at Pastor Cobbett and said, "We taught the British all about that."

Once the plane captain, Harry Faber, said, "It was almost a miracle! I was scared silly, but when I got my last instructions from your radio I took off the headphones and said, 'Here we go!' Then I heard a voice as clear as I can hear yours saying, 'You are in God's care.' And even though the plane exploded, we all got out."

"What did the voice sound like?" Mr. Morgan asked.

"Deep. Powerful. Speaking right to me."

"It was a miracle all right," Mr. Morgan said disgustedly. But when the picket boat came to take the flyers on to Samoa, he followed them right to the tip end of the wharf and shouted, "Give those Japs hell!"

Now he was truly at war. The picket boat gave him a large map and some colored pins. He kept it at the Chinaman's, and there he and Pastor Cobbett would sit hour after hour marking out the radio reports. We called them Churchill and Roosevelt, and when portentous things happened like El Alamein or the entry into Paris, the entire island would celebrate.

When the war ended, an American warship came to Matareva to give the island a scroll thanking us for our

part in saving an American crew. The pastor had a big
day! He arranged formal ceremonies and appeared in
his black suit to give a long invocation. At the end
of the prayer an American flag was hoisted over the
church and the American officials gave Mr. Morgan a
medal "for improvising a landing strip under extreme
difficulties." They also left the flag, which to our surprise Mr. Morgan nailed on the wall of his front room.
When boys of our village came to talk with him about
America, he served citronade and said, "Now there's
one country you ought to see!"

He lived in this way until 1946, when a schooner
from Australia dropped by and landed a young man
in khaki shorts. Before he had left the wharf our girls
were screaming, "Harry Faber! American pilot! He
come back!"

He hurried right to Mr. Morgan's house and clapped
the tall man on the shoulders. "I swore I'd get back
here to say thanks." He brought us six crates of things
contributed by members of the crew we had saved.
There were radios, iceboxes, many jazz records, books
and more than a dozen fine Army blankets. "All
stolen," he said proudly.

We made a great festivity for Harry, and the record
player was set up in Mr. Morgan's front room, beneath
the flag, where we gathered many nights to hear Bing
Crosby.

But before long we noticed that Harry Faber was
rarely at these pleasant sessions, and my mother, who
always hears these things first, said that he was spending his nights with Turia Vanaavoa, as Mr. Morgan's
daughter was now called.

Soon everyone on the island knew about the love

affair, except Mr. Morgan, whom no one told such things. Then one day an old woman said approvingly, "Wouldn't it be wonderful if the American married your daughter?"

It took about a minute for the implication of this question to reach his brain. He looked very puzzled and asked, "Turia . . . Vanaavoa?" He seemed unable to remember that this girl whom he had rejected was his daughter. But next day he found a piece of paper and suddenly his life flamed into purposeful being, as if Turia, and dead Maeva, and lost America, and even the vanquished wardens had all thundered down upon him like stormy waves upon the reef.

He read the paper twice and said, "Damn such nonsense." Then he carried it straight to Pastor Cobbett and jammed it under his nose. "What do you make of that?" he growled.

The pastor lifted his spectacles, cleared his throat and read the following poem, which is now famous in Matareva:

SONG OF A TROPICAL TRAMP

I have wandered through the islands with hibiscus in
> *my hair,*
I've surrendered my ambitions for a life that laughs at
> *care,*
I have loved an island maiden when the nights were
> *far and fair:*
> *And I've seen the constellations upside down.*

I have watched canoes go gliding on a fairy-tale lagoon,
I have heard the sun come raging up a day, a year too
> *soon.*

Then I've waited for Turia and the rising of the moon:
And I've heard the wild sharks twisting near the
*　　shore.*

When the schooner fled outside the reef to run before
*　　the gale,*
When palm trees bowed their heads to hear the hurri-
*　　cane's wild wail,*
Then her lips on mine were golden brown and mine on
*　　hers were pale:*
For I've seen the stars surrender to the storm.

Sometimes within the city streets I hear a curlew cry,
I see the reef spume leaping up to meet a cobalt sky.
Then the island fever has me and I think that I must
*　　die:*
For I've seen the atolls baking in the sun.

Pastor Cobbett finished reading and put down his spectacles. "What's it mean?" Morgan asked.

"The usual bad poetry a young man writes," the pastor explained. "I never wrote any, but I recognize the stuff."

"Is it anything serious?"

Cobbett rose and stood with his hands behind his back as if about to deliver a sermon. Then he saw his friend's agnostic face and changed his mind. "Two kinds of men come to the atolls," he said simply. "You came here and made a life. You were one of us, and our problems were your problems. You helped us, for better or worse. But other men come like birds of passage. They think it's part of growing up. To see strange places. To love strange women. Maybe they're right, but it's hard on the places. It's very hard on the women."

"That's what I thought it meant," Mr. Morgan said grimly. "But I never found much time for reading." Clutching the poem in his hand he strode back to his house, where he found Harry Faber reading a book. "You write this?" he asked.

Harry looked at the poem and said yes.

"It's time you left Matareva," Mr. Morgan said.

"What do you mean?"

The old man began to shout, the only time we ever heard him raise his voice. "Damn it all. I didn't save your life so you could come back and make a fool of my daughter." We were dumbfounded! We had even forgotten that Turia Vanaavoa was his child, and now after all the years he trembled with fatherly concern!

"Wait a minute, sir!" the flyer protested.

"I said it's time to go, Harry. You smart guys who come down here like birds of passage. There's a schooner out there. Get on it!" And that night Harry Faber was on his way to Tahiti.

The girl Turia was heartbroken. She had a copy of the poem and a guitar player set it to mournful music, which our wahines still sing with tears in their eyes. Mr. Morgan amazed us by insisting that Turia come back to live with him as his daughter. The Vanaavoas made no protest, for they had enjoyed the girl as she grew up and now it was time for her to have a life of her own. She started going with a young man of our village and when she became pregnant told her father that she wished to get married. "It's high time," he said.

The wedding was held in church, the last occasion

on which Mr. Morgan ever wore a tie. Later he gave a
reception in his house, but we noticed that the American flag had been taken down. He gave an embarrassed
speech about his daughter's happiness and then disappeared. When I went home I saw him sitting on the
sea wall, the solitary man whom life had subtly surrounded as the coral polyps working on our reef once
surrounded a portion of the vast sea and made it
habitable. I was inspired to rush up to this man and
say that we were proud he had made Matareva his
home, but as I moved to do so, I saw that he was sitting with Pastor Cobbett. What they were talking
about I do not know.

Povenaaa's Daughter

*He saw these massive forms, this
somber beauty, the mysteriousness
of this race.*

NORTH of Tahiti the *Hiro* began to roll, and before
long all passengers were seasick. That is, they were all
sick except a remarkable Polynesian woman of fifty
who sat on one of the forward hatches munching some-
ing she had pulled from a paper bag.

She was ridiculously fat. Her jowls seemed to run
down onto her shoulders, and her body, from neck to
knee, was one unbroken ball of suet, covered by a blue-
and-red Mother Hubbard which swayed solemnly about
her ankles with each motion of the wallowing ship.

The bag from which she selected her dainties was
quite greasy, and two men, long hovering at the vomit
point, were thrust over when they saw what this large
woman was eating. For Maggi—that was her only
name—was eating fish heads. She would lift one from
the bag, inspect it, then crack it with her teeth. There
would follow a sucking sound, a smacking of lips and
then more cracking, as if a dog were worrying a mar-
row bone. When she had quite drawn out all the goodness from the fish head she would toss the skeleton
in an arc over the rail and into the sea. Then she would
loudly suck each of her eight fingers before probing

103

once more among her inexhaustible supply of delica-
cies.

At the ship's rail hung a limp Chinese, so sick he
thought he must die. Four times, just as he hoped he
was becoming accustomed to the wicked roll of the
Hiro, a fish head went whirling past his face and he
would collapse with retching. As the fifth head passed
an inch from his nose he stormed in outraged protest,
"For the love of God, fat woman! Stop eating those
fish heads!"

The woman in the Mother Hubbard put down her
paper bag, wiped the grease off her huge cheeks, and
looked at the miserable Chinese. Placing her hands
at spots where her hips had once been she taunted,
"You've thrown over more than half of yourself. Jump
after it!" Then, with ponderous grace, she rose and
lurched over to the rail, where she swatted the sick
man on the back. "Throw it up, Kim Sing!" she cried.
She drew a greasy fish head from her sack and rubbed
it under the Chinese's nose, holding him by the waist
as he heaved in agony. "That wasn't so bad, was it?"
she asked like a mother.

Affectionately she dragged the near-dead Oriental to
her hatch. After consuming two more heads she tossed
the bag into the ocean and wiped her hands on the
ample hem of her dress. Then, belching twice, she
adjusted her huge bulk to the ridges on which she sat
and asked, "Did you accomplish anything in Papeete?"

For a moment the sick man was unable to reply, but
somehow the vast amplitude of the woman encouraged
him and he said, "I made a contract for all my vanilla."

"Good!" she said with a crisp finality that meant

she was saying nothing about her own mission to the capital.

But toward morning the Chinese saw her smiling to herself in considerable satisfaction and he asked, "What did you find in Papeete that makes you smile, Maggi?"

She was not to be tricked. She laughed to herself for a moment, then rose and hurried to the rail. She peered into the stormy night and caught, along the horizon to the east, the first faint glow of dawn. It was a mere thread of pale light, yet as it played upon the tempestuous waters she could see, past the prow of the ship, waves breaking upon a reef. She studied the scene for some moments until she was satisfied that it was indeed her reef. Then she returned to the hatch and cried in a loud voice, "We'll soon be there!"

This caused a great commotion among the restless steerage passengers and they crowded the rail to catch the first sight of Raïatéa, the ancient island from which all of Polynesia had been settled in the old days. In the dark mistiness of dawn they saw the island mysteriously appear out of the ocean, the spray high upon the reefs, the rain clouds low upon the historic hills.

Then suddenly, like the shifting mood of a wind that scurries across the surface of the sea, the passengers stopped mumbling to themselves, and Maggi, forgetting the Chinese, elbowed her way forward to the prow of the ship, where she stood in the morning rain. She stood with her head cocked as if she were listening for a sound. But she was not, for on one of the off-shore breezes came that most puissant of all island smells: the sweet, rich, perfumed, heavy, unforgettable odor of vanilla, ripening after harvest. The

alluring sweetness filled the ocean. It was like the fra-
grance of many flowers, the richness of fine food, the
sweetness of tropic sunshine. It was the smell of dawn.
It rolled in blankets from the shores of Raïatéa, the
symbol of wealth, the reward of labor. Fat Maggi
breathed heavily and thought, "I would give everything
I smelled in Papeete for this. They speak of Paris!
Pouf!"

As the *Hiro* warped its way to the creaking wharf,
Maggi waited impatiently at the gangplank and even
before it was secured started to let herself down onto
the dock. A group of cheering young men helped her,
yanking her red-and-blue dress awry, but as soon as she
felt the earth under her feet, she shook herself loose
and plopped onto her head a pandanus hat, which she
secured with one hand while running as fast as her
bulk would permit through the copra sheds and down
the main street of Raïatéa.

As she hurried along many villagers called to her,
seeking news of Tahiti. But on this day Maggie had no
gossip to spare. She hurried on and at last half-galloped
through the open doors of the island's only hotel.

"Povenaaa!" she bellowed. "Oh, Povenaaa!"

The hotel into which she had thus burst—Le Croix
du Sud—was such a place as would have captured the
imagination of Joseph Conrad had he voyaged to
Raïatéa. It was a two-story affair with an interior balcony off which opened several dismal rooms. The
ground level was crammed with small, square tables,
each attended by four chairs. An open kitchen, with
many battered pots and pans, led to the rear and a
dirty bar edged one side. A Japanese octagonal clock
had run down some years before and now showed

three-twenty, while a fly-specked portrait of Clemenceau surveyed the bar. And in one corner, barefooted and with a torn shirt, huddled a thin, unshaved Polynesian man, sleeping off his drunk. This was her neighbor, Povenaaa.

Maggi's cries having had no effect upon the sleeper, she let fly with a solid kick and shouted, "Povenaaa! What a morning to sleep!"

The drowsy man twisted on his numbed hip, punched two dirty fists into his eyes and looked up protestingly. When he recognized Maggi he scrambled to his feet, using her solid body as a post by which to haul himself to attention.

"Maggi!" he cried, embracing her warmly. "I didn't expect you!"

"Oh, Povenaaa! What news?"

He became all attention. He took off her hat and placed it carefully on a hook. He held a chair for her and banged furiously on the table for service. "Hey, there! Two breakfasts!"

A misanthropic servant stuck his head out from among the pots and asked dolefully, "Who's going to pay for two breakfasts?" Then he saw Maggi and smiled wanly. "For you, two breakfasts."

He produced coffee cups which weighed a pound each, great brutal things, cold brioches and rancid Australian butter, served in a tin with a jagged edge. As Maggi sipped the chicory-laden brew, Povenaaa twisted his toes around the rung of the chair and asked impatiently, "What's the news, Maggi? Money?"

The big woman tried to play coy and savored her coffee down to the sticky sugar. Then she straightened her Mother Hubbard and said with tremendous import,

"What we've waited for, Povenaaa. The Americans are back!"

The effect of this news on Povenaaa was electric. He rubbed his unwashed face, pressed down the front of his dirty shirt and cried ecstatically, "Ah! *Les Américains!*"

"Yes. The yachts have began to arrive."

"Lots of men?" Povenaaa drooled. "Lots of money?"

"Like the old days," Maggi replied, and the two neighbors sighed nostalgically. Then abruptly, as if a deal had been concluded, Maggi slapped the table and cried, "Well! Why do we wait? Get Teuru!"

Povenaaa rose creakingly, shook the hangover out of his joints and went uncertainly to the door, bellowing, "Teuru! Teuru!"

From a clapboard house down the road a young girl appeared. She had been interrupted at her toilet, for she carried a brush with which she tugged at her long black hair which fell to her waist. She was barefooted and wore a cotton skirt with a skimpy bandanna halter. She was not a girl of extraordinary beauty, but she was handsomely proportioned and majestically straight in the Polynesian fashion. But her most memorable gift was a gamin smile and flashing black eyes that brimmed with an inner merriment.

She stood in the dust of the road, looking for her father, and when she saw him stumbling out from Le Croix du Sud she laughed affectionately and said, "Father! Stop the noise! You're drunk again."

"No, Teuru! Such news!"

His daughter remained in the road, brushing her hair, until Povenaaa shook her by the shoulders. "Maggi's back!" he cried like a little boy relaying Christmas news.

"So soon?"

"And with such glorious news!"

With much nervous excitement Povenaaa led his daughter into the hotel and arranged a seat beside Maggi, who pinched her on the chin and cried, "I'm so happy for you!"

Before Teuru could ask why, some tourists from the *Hiro* entered the hotel and the men could not keep their eyes off the young girl, for it was deliciously apparent that she wore nothing beneath her cotton skirt, since Povenaaa had forced his daughter into her chair in such a way as to expose a splendid leg.

The men's eyes popping at the bar gave Maggi intense pleasure, but after the peep show had continued for some minutes, unknown to Teuru, the fat woman leaned over and with ostentatious prudery pulled down the offending dress. "Never show that much," she whispered, "except on purpose."

Povenaaa clasped his hands and giggled, "Teuru! You're going to Tahiti!"

At this Maggi clasped her young friend's hands and cried, "Oh, what I could do in Papeete these days if I was seventeen, like you."

"What's happened?" Teuru asked, caught up in the excitement.

Povenaaa giggled again. "The Americans! They've come back!"

"Yes, thank God!" Maggi drooled. "And you're going down to live on the best things dollars can buy."

"But I've never been to Tahiti," Teuru protested.

Maggi pulled her chair away from the bar and whispered, "You'll go, Teuru, and on the first day you'll meet a rich American on his yacht. All across the Pacific he'll have been dreaming of you."

"But I've never seen an American," Teuru pointed out.

Maggi ignored the interruption and said, "He'll let you live in his cabin. You'll eat your meals at the Yacht Club. Chinese girls will sew your dresses."

"You'll wear shoes, of course," Povenaaa interrupted. "White men like their girls to wear shoes."

"And if you find a handsome young lover," Maggi continued, "You'll have enough American money to pay his rent at the Hotel Montparnasse, where you can meet him at night."

"When the rich American is asleep," Povenaaa explained.

"And when the yacht sails there'll be another one coming in," Maggi said, recalling her boisterous youth in Papeete. "And who knows? Maybe later you will even get married."

Teuru listened to this recital with close attention. Povenaaa had always told her that some day the rich Americans would be coming back and it would be heaven for pretty girls. "And you'll be pretty!" he had assured her.

"But I wouldn't know what to do," she blushed.

"Do!" Maggi roared. "You don't do anything!" Then she dropped her voice and said, "With American men it's very simple. Look at that fellow at the bar. He's French, but all men are more or less the same. Povenaaa and I will leave. I'll manage to pull your dress up the way it was before. Watch what happens!"

As the big woman led Povenaaa from the hotel she hiked Teuru's dress accidentally, and all the men at the bar snapped to attention. A wife complained, "You haven't stared at me like that for ten years, Henri." To which he replied, "Ah, yes! But you haven't looked like that for fifteen."

Then one of them reacted as Maggi had prophesied. In three minutes he was trying to buy Teuru a drink. "I don't drink," she laughed. "My father does enough for both of us."

"Was that your father leaving here a moment ago?"

"Yes."

"Remarkably handsome fellow," the tourist said.

"You sound very silly," Teuru replied, whereupon the man coughed. At this point Maggi and Povenaaa returned. The Frenchman was completely confused and became more so when Povenaaa said, "Thanks, I'll have a cognac."

When the tourist had been eased away, after paying for the drinks, Maggi said, "See! It's simple! And with an American—much easier." Dramatically she fumbled in her bag and produced a slip of paper. "*Voilà!* M'mzelle Teuru! Her ticket to Tahiti!"

The excitement of an actual ticket on the *Hiro* and the lure of Papeete were powerful, and Teuru's dark eyes bubbled with merry anticipation, but suddenly they sobered and she said, "I can't go."

"Why not?" Maggi snorted.

"I promised . . . Kim Sing . . . to work his vanilla vines again."

Povenaaa exploded. "The Chinaman's vanilla! You compare that to a rich American!"

Maggi said quietly, "You were too young during the

war, Teuru. We never smuggled you across to Bora
Bora. But the lucky girls who did reach the American
camp—they lived in paradise."

"A true paradise," Povenaaa cried. "Canned food.
Jeep rides. Trips in the airplane. Whole cartons of
cigarettes."

Maggi explained, "There's no reason to be afraid
of Americans. I remember when they had a certain
major who was what the men called an old bitch.
Nobody could do anything with him. So I sent Hedy
over and half an hour later she had his pants off."

Inspired, Povenaaa went to the door and roared,
"Hedy! Come here!"

In a moment the heads at the bar almost snapped
off, for into the doorway came a slim Polynesian girl of
twenty-four. She held a very blonde child by the hand,
and these two created a sensation of perfect beauty.
Hedy—she had been so designated by the Americans—
had the delicate quality of the actress from whom she
had been named, but the frangipani flowers in her hair
were her own device. When she spoke her voice was
childish and musical. She did not want her daughter
to enter the bar, so she said, "Major, you go back
home." Then she saw Maggi and cried in her tinkling
voice, "Good return, Maggi!"

"For you it's good," Maggi chuckled.

"You bring a message?" Hedy asked, keeping her
eyes shyly upon the floor so that she would not have
to look at the strange men along the bar.

"Such a message!" Povenaaa beamed.

"The Americans!" Maggi whispered, "They're back."

Unlike Teuru, Hedy knew how to appreciate this

luxurious news. She smiled with delicate satisfaction, moved a little nearer Maggi, and sighed, "During the war they used to say, 'Come peace, baby, you'll see me back here with a fist full of dough.'"

"She talks just like an American," Povenaaa said proudly.

Hedy sighed again and sort of hugged herself. "I should like to be in Papeete now!"

"And here's your ticket!" Maggi cried, producing another strip of paper.

"Oh, Maggi!" Hedy cried, embracing the fat woman. Then she pouted, "But what about Major?"

"I was thinking about Major," Maggi said softly.

There was a long moment while Hedy and Maggi stared at each other. Then, impulsively, the younger woman kissed the older and laughed, "You've always wanted Major, haven't you? Well, she's yours."

Povenaaa was sent to find Major and returned shortly with the fair-haired little girl, who ran promptly to her mother, but Hedy lifted the child deftly into Maggi's voluminous lap. "Maggi's your mother now," Hedy said gently.

The little girl looked first at her mother, then at her new mother. Both women winked at her, and before the winks had rustled to rest, little Major—named after an American officer long since forgotten—accepted the new order. Hedy patted her approvingly and whispered, "You be good. Hedy's going to Tahiti."

Then Povenaaa spoke, officially, "You girls will love Papeete. I want you to behave yourselves. No drinking. Don't become bums like me. And remember that Americans do not shoot pistols all the time like the

movies. I've known some very decent men." Then he
stopped. He saw tears in his daughter's eyes. "What's
the matter, Teuru?" he snapped.

"I want to see Papeete," she said haltingly. "I think
I would like Americans, but . . ."

"Poor little Teuru!" Povenaaa whispered. But her
indecision frightened him and he realized he must tell
the whole truth. "You must go," he pleaded. "For
my sake if for nothing else. For if you could save only
three hundred American dollars . . . Well, I could
buy that surplus jeep on Bora Bora." He looked at
Teuru in triumph, as if the coveted vehicle were already his. "And with a jeep! Why, I could be a very
important man in Raïatéa. With a jeep, that is."

The *Hiro* blew its whistle once. "I must pack!"
Hedy cried. "Maggi! You must help me."

The two women, taking the child, bustled out, and
one of the men at the bar came to Povenaaa's table.
"Your pardon, sir. Who was that remarkable girl?"

"The big one or the little one?" Povenaaa asked.

"The . . . younger one."

"Name's Hedy. She's going to Tahiti." Then he
grabbed Teuru's hand and started for the door, where
he turned and added proudly, "And my daughter's
going, too."

The *Hiro* blew its whistle twice, and then followed
an amazing pageant of Polynesian life. Everybody on
the dock began to weep. Maggi lowed and whimpered
like a grief-stricken heifer. Povenaaa blubbered help-
lessly, repeating over and over again, "My daughter!
My daughter!" Stragglers who had drifted down merely
to watch the *Hiro* were caught in the lamenting and
they too wept in an abandonment of sorrow. Tahiti

lay less than a hundred miles away, and the ship sailed each week, but the sorrow in Raïatéa could have been no greater had the passengers this day been destined for the Arctic wastes.

In a final debauchery of despair Maggi shrieked, "Hedy, look after Teuru!"

Hedy burst into passionate tears and screamed, "Povenaaa, I'll show Teuru what to do."

The *Hiro* blew its whistle the last time and stood out into the channel, and as it did so a transformation came over Hedy. She stopped weeping instantly, lifted her lovely head into the breeze and looked southward. "Oh, Teuru," she whispered happily. "Tomorrow night we shall sleep in Papeete!" Then a frown puckered her forehead and she added, "But I wonder with who?"

Teuru blushed. A delicate color came to her cheeks, shining for a moment under the soft brown skin. "It's all very well to joke about such things, but . . ."

"Sssh!" Hedy warned. "Those gentlemen are looking at us. I'll bet they want to buy us some beer." But when she turned she saw that Teuru was weeping. "Why are you crying now?" she asked sharply. "The boat's sailed."

And Teuru sniffled, "You've been away from home before. I haven't."

But by the following evening, when the *Hiro* like an exhausted porpoise rolled on toward Tahiti, Teuru's bubbling good humor returned and she shared in the general excitment as the glorious climax of their journey unfolded. To the west sprang the peaks of Mooréa, crimson in sunlight. Ahead loomed the stumpy, cloud-wreathed hills of Tahiti. Seagulls dipped majes-

tically about the ship, welcoming it as if it were a
rich caravel, and even the seasick cattle revived as they
caught the scent of land.

"Hedy!" Teuru cried. "Look at those beautiful
ships!"

"They must be the yachts," Hedy said, straightening
her dress.

"And the white spires."

"Churches," Hedy guessed, keeping her attention focused on the yachts.

"But what's that?" Teuru cried.

To starboard, tied up to the quay that ran along the
water front, stood a huge ship painted white. Along its
deck moved sailors, also in white, each with a red
pompon on his hat. "It's a French ship," Hedy sniffed
scornfully. "You stay away from the French."

"It's lovely," Teuru said happily. "Even if it is
French." Like most residents of the northern islands,
she had inherited a revolutionary hatred of the French,
who had subdued her islands last and with force.

"Ah!" Hedy cried. "Those yachts are American!"

But Teuru was fascinated by the warship, and as the
tired old *Hiro* limped into port she stood at the railing
and stared at the cruiser *Jean Delacroix* as long as it
remained visible. Then, perforce, she had to look elsewhere, and for the first time she saw the rich panorama
of Papeete.

Along the quay important Frenchmen bustled in
coats that seemed too tight. Chinese rode bicycles
that teetered perilously, while handsome native men
from the fishing boats hauled bonita onto the cobbled
stones. Girls in Paris frocks walked slowly back and
forth in twos and threes as officials in uniform bustled

about giving orders and a nest of tourists lolled in a
rented sports car blowing their horn at everyone.
Three nuns waited on the dock for a sister reporting in
from an outstation, and innumerable black and white
and yellow boys ran screaming into alleys.

There was a color about Papeete that night that
Teuru would never forget. The white clouds turning
to purple. The silvery flash of bonita as they scintil-
lated in the sun. The golden-yellow towers of the
Douane. The majestic motion of many people as their
various colors blended, and everywhere the glorious
flowers of Tahiti.

That was how Povenaaa's daughter arrived in Papeete. She stepped upon the dock barefooted, in a close-
fitting green-and-white pareu, her long black hair
reaching her waist, a frangipani behind her left ear, a
little wicker suitcase in her hand, and on the back of
her head, a straw hat. She took a deep breath of the
new air and whispered, "We're here, Hedy."

The older girl presented a much different appearance. She wore shoes, very high in the heel, and a dress
drawn tightly about her small waist. Her hair was done
in plaited strands wound into a crown. For lips she had
two scarlet dabs, but against the white flowers in her
hair they seemed appropriate. She handed Teuru her
suitcase, explaining, "American men don't like to see
pretty girls lugging things."

As if she had lived in Papeete all her life, she led
Teuru off the dock and westward to where the yachts
were anchored. She knew she had little time, for the
sun already had the peaks of Mooréa aflame. Then
abruptly she stopped. Suddenly she was no longer in a
hurry. Motioning Teuru to stay behind, she sidled

along the water front to where a yacht was tied stern to. A man of fifty was leaning over a board, cleaning fish. Hedy laughed musically and the yachtsman looked up.

"Watcha laughin' at?" he demanded.

"That's no way to clean a fish!" Hedy taunted.

"Whatsa matter with my way?"

"You'll cut yourself." She leaned slightly on the ropes, swaying with the motion of the ship. Then she laughed again.

"You think you could do it any better?" the yachtsman asked.

"Sure!" Hedy cried, using a French accent she had found irresistible during the war.

"If you're so smart, let's see." The man reached aft with a boat hook and steadied Hedy as she swung herself aboard. "What's your name?" he asked.

"Fish-cleaner," she teased.

"No. Your real name."

"Hedy," she replied.

"Like Hedy Lamarr?"

"Yes. An American major said I looked like her." The petite girl leaned over to survey the mutilated fish, but she was careful to keep her lovely profile steady for several seconds.

"Say!" the yachtsman cried. "You do, at that!" He moved toward her, attracted by her extravagant charm, but as she did so she lifted the fish and laughed at him with tinkling music.

"You've ruined the fish," she said.

"Where'd'joo learn to speak English so good?"

"Oh!" she cried. "My bag!" She ran to the stern and started to shinny down the ropes.

"Don't go!" the American cried.

"I'll be back," she reassured him.

"What are you going to do?" Teuru whispered.

"Stop here for a while," Hedy said.

"What am I to do?" Teuru pleaded.

"Well," said the self-assured little beauty with a flip of her head, "there's a lot more yachts."

"I couldn't do that."

Suddenly Hedy was all tender affection. "You're right! You've got to take these things very slowly. I remember when Maggi smuggled me ashore at Bora Bora. I was scared to death. I knew I'd never be able to talk with a major. An American, too."

"Were you?"

"Oh, yes," Hedy replied. She kissed Teuru good-by and the girls began to cry.

"Whatsamatter down there?" the yachtsman shouted.

"My friend," Hedy blubbered.

"Whatsamatter with your friend?"

"She's never been away from home before!"

"Well, bring her along."

There was fresh sobbing, rising to a wail of remorse and lonely anguish. The American was totally bewildered as he watched his girl open her purse and hand the barefooted stranger a fistful of francs. He was even more surprised when Hedy wiped her eyes, flashed him a wonderful smile, pitched her bag aboard and shinnied up the ropes with the friendly cry, "All right! Where's that fish?"

Teuru was now alone in Papeete. Stuffing Hedy's benevolent francs into her suitcase, she pulled out a slim scrap of paper on which Maggi had scrawled two words: HOTEL MONTPARNASSE. She was about to seek a

policeman when she beheld a sight that would have
made the heart of any young girl dance with pleasure.
Down the quay came three French sailors in dazzling
white uniforms and red pompons. Their shorts stopped
crisply at the knee and they wore hard-ribbed white
socks and highly polished shoes. They were laughing.
They were laughing and making a great fuss, so that
Teuru had to laugh, too.

They saw her hesitating at the edge of the road and
quickly surrounded her. In French the tallest cried,
"Ah, the village maiden comes to the city!" Then they
offered her a cigarette.

"Ah! Virtuous maiden! She doesn't smoke!"

"I'm looking for a hotel," Teuru explained.

"*Voilà!*" the sailors shouted.

"What happens here?" a policeman asked, patting
himself on the belly.

"We're showing m'mzelle to her hotel!" the tall
sailor announced, making a little rhyme which his
friends mimicked in mincing style.

They grabbed her by the waist and swung her down
the street, so that she had to dance with them. Then
they lifted her high into the air and planted her bare
feet on the sidewalk. "The hotel of m'mzelle!" they
cried, and then the leader said very seriously, "Let it
never be remarked that the men of *Jean Delacroix*
were not gallant. Your official welcome to Papeete."
And he kissed her firmly on the lips.

"So too the engine-room crew!" cried the next sailor,
holding her face to attention and wiping off his lips
with his shirt sleeve.

But the third sailor stood back. He blushed considerably and indicated that he would not force his atten-

tions on Teuru. His companions mocked him and the leader cried, "M'mzelle! Our good friend Victor, he does not like girls! Therefore, on behalf of Victor, I salute you again." He lifted her into his arms, but this time Teuru did not feel his lips, for over his shoulder she saw the confused, scarlet face of Victor.

When the sailors left, their six handsome white-ribbed legs making rare patterns in the dusk, Teuru watched them for a moment, then laughed and hoisted her suitcase, turned on her bare feet and marched into the Hotel Montparnasse. This establishment, so inappropriately named, faced the peaks of Mooréa, but otherwise its facilities were unspeakable. It had served wastrels and wanderers for almost a hundred years, and in that time Rupert Brooke, Stevenson, Henry Adams, and Gauguin had lounged upon its dirty veranda, staring at the pantomime of Papeete. Now it was run by a German woman who wore stiff black lace collars, as if to bring to the hotel a respectability it had never owned.

"What do you want?" Frau Henslick snapped.

Teuru thrust the piece of paper onto the counter and Frau Henslick shouted, "What am I supposed to do? This says nothing."

"Maggi sent me."

"You mean the fat woman?"

"Yes!" Teuru beamed. "She said you might need help."

"I do," Frau Henslick cried. "I always do." She came from behind the counter and examined Teuru as if she were a horse. "Got your teeth?" Teuru opened her mouth and the woman nodded approvingly. "Can you work?"

"Yes," Teuru said. "I'm a good worker."

Suddenly the German woman screamed, "When you work here I want you to sleep in your own bed."

"What do you mean?" Teuru asked.

The German woman screamed even more loudly, "You island girls!"

That ended the conversation. Frau Henslick led Teuru to a dingy room, kicked open the door and said, "You start work at six in the morning." Before the girl could reply, the angular woman had disappeared.

It was then seven, and Teuru was hungry, but before she could ask about food she heard the heavy shouting of a man: "Damn it! I want some hot water!"

There was some scuffling and Frau Henslick banged open Teuru's door. "You!" she shouted. "Take this upstairs to Mr. Roe."

Teuru lugged the pitcher to the upper hall and then wondered where she should deliver it. Reasoning that if she waited the man would shout again, she heard an irritated bellow issue from Room 16: "You old sow! Where's the water?"

Cautiously she pushed open the door and faced a young man standing in his shorts. He was redheaded and had a week's growth of beard. "Thanks," he said, turning his back on her.

At the door she asked, "Are you an American?"

"Yes," he said, swabbing his face.

"I've never seen an American before."

"We're pretty sturdy stuff," he said, lathering his beard.

She started downstairs, but he came to the door and called, "You eaten yet? Good. I'm just getting over a

four-day drunk. How's about holding me up till I get
to the restaurant?"

"I'll put my shoes on," she said.

"Don't bother. I never wear any."

He made her sit down while he shaved, cursing the
blade. Finally he asked, "Do I look pretty awful?"

"You look pale," she replied.

He studied the mirror and shuddered: "Let's get out
of here!"

He took her to the Yacht Club and insisted that she
order the best of everything. He himself took poached
eggs but couldn't manage them. Instead he sat back
and admired the way she stuffed down the meat and
vegetables. "I was hungry," she said.

"I feel nourished, just watching you," he laughed,
but she made him eat some of her meat and he said it
tasted pretty good, so he ordered some more, and while
he pecked at it, she told him of Hedy.

"Which yacht was it?" he asked. When she described
it he said, "She'll be a wizard if she gets a nickel out
of that old bastard."

"Do you know him?"

"I came down here with him," Mr. Roe said.

"You will go back with him, too?"

"I'd sooner be dead." From the street came the
sound of music and he said, "Would you like to
dance?"

"I have no shoes."

"You forget, neither do I." He led her to Quinn's, a
place Maggi had often mentioned, and there Teuru
saw the gaiety of this island. As soon as Mr. Roe entered, everybody shouted to him and couples stopped

by his table to ask what was new. He made no move to
dance and she was not surprised when a very beautiful
girl in shoes took him completely away. He did not
return to Teuru at all but sat across the floor drinking
gin and growing more glazed each hour.

In her embarrassment Teuru was about to leave
when there was commotion at the door and the three
French sailors roared in. The leader saw Teuru at
once and swung her onto the floor. He was good at
native dances and flourished his hips as well as an
island man. Soon Teuru felt her hair swinging about
her shoulders, and then, as earlier that night, she
saw across the room the penetrating stare of thin-faced
Victor.

When she joined the sailors at their table, the young
man rose properly, bowed and said, "My name is Victor de la Foret," and in those brief words he opened
for Teuru a completely new vision of life, because
when she said that she was from Raïatéa, he replied,
"I was born there."

"You were?" she asked. "I never heard of you."

"In spirit," he explained. "I had an uncle who
served in these islands, and from the time I was a boy
. . ." Nervously at first and then with a rush of golden
words he told Teuru the history of her island: the hills
that contained the sacred marae, the straits from which
the canoes set out to populate the Pacific, the forgotten groves where the lewd ritual dances were held.
He was only twenty-one and he had never seen Raïatéa, but he knew the island better than Teuru, who
had left it only yesterday.

When Quinn's closed the young couple walked along

the quay until they found a bench, and then he told
her of the map he had drawn of Raïatéa, many years
ago. "It was marked with a star," he said.

"What for?" she asked.

"Raïatéa was the source. Women like you bore brave
sons and they risked all the dangers of the sea."

For a moment these new ideas cast a spell over
Teuru and she was back in the age when men of Raïatéa ruled the oceans. Not until that night had she
known that she carried such blood. Better than she
could have liked any American, she liked this young
sailor, and impulsively she reached out her brown hand
and touched the red pompon. "It dances," she said,
"on your white hat."

Victor drew back and even in the faltering light she
could detect his blush. "You shouldn't have done
that," he said nervously.

"Why not?" she asked perplexed.

"It's a rule," he said. "A silly rule."

"What is?"

"A girl . . . who touches a pompon . . . a sailor's
red pompon, that is . . ."

"I'm very sorry," Teuru apologized.

"It's nothing," he assured her. "A stupid rule. But
she must kiss him."

This was not play-kissing and Teuru rose in embarrassment and started to leave, but Victor caught
her by the hand and said quietly, "Tonight . . . when
the others were kissing you . . . I was afraid."

In stately grace the barefooted girl bent down and
placed her lips on his. Her long hair fell about his
shoulders and across his eyes. At first he did not move.

Then, in an excess of joy, he flung his arms about her and pulled her down upon his knees. "You are like the queen of my island," he whispered.

These words were very sweet to Teuru, but she was somewhat perplexed—recalling all that Maggi had told her about how men behave—when Victor made no move to kiss her again but spent the night asking her detailed questions about Raïatéa. Toward morning, when pale light was quivering upon the tips of Moorea, a bugle sounded on the *Jean Delacroix* and Victor said he must leave.

"I must see you each day," he whispered. Then, staring at his shoes, he confided his secret. "I joined the *Jean Delacroix* to see these islands. Because, you understand, I am going to write a great poem about Raïatéa. In the ancient days, of course."

A policeman stopped by the bench and said, "You'd better get back to your ship, vice-admiral."

"Will you talk with me again tonight?" Victor begged, and Teuru said that she would. She reached the Montparnasse at five minutes to six and Frau Henslick screamed, "Come in, you baggage. Are you sober enough to work?"

"I'm all right," Teuru replied. Indeed, she thought the words had never really applied to her before that moment. She felt all right.

"Then go up and see what Mr. Roe's making such a noise about."

There was a wild clatter at the head of the stairs, followed by a bucket bouncing down, step by step. "I said I wanted some ice!" Mr. Roe stormed.

"Get him some," Frau Henslick ordered.

Teuru hauled some up to Room 16 and Mr. Roe shouted, "Bring it in!"

Gingerly Teuru pushed open the door, keeping her eyes down, for Mr. Roe was wearing almost nothing and in his bed slept the pretty girl, who now did not have her shoes on. By no gesture did Mr. Roe acknowledge that he had ever seen Teuru, and it was apparent that he knew nothing of the evening before.

All that morning Frau Henslick kept Teuru hopping so that when siesta time came the girl did not even bother with food but fell into a death-like sleep for two hours, awakening only when the German woman shook her. "Mr. Roe wants you again," Frau Henslick said.

"He makes a lot of trouble," Teuru said sleepily.

"He pays his bills," the landlady said simply, and thus Teuru was introduced to the rules of Hotel Montparnasse. People who paid were let alone. Teuru learned never to enter any room unless invited. Each night after eleven stray girls from all the outlying islands wandered through the hotel, checking up to see if all the men were sleeping well. It was not uncommon for two or sometimes three girls to spend the night in one visitor's room: one in bed and two on the floor. If no other place was available, they crowded into Mr. Roe's room, for he never bothered them, and if, as was often the case, he found them in his bed when he got back, he would curl up in a chair on the verandah, unless he was very drunk, when he would roar, "Get the hell out of here. I've got to get some sleep." And there would be a scurry of bare feet down the corridors.

Teuru was not bothered by the Montparnasse because she herself lived in a kind of dream world. During almost every free moment she was with Victor de la Foret. On rented bicycles they rode and then clambered up to the pool of Pierre Loti where, generations before, the romantic novelist had wooed his island girl. They danced, went to boxing shows and sat in the movies. But most of all they talked. Teuru, who had been a quiet girl—Povenaaa's chin was always bobbing —now found herself able to speak for minutes at a time, relating her memories of Raïatéa. True, she sometimes wondered when they were going to get around to those things that Maggi had said "were all that men wanted, anyway!"

When Victor finally did, Teuru was completely shocked. It happened one night while they were sitting on the bench. The young sailor caught Teuru by the waist and cried, "We are going to get married!"

"Married!" Teuru repeated. She was astounded at the idea. After all, she was only seventeen, not nearly of an age to marry. She had not yet lived with a man, she had borne no children, knew nothing of life. She suspected that it was both unfair and ungallant of Victor to propose such a thing and in extreme perplexity she told him he had better go back to his ship.

"But will you marry me?" he begged.

"Not right away," she parried, and as soon as he had left she scurried across the quay to Hedy's yacht and scrambled aboard. In the darkness she upset a bucket and heard a gruff voice cry, "Get off'n this boat, you crooks!"

"Hedy!" she whispered. "It's Teuru!"

There were muffled protests but soon the Polynesian

girl appeared. She embraced her friend and said, "The skipper complains a lot, but he bought me this robe."

They sat on the deck and Hedy listened carefully while Teuru explained about the wedding proposal. "I warned you!" Hedy cried indignantly. "I told you Frenchmen were no good. To expect you to marry him. So young! And no money!"

"What shall I do?" Teuru begged.

"You go back to Raïatéa. Maggi and Povenaaa will tell you I'm right."

"Will you ever get married, Hedy?"

"Of course. In two or three years."

"Then why can't I?"

"At your age! You haven't even had a baby yet. You go home."

So next morning Teuru informed Frau Henslick that she'd be sailing on the Tuesday *Hiro*. The German woman bawled at her for being an ingrate, but Teuru was determined. Nevertheless, as the day ended she nervously watched the *Jean Delacroix*, waiting for the white suit and red pompon she had grown to love.

She was surprised, therefore, when Victor did not appear at the accustomed hour, and she was wandering idly along the quay when a young man in civilian clothes . . .

"Victor!" she cried. "I hardly knew you!"

"I was keeping it as a surprise. My enlistment's up and I cabled Paris for special permission to stay out here." He dropped his voice and added, "So that we could get married."

"But we can't!" Teuru objected. "I'm going home next *Hiro*."

"That's what I planned, too," he said eagerly.

"What did you plan?" Teuru asked, half in tears.

"To go with you . . . to Raïatéa. Our first home! We'll get married on Monday."

"But Povenaaa would never let us!" Teuru protested.

"We'll talk with M'sieur Povenaaa," Victor insisted, and on Tuesday they were aboard the *Hiro*. There was a fine cry as Hedy and her American saw them off with many flowers. Frau Henslick was there, too, with more flowers, and an old woman from Raïatéa who just came down for the general lament. Victor said, "I am sure it must have been like this when the canoes set out for Hawaii. But Raïatéa's only a few miles."

Teuru said, between tears, "It's always so sad to part."

That night they sat upon a crate of knitting yarn and watched the timeless race of the moon across the tropical heavens. As new constellations appeared, Victor named them, and all around was the music of a small ship plowing through starry night: the lowing of cattle, the whispers of women talking, the patient throb of the reluctant engines, the cry of a night bird, the echo of waves against wood.

Teuru sat close to Victor and in spite of Hedy's warnings, in spite of what she knew Povenaaa and Maggi would say, she wanted to marry this Frenchman. She was about to tell him so when a mysterious sound came from the port quarter and Victor rose. He peered into the darkness and asked, "What is that noise?"

Teuru stood beside him, her face pressed into the wind, and before she could speak the first probing dagger of light cut across the waves and poised above the hills of Raïatéa.

"My island!" de la Foret cried, and there was something in his passionate recognition of a land he had never seen that bewildered Teuru, yet at the same time she felt that she had found the one man with whom she could live forever happily. They stood like enchanted voyagers from another age as the pitching *Hiro* approached the island. These were the hills that had bred the bravest navigators the world has ever known. These were the valleys of the most lewd pagan rites, the sacred altars where human sacrifices had been dragged by the hair, the living monuments of a towering civilization—lost.

But their reverie was broken by shouts coming from the wharf. Some children had caught sight of the lovers and were screaming, "Povenaaa! Teuru has her American!"

The happy message sped through the crowd, for all the island knew of Teuru's mission, and all the villagers beamed approval of the handsome young American. Then, as the *Hiro* docked, there came a fresh commotion and the crowd fell back to make a pathway for Maggi, puffing and on fire. She took one look at the young people and shouted, "By God, girl! You've done it?" Then she turned and shouted, "Get Povenaaa!"

In a moment half the children on the quay were paging the town bum, and soon he appeared, barefooted, his pants falling away from his hips, his face a thicket of whiskers. Then, as his bleary eyes focused, he saw de la Foret and he cried in Polynesian, "I knew my daughter could catch herself a rich American!"

The gangway was lowered and Povenaaa received his first shock of the day, for when Teuru led Victor

ashore, the first thing the young poet did was to stoop
down and kiss the earth of Raïatéa. "My God!" Povenaaa cried. "Is he sick?"

Maggi shook her fist at the *Hiro* and swore, "You'd
give Jonah the seasickness."

Povenaaa led the procession to Le Croix du Sud and
when the rancid butter appeared with the sour
brioches he asked expansively, "And what part of
America do you come from?"

Victor smiled and said, "I am a Frenchman."

There was a horrible silence while Maggi stared
dumbly at Povenaaa's gaping jaw. Teuru tried to help
things out by saying that Victor was really a French
sailor, but that he'd been discharged on Saturday.

"Oh, my God!" Maggi groaned.

Now Victor tried to soothe things. "I've come here
to marry your daughter."

"No!" Povenaaa exploded. "No French pig shall . . ."

"Father," Teuru pleaded. "Let's go home."

"I think we better," Maggi said limply. With anguish she paid Povenaaa's bill—what a hollow celebration this had been—and then started for the weatherbeaten house.

Once inside, Povenaaa miraculously produced four
rickety chairs and demanded, "Now what's all this
about?"

"I want to marry your daughter," de la Foret said
forcefully.

"No! She's too young!"

"And besides," Maggi added, "Frenchmen are not
welcome here."

"She's right!" Povenaaa stormed. "No Frenchman
will marry my daughter."

Now Teuru spoke. "But I love him. He's very gentle. He's a poet."

This caught Povenaaa off guard. He stopped blustering and leaned forward. "Poets are very famous. Do they make a lot of money?"

"No," Teuru interrupted. "Not yet. But some day he will. He's writing a long poem. About Raïatéa."

"Son of a pig, it's strange!" Povenaaa mused. "The world full of rich Americans and my daughter picks a poor French poet."

Ignoring de la Foret completely, Maggi took Teuru's hand and said, "I understand Hedy got herself a beautiful yacht. How did she get a yacht and you a poet?"

Teuru blushed and explained, "She didn't fall in love. I did."

This was enough for Povenaaa. He rose to his full height and announced dramatically, "There will be no marriage! Not between a poet and a girl only seventeen."

"What shall I do?" de la Foret cried, anguished that he must lose Teuru.

"You stay here, of course," Teuru replied.

"Here?" he repeated.

She lifted his bag and carried it into her small room. Next she fetched hers and placed it beside his. Then she stood in the doorway and motioned to him.

"You mean . . . I'm to stop here? With you?"

"But there's to be no marriage!" Povenaaa warned, defending his daughter from the unwelcome intruder. When de la Foret remained rooted in bewilderment, Povenaaa reached out and pushed him into Teuru's room. "You can stay here for the time being," he said grudgingly. "But no marriage!"

Disappointed and disgusted, Povenaaa slammed the door on the young lovers and slumped down beside Maggi. "A dog's luck," he mused bitterly.

"It's too bad," Maggi consoled. "But it'll work out . . . in time. The important thing is, be firm! Don't let them get married. He'll leave one of these days."

Povenaaa scratched his bewhiskered face and asked, "A poet? Do you suppose that's much better than a sailor?"

The disillusionment of young Victor de la Foret was catastrophic. It was not the disillusionment of love, for never had he been so happy. In the morning Teuru rose from their bed and polished the thin bamboo wafer she used on the vanilla flowers. Then she threw around herself a blue-and-white pareu and combed her radiant hair. Sometimes she would bring in a pawpaw, some limes, a mango or a pot of black coffee. They would eat together while the morning birds made a symphony among the trees. Then she would kiss him good-by and walk like some ancient goddess toward the vanilla plantations.

Nor was it the disillusionment of life with Povenaaa, who worked each night to bring America into the conversation. The disappointed father made it emphatic that a Frenchman was a pretty poor substitute for a Yank. He also delighted in dandling Major on his knee, adding that he guessed no babies in the world were as pretty as American babies. He said—staring boldly at Teuru—that he guessed any girl in the world would be mighty happy to have a child as intelligent as Major. He taught the child to sing an amazing version of "Yankee Doodle." Worst of all, in an old copy of *Life* he found a full-page color shot of a jeep. This he posted right where Victor and Teuru had to face it as they ate. But for the most part Povenaaa proved a decent sort, even though he used to ask Maggi almost every night, in a voice so loud that Victor had to hear, "I wonder when he's leaving."

No, the tragic disillusionment that overtook Victor de la Foret was that of Raïatéa itself. Where had the once great civilization fled? How could the godlike subduers of the vast Pacific have degenerated into Povenaaa? Why, only last week sailors of Raïatéa had fled back to port when a trivial storm overtook them at sea. He studied the relics of the island, hoping to find an answer, but in no stone could he detect a trace of the grandeur that had once inhabited this land.

Strangely, he found his only solace in Maggi, who often sat with Major on her lap, droning about the old days. She could recite the names of all the canoes that had penetrated the oceans even to Peru.

"But what happened, Maggi?"

"Now we stay home."

"But where did the grandeur vanish?"

"It's still here. You ever see Major's mother? Very grandeur, Hedy!"

"I mean the spirit of life."

"It's here. Some time Teuru will take you to a real island dance."

Word arrived that there was to be one on nearby Bora Bora and Victor arranged for a long boat to make the trip. He rode aft with Teuru and for a breathless moment he could believe that he was sailing with the immortal canoes. Ahead rose the fantastic cliffs of Bora Bora, radiant in the sunlight. About him the birds wheeled as they had generations ago during the hegira. In counterpoint to the throbbing of the engine he could hear the men of Raïatéa chanting songs whose very meaning had been lost in the dust of years. This was the historic grandeur of Polynesia: brown bodies thrusting forward into the unknown sea, frail boats riding to the sunrise. Ahead the sure knowledge that somewhere there must be an island. Behind the security of a beautiful homeland.

He had a further sensation of historic reality when he decamped onto the shore of Bora Bora where the cliffs dropped into the fairy-tale lagoon. As dusk came on, lovers from all over the island gathered and a tom-tom beat out traditional rhythms. Men leaped into the ring and began furious gyrations. Soon they were joined by handsome girls. They danced, as if demented, a sexual ritual that probed far back into the past, until with furious cries the men caught the girls by the waist and threw them toward the jungle's edge. There was a timeless moment when the men leaped beside the girls as lovers ages ago had done before dragging the women into the bush. But now came a nervous giggle and the girls rejoined their friends.

The spell broken, de la Foret had to recognize not some dim memory of the past but the harsher actualities of now. This once godlike people! Look at them! Their teeth falling out from white man's food. Their health ruined with white man's diseases. Even the flaming moon that had once risen above the volcano to shine down on rare, savage bodies now limped up from a dead volcano and shed a pallid light upon a doomed and dying race.

"Teuru," he whispered, "let's go back." She understood his disillusionment and tried to round up the

Raïatéa sailors, but they were afraid to set forth in the darkness.

That was the beginning of de la Foret's illness. He had no fever, no disease. He was sick of that almost incurable malady: today. When he watched Povenaaa trying to sell his daughter to some rich American, he was sick. When he dissected the trivial life of modern Raïatéa, he was sick. There had once been a glory, but today it was vanished. Therefore he was ill with today's illness.

His poem never got beyond the first canto. True, that fragment was superb and was published with distinction. It dealt with Polynesia as a physical world: the sky, the stars, the lonely islands. It was when people were introduced that the poem turned to rot. Victor was aware of this and stopped writing. "I am sick," he repeated.

"You must come with me while I work the vines," Teuru laughed, and it was there that de la Foret rebuilt himself. Day after day he watched Teuru move among the vines, grasping in her firm left fingers the flowers that looked like orchids. In her right hand she carried the bamboo wafer, which she deftly stroked along the stamen, collecting pollen. Then, with a twist of her left thumb, she snapped open the flap that protected the pistil and deposited upon it the pollen from her bamboo. Then she allowed the flap to snap back in place, whereupon she squeezed the pistil to be sure the pollen penetrated it.

"It's so tedious," Victor complained.

"Vanilla's too important to trust to luck," she explained. She said that every flower impregnated by her gentle method would produce a vanilla bean. Those she missed would die that night. "I do the work of bees and flies," she said.

Since the flowers opened at eight and closed at four, Teuru and Victor spent most of each day in the sunny fields, reworking the same vines daily to pollinate each new flower. "Povenaaa must be a rich man with so much vanilla," de la Foret observed as he watched the long beans ripening in the sun.

"They're not Povenaaa's!" Teuru laughed. "They belong to Kim Sing."

Then the sickness returned. The sunny islands of Polynesia were now owned by Chinese and Frenchmen and Germans. Everyone prospered. Only the Polynesians withered.

"You spend so much care on a Chinaman's vines," Victor protested. "Who cares for you?"

Teuru blushed. "Yes. Povenaaa was asking that last night."

"What do you mean?"

She would not reply but that evening Povenaaa was most blunt. He had Major on his lap and asked, "When will you have a white baby, Teuru?" His daughter blushed and made no reply. "Well!" Povenaaa continued. "You have a man for eight months now. What's the matter?"

Victor was outraged. "You shouldn't talk like that," he protested.

Maggi looked at him and sniffed. "Poets, hmmmm. I'll bet Hedy isn't fooling around with poets." She sucked at a bone and then called for Major. Swinging the child onto her lap she counseled, "Don't you ever bother with poets, Major."

Humiliated, young de la Foret left the table. Teuru

found him along the shore. "What kind of father is Povenaaa?" the poet cried.

"He knows I ought to have a baby pretty soon," Teuru replied.

"Stop it! Are you trying to drive me mad?" He pushed her away and stormed along the beach. When Teuru tried to keep up with him he shouted at her in a high, tormented voice and told her to go home. She sought out Maggi and reported the strange behavior.

"Was he crying?" Maggi asked.

"Yes," the perplexed girl replied.

"Good!" Maggi said, straightening her Mother Hubbard. "When a white man cries it means that pretty soon he's going home."

"Why?"

"I can't explain it," Maggi said. "Every time you think you understand a white man, something like this happens. But I noticed that whenever one of my men cried I could start packing his things."

"Why are white men so hard to understand?" Teuru asked.

"Because they're all fools," Maggi explained.

"But you yourself said there were some wonderful white men on Bora Bora."

"Yes, but they were Americans."

"But Hedy told me that when the major found she was going to have a baby, he cried."

"What about?" Maggi asked suspiciously.

"About his wife in America."

Maggi shrugged her shoulders. "It's as I said. White men are very strange."

Victor returned late that night. Lighting a small lamp by Teuru's bed, he scanned the poetry he had tried to write. It was apparently very bad, for one by one the sheets were burned. Teuru feigned sleep and watched him. Then finally she asked, "Have you nothing you want to keep?"

Startled, he dropped a flaming page and had to extinguish it with his foot. When he had done so he sat on Teuru's bed and held her dark head close to his. "Yes," he muttered. "I have one thing to keep."

"What?" she inquired prosaically.

"My memory of you." Then, as if he wished to explain exactly the meaning of this day, he launched into a long apostrophe to the fact that in the midst of a dying and degenerate world he had found one clean, pure symbol of the ancient grandeur: Teuru's placid beauty.

"What's 'placid' mean?" she asked.

He realized that she had not understood anything of what he was trying to say, and she, realizing that he did not intend making love, sighed and pulled away. "I've got to sleep," she said. "I must be up early."

When she rose, he had gone. He did not return and she heard that he had slept on the hotel floor like an ordinary tramp. When the *Hiro* arrived Major came running in with her childish news: "Victor go away!"

At first Teuru felt nothing. Victor was going back to France. Good. She went about her work, but as she did so she saw a vision of the young sailor in crisp whites, with a forbidden red pompon on his hat, and she burst from the house and dashed along the dusty road to the dock.

The *Hiro* was standing out into the channel, but she could see Victor against the railing. She was disposed to call out to him, but instead she stayed among the shadows and watched the boat recede into the distance. It was strange. As a girl she had often come to see the *Hiro* sail and aboard there might be some girl she had never really liked, but at the moment of departure she would break her heart with weeping over the loss of this unimportant girl. Now Victor was leaving and she felt nothing. But then he put his hand over his eyes, as if he were shielding them from the morning sun in order to locate someone on the quay. She started to wave her hand and cry "Victor!" but she realized that the *Hiro* was already too far from shore.

At last she turned to resume her work in the vanilla fields, only to find Maggi and Povenaaa weeping bitterly, consoling each other. "He was a fine young man," Maggi said.

"For a Frenchman," Povenaaa said, "he was all right."

Then Maggi with fortitude wiped her eyes and announced, "But we must forget him. Look!" And she produced a ticket for Teuru on the next *Hiro*.

"Only this time," Povenaaa begged, "an American. Please."

There was a somber quality in Teuru's return to Papeete. The day was overcast and the brooding hills were enveloped in fog. Along the beautiful quay there was a gaping wound: the *Jean Delacroix* was missing. There were no sailors with red pompons, and the water front looked as if it had been betrayed. Even Hedy's yacht was gone.

But Hedy herself was waiting at the gangplank. The slim girl had a scar across her right cheek. After she had fallen into Teuru's strong arms she said, "He hit me with a dish. Night before he sailed."

"Was he a good man?" Teuru asked.

"Pretty good," Hedy said reflectively. "I managed a lot of presents and some money."

"What are you doing now?" Teuru asked as she trudged back to her old job at the Montparnasse.

"I have another American," Hedy reported.

"You're lucky," Teuru said.

At the hotel Frau Henslick screamed, "So you've come back! Put your things in your old room. There's a Hikeroa girl in there now. Kick her out. She's no good."

Teuru was unpacking when the German landlady returned and announced, "Under no circumstances are you to give any food to that bastard Johnny Roe." This, Teuru figured, meant that Mr. Roe had stopped paying his bills. She was alarmed, therefore, when the American shouted for some ice. She filled the bucket and started upstairs.

"Remember!" Frau Henslick warned. "No food!"

Teuru was quite unprepared for what she saw. In bed lay the young American, very drunk. That was normal, but the once neat room was a shambles. Clothes were scattered everywhere, men's and women's, and as she picked her way among them she saw that Hedy was perched in the armchair, peeling an orange.

"Surprise!" Hedy cried. "I live here now!"

"Let's have the ice," Mr. Roe moaned.

"Don't worry about him!" Hedy laughed. "This is no yacht, but Johnny's a lot more fun."

"You ought to keep the room cleaned up."

"Johnny don't care. And besides, I can see where things are."

Mr. Roe was in as bad a condition as his room. His

face was a pallid white and his hair needed cutting. "I think he ought to have a doctor," Teuru said.

"He's drunk."

"How does he live?"

"Traveler's checks. They're wonderful. I sign his name here, and a Chinaman cashes them."

"Then why don't you pay his bills? So I can bring him food?"

"We go out to eat now and then," Hedy assured her, but it was obvious that most of the money went for her clothes and his gin.

So from time to time Teuru spent her own money to provide Mr. Roe a decent meal. She delivered it secretly so that neither Hedy nor Frau Henslick could berate her. One day she was sure that Mr. Roe was dying, but that very evening he and Hedy appeared at Quinn's. He was handsome in pressed whites. Hedy was breathless in a halter bra, a sweeping dirndl and gold slippers. Mr. Roe recognized Teuru and asked her to dance.

"I must owe you a lot of money," he apologized.

"You ought to stay sober and eat more," she advised.

She hoped that he would invite her to dance again, but he soon became staggeringly drunk and danced no more. There were moments, these days, when Teuru was almost unhappy. She would step out of the hotel and see that gaping empty space where the *Jean Delacroix* had anchored and she would recall Victor and his flashing white uniform. At such moments she would wish that somehow they could have married.

But it was difficult for Teuru to remain melancholy for long. Her happy, bubbling nature would assert itself and she would be swept once more into the rich pat-

tern of Papeete life. In the evenings she would walk
through the colorful streets, her head high, and she
would find a dozen things to laugh at: tourists avoiding
Chinese as if they were killers, little girls acting like
big girls and whistling at sailors, a Paumotu fisherman
wrestling with a turtle. One night she stood for
some time chuckling at a tiny Chinese seamstress trying to fit a very sour white woman with a white dress.
Teuru's eyes bubbled with merriment as she watched
the white woman trying to look important. Then she
heard a rasping voice cry, "Don't move. Keep the light
on your face."

She turned and saw a wretched little man of more
than forty, pencil in hand, sitting in a doorway. His
head was large and dirty. His clothes were borrowed
and also dirty. He did not have good teeth and he was
sketching Teuru's head.

"I must go now," she laughed.

"No!" he pleaded, and there was something in his
voice that commanded her to stay. So she continued to
laugh at the Chinese seamstress and the white woman,
while the little man made hurried scratches on his pad.

"What are you doing?" she asked.

He showed her the sketch. "That's you," he said.

On that first night she talked a long time with Earl
Weebles, even bought him some beer, which they
shared in a grubby cantina while he explained what
sculpture was. "I can take a piece of marble," he began. Then he laughed nervously and said, "Damned
little marble I see these days. But I can take mud or
cement or even butter. And a human being grows
right out of it."

"I don't believe you," Teuru laughed.

So he took her to his small room and for five successive evenings she returned and posed for him while he hacked away at a chunk of tree he had somehow lugged into the room. "You understand," he said in his rasping voice, "that I can't pay you."

But she was so convinced that this little man loved what he was doing that she sat willingly, amused by his earnest comment. "England's a rotten place to live," he said. "Too cold. I almost died there. Tuberculosis. But I always dreamed of Tahiti."

"How did you get here?" she asked.

"Damned near didn't. Got caught passing bad checks."

"Where did you learn to carve?"

"Never learned. Just started one day. Used to spend my last thruppence on museums. Went to Paris, too. Fine museums there. You ever been to Paris?"

"I've only been here twice," she laughed.

"You are very beautiful," he said. "Now! Would you like to see yourself?"

He stepped aside and allowed Teuru to see her portrait. She was astonished that wood could be hacked away until it looked like a human head. "My face isn't as lumpy as that!"

He explained, "I didn't try to make your face exactly as it is. I wanted to show it springing from the deep heart of Polynesia."

"What do you mean?" she asked.

"Your people," he said earnestly. "They are the most beautiful human beings I've seen. You are intended to represent them all." Then he tied a rope around the head and started lugging it into the street. "We'll see if we can sell it."

He hawked it through Quinn's, but nobody wanted it. He tried the Col Bleu with no more luck. There was a steamer in from Sydney and he offered it for two hundred francs, five dollars, thirty bob, any sum at all. He asked Teuru to stand beside it so the passengers could see the likeness.

"Don't look much like 'er," an Australian fireman growled, but he bought it for ten shillings. With the money Weebles took Teuru to Quinn's and ordered drinks. He danced, too, coming not quite as high as her forehead. Later, in his studio, he uncovered a three-foot piece of marble and said, "I've been saving it for something worthy. Would you pose for me?"

"Sure," she laughed, resuming the chair.

"I mean . . . undressed?"

She slipped off her clothes and stood in the wavering light, unconsciously assuming a pose that illustrated her strong peasant blood. "It is perfect!" Weebles said, but on that festive night when Teuru first stood in his room, he did not start to work upon the statue.

Teuru now entered upon a complicated life. During the day she listened to Frau Henslick's ranting. Occasionally she slipped out to get Mr. Roe some food, and in the evenings she posed for Earl Weebles as he carved out the series of heads and torsos that he peddled hopelessly through the streets of Papeete. But once after midnight, as she was preparing her bed in the studio, where she now slept, Weebles started to cough and blood came.

Oten Teuru had seen this blood-cough in the islands and she knew its meaning. She tried to stifle her cry of pain, but it escaped, and Weebles, with his death sentence smeared redly upon his fingers, said, "That's why I stole money to get out here."

"But you mustn't stay in this tiny room."

"I can work here. That's what matters."

"No!" she protested. "You are killing yourself."

"What else can I do?" the pathetic little man asked, chopping away at his work.

"You can come home with me," she said simply.

She would accept no argument. Earl Weebles was dying, that was plain, and if he remained in this narrow, choked Papeete hovel he would die very soon. But in Povenaaa's big house in Raïatéa he might live for many years. Accordingly she took her savings to the shipping office near the cathedral and said, "I want two tickets to Raïatéa. There'll be a lot of baggage." She spent three days trying to sell Earl's accumulated statuary but in the end she had to give it away. His tools she packed and sent aboard the *Hiro*.

As the little ship rolled northward to the rich vanilla lands it would have been natural for the eighteen-year-old girl to contemplate on why she, a girl of bubbling vitality, should be dragging along with her a consumptive and dying Englishman, old and ugly; but she did not engage in such speculation because what she was doing had been done in Polynesia since the first day Captain Cook discovered the islands. The natives, rich and happy in their relaxed life, had instinctively reached out to protect the embittered or confused or deteriorated white man. It was a rare Polynesian family that did not have a record of some outcast cured of despair. The easygoing, sun-drenched natives kept white men as families near London or

New York might keep beloved puppies. The wastrels
were welcome to hang around the cool porches. They
were welcome to sleep with the unmarried daughters.
And if the time ever came when they were able to return to what they called civilization, there was a pang
of regret in the bosom of the Polynesian family that
had—perhaps only for a brief period—protected them
as treasured pets. So on the northward journey Teuru
stood barefooted, her fine head and chest forward to
shield little Earl Weebles from the rain.

The arrival in Raïatéa was not gala. Maggi took
one look at the little shrimp and washed her hands of
the whole affair. "Another passage wasted," she
snorted, adding in a loud voice so that all on the dock
could hear, "They tell me, however, that Hedy caught
herself another rich American."

To Povenaaa an Englishman was no better than a
Frenchman. He made it a point to stumble over
chunks of statuary and then moan as if his shin had
been fractured. At night he would sit on his porch and
shout across to Maggi, "I wanted a jeep and look what
I got. A stonemason that don't even know how to build
a house."

But Povenaaa's troubles were only beginning. Teuru
made him haul clay to Weebles' room, and big rocks
and stumps of trees. She bought him not a jeep but a
broken-down old mare and it became a common sight
to see sweating Povenaaa, his pants slipping down,
straining along the roads, cursing bitterly while he
dragged behind some huge object that raised a storm
of dust and flies.

For the closer Earl Weebles came to death, the
grander became his designs. His largest group showed

Povenaaa, Maggi and Teuru standing by the prow of
a ship at the critical moment when it hesitates at the
edge of the ocean. Povenaaa was transmuted into a
fearless navigator. Maggi was the symbolic matriarch
bearing food and determination into the canoe. Teuru
was pregnant, carrying the seed of Polynesia to a new
part of the world. In this majestic group there were no
fragments of a dying race, no wormy, whining Povenaaa. Here was depicted the dayspring of Polynesia.

It was this way with every statue Weebles carved.
He did not record the death about him in Raïatéa,
for in the midst of his own death he saw life. He witnessed the eternal on-springing of humanity, and in his
Raïatéa pieces he created a testament of life. Consider
only his figure of the fisherman. He wanted to use Povenaaa for this, but Teuru's father said he'd be
damned if he'd take off his clothes again for that
shriveled-up Englishman. So Weebles found an old
man, useless for anything, and handed him a spear.
What evolved was the figure of a man rich in years,
poised for one last try at the reef bonita. There was
grandeur in the sagging belly line, compassion in the
old head.

Earl Weebles saw these things. He said, "Raïatéa is
the most beautiful spot on earth." It was also apparent
that he considered Teuru the most beautiful woman
he had ever seen. Endlessly he copied her placid
beauty. She would come home from working the vanilla vines, laughing, her hair about her waist, barefooted and strong, and he would insist that she stop
just as she was, and he would prepare the sketch upon
which he would work that night.

It was curious that she never thought of him as an

artist. He was merely an unfortunate man who needed
a last home. She worked for him, posed for him, slept
with him and comforted him when coughing spells
attacked. She even enlisted the aid of her cautious employer, Kim Sing.

This happened when she found that Weebles needed
new tools, a sketchbook and some medicine. Her own
money had been used up and Povenaaa had none. So
she went to Kim Sing. "Why do you need so much
money?" he asked.

"To buy rocks with."

"Rocks!"

"Please, M'sieur Kim. My friend needs many
things."

"Can he pay back the loan?"

"He could give you a piece of sculpture, perhaps?"

The canny businessman laughed. "None of that
stuff!"

"Then I'll pay it back," Teuru said.

"How?"

"You yourself said I was your best workman."

"It would take a long time."

"I'll be here a long time," Teuru insisted.

"But why should you do such a thing?"

"Because Weebles needs the money. Now."

"Are you in love with this man?"

"Of course not."

"Then why do you seek the money?"

"Because he's very sick," she said.

By such persistence Teuru mustered the help of
many people in behalf of Earl Weebles. In time she
even wore down fat Maggi's contempt, whereupon she

arranged for the sculptor to take his lunch at Maggi's, so that he could have hot food.

"I don't object to feeding you," Maggi puffed. "Most island families have some no-good bum eating their food sooner or later."

"Why do you tolerate it?" Weebles asked humbly.

"When I was young I liked to have a white man around. It was fashionable."

Weebles wiped his chin and said, "I could never express in words . . ."

"I know," Maggi broke in. "I must say that for you. You're grateful. You take the French poet that lived with Teuru last year. What a simpleton! Used to ask me, 'Maggi? Where has the grandeur gone?' I told him if he ever got a good hold on Hedy he'd have more grandeur than he could handle."

"The grandeur gone?" Weebles repeated incredulously. "I've never seen such grandeur before. The hills quiver with meaning."

"And you haven't seen Hedy yet!" Maggi added. In time she grew to like the wizened Englishman. "Weebles!" she cried one day. "Why don't you move over here with me?"

The little man looked up in amazement at the woman who weighed more than twice as much as he. "Not that," she roared, banging the table until the plate of fried fish clattered. "I was thinking that if you left Povenaaa's . . . If I took care of you . . . Then Teuru could go back to Papeete."

"Does she want to go?" Weebles asked quietly.

"Of course she does. She's got to catch herself a rich American."

There was a long silence, one of those hazy, fly-buzzing pauses during which the bedraggled Englishman stared at the fat woman. Finally he muttered, "I won't be there much longer."

"The sickness?" Maggi asked, banging her chest. "It's bad, eh?" Weebles nodded and Maggi changed the subject abruptly. "But you've got to do something with all that junk."

"What junk?"

"Those heads. Those things you carve."

"What do you mean?"

"I mean," she said, banging the table, "that pretty soon it's going to cave in Povenaaa's floor." That was when she started hauling one piece after another down to the *Hiro*, peddling them among the passengers. She sold by weight, asking a dollar a pound, but she was usually so sweaty and puffing when she lugged the stuff aboard that she would accept any reasonable offer.

Weebles was delighted. He had, in his lifetime, sold very few pieces and he glowed with satisfaction when Maggi reported good luck. "Remember that head of Teuru that looked like a cow? This morning I stuck a Swiss woman with it."

Weebles loved beer, and in the evening when a sale had been made he would stand treat at Le Croix du Sud. Once, as Teuru raised the amber glass to her amber lips, the sculptor stopped, enraptured. He put down his glass, deeply affected, and begged to be excused. They heard him coughing outside and he waited in the road until Teuru left the bar. They walked through the deserted streets, down to the wharf where the sweet vanilla beans were waiting shipment.

"I've never been able to talk well," he said.

They had never said much, Teuru and Weebles, but this night great agitation gnawed him and he said, "You're very young . . ." but the precise words would not come, and he stood there by the straits from which the great navigators had set forth. His hands reached for hers and he felt the subtle structure of her bone and flesh. Finally he blurted out, all at once, "You have wasted these months on me."

There was a world more he wanted to say, but he was silent, an inchoate chunk of confusion which no chisel like his own had ever quite polished to completion. When they got home he begged her to pose for him once again, and Teuru stood there naked in her father's room. The statue was never completed, of course, for that night he died.

He was buried, as he would have wished, near the straits of Raïatéa. When the funeral was over Povenaaa said, "Now we can get some of this junk out of here." He ordered the whole collection to be hauled away, but this was a silly command because he had to do the hauling. The smaller pieces he gave to people about the island who had posed for Weebles at one time or another. But he was stuck with the big ones. He tried to make Maggi take some, but she would have none of them.

"If I look like a blown-up whale," she snorted, "I at least don't want a picture of me around the house."

It was she who finally talked some sense into Teuru's head. She said, "It's all very well to be nice to men. A girl ought to be. Lord knows, I was in my day. But it's also necessary to look out for yourself. How do you suppose I bought this house? A rich American, that's how. Now you get on back to Tahiti and find yourself a real man."

She bought Teuru her third ticket to Papeete and whispered consolingly as the *Hiro* blew its whistle, "You've had a no-good Frenchman and a half-dead Englishman. Get yourself a strong American and start having babies."

This time Hedy did not meet Teuru at the Papeete quay. Alone, the nineteen-year-old girl trudged back to the Hotel Montparnasse, where to her surprise Frau Henslick greeted her with an embrace. "You're the only girl I've ever been able to trust," she shouted. "That Hikeroa girl has your room again. Throw the tramp out."

Cautiously Teuru motioned up the stairs with her thumb. "Hedy still here?"

Frau Henslick put down her pencil and beamed. "She's the smart one. She's married."

"To the American?"

"That good-for-nothing drunk?" And although Teuru could hear no disturbance, Frau Henslick suddenly screamed, "Shut up, you lazy bastard."

"What's the matter with him?" Teuru asked.

"Nothing. Hedy stayed around till the traveler's checks were used up. Then she married this rich Austrian refugee. He runs the new curio shop."

Frau Henslick directed Teuru along the quay to a bright new store. Inside, a nervous Austrian tended shop, hovering like a frightened hummingbird above trays of exquisite jewelry. "Is Hedy here?" Teuru asked.

The Austrian fluttered to the back of the shop and

with obvious uxoriousness called for his wife. In a moment she appeared, gloriously pregnant. She posed for a moment beside her birdlike mate and then said, "M'sieur Kraushoffer—you must never call him Herr Kraushoffer. He wants no more of that. He's a real sculptor, not like that dirty Englishman." She pointed out the delicate filigree work M'sieur did. "It sells very well."

In proof she led barefooted Teuru onto the sidewalk and pointed to a spanking new Renault. "Ours," she said simply. She made Teuru climb in, and they took turns blowing the horn. Then she kissed her friend and whispered, "M'sieur Kraushoffer has a rich friend. Tonight put on your best dress and eat with us."

The dinner was excellent, and Hedy was quite the grandest lady Teuru had ever seen. She commanded the servants what they must do, served the wine with a dazzling smile and continually referred to how clever her husband was. The other guest was a moody Bavarian, Herr Brandt. He was, he announced, considering a business in Tahiti. He used many words that Teuru did not understand and wound up by trying to rip off all her clothes. She was not averse to lovemaking, for Maggi had long ago instructed that this was natural for a girl after she was fifteen and that men seemed to enjoy it greatly. But Teuru compared rough, cold Herr Brandt with kind, gentle Earl Weebles and as a logical conclusion she smashed the German across the nose and ran back to the hotel.

In the morning Hedy appeared. She was furious, said that Teuru had insulted her husband's friend and that she must never come back to the shop again. Never. Tears followed, with Hedy admitting that Herr Brandt

had tried to do the same with her once, and that she
had struck him too. She gave Teuru a wrist watch and
said, "Take it up to Johnny. We broke up in a terrible row, and I stole most of his things. But I'm not
mad at him any more." She fluffed out her pretty dress,
said good-by and walked down the quay, calling
"Bon jour" to all the other respectable married women
of the town.

It was some time before Teuru found occasion to
deliver the stolen watch, but when she did she was
dismayed at what she found. In a dark room, surrounded by filthy confusion, redheaded Johnny Roe
lay sprawled on a bed he had not left for four days. He
had not shaved. He had not washed. He had not eaten.
He was a horrible cartoon of a man, so that even the
stray island girls now let him alone at night.

"Mr. Roe!" Teuru called gently. In a month-old
stupor he rolled his head slightly and stared at her.

"Who's there?" he mumbled.

"I've brought your watch back. You must get up."
She threw him a pair of shorts and insisted that he
crawl into them, but when she tried to lead him along
the hallway to the bathroom he collapsed. Teuru
called for Frau Henslick, who hurried to the top of
the stairs. When she saw it was Roe again she became
raucous.

"I'll never touch that drunken swine again. I've
hauled him back to his room for the last time." She
stood over the crumpled body—the most recent in a
distinguished line of men who had tried to drink themselves to death in the Montparnasse—and reviled the
American while Teuru ran along the quay searching
for someone to help her lift the inert form. Finally she

got Johnny spread-eagled on the sheets. Then she washed and shaved him, holding his face tightly when the dull razor grabbed. He was bleeding when she finished, but he was beginning to look like a human being.

It was three days before he could walk to a meal. In that time Teuru had actually to chew small portions of meat and place them between his lips. She had also to buy him the gin he whimpered for, giving him a little less each day until she had weaned him back to strength.

Frau Henslick was outraged. She said that Johnny Roe should be tossed into the bay. "Shark's meat! That's what he is!" She said that as soon as he could move she was going to have him tossed in jail. And as for that room! Out he must go!

Teuru solved this by moving him down to her room, and it was there, in a grubby back hallway of the Montparnasse, that she finally learned how truly sweet it was to be in love. It was as Maggi had said, "Quiet bits of heaven." For Johnny Roe had come so close to wrecking himself that he could appreciate what Teuru had done for him.

"See what the Chinaman will give us for the watch," he suggested. She became adept in hagglig over prices with the pawnbrokers and she hoarded both her salary and the loans on his jewelry. Like a French housewife she husbanded their wealth and spent it on things that would be good for Johnny. It was very good to watch him come alive.

"What happened to you?" she asked.

"I'd always heard about these islands. After the war I wanted to see them."

"Were you in the war?"

"Like everyone else."

"Why is it so many white men want to come to Ta-hiti?"

"You've got to have somewhere you want to go," he replied.

"What did you want to find?"

"You, I guess."

"We're out of money," she replied, changing the sub-ject.

"I'll have to get a job—somewhere."

"What can you do?" she asked.

"Best thing I ever did was fly a plane."

"Maybe I can figure out something," she said.

And that was how Teuru, Povenaaa's daughter, finally arrived one day in Raïatéa with an honest-to-God American. As the *Hiro* docked Maggi and Po-venaaa waited ecstatically. They studied the clean-shaven, good-looking young man and Maggi cried in Polynesian, "I knew you could do it!"

It was a much different story, however, when the four of them faced the rancid butter of Le Croix du Sud. Povenaaa got right to the point. "I better hurry over to Bora Bora, because there's only one jeep left."

"You buying a jeep?" Johnny inquired.

Povenaaa winked broadly and patted Johnny on the arm. "It's good to see you here, son. How long you intend to stay?"

"As long as Kim Sing . . . that's his name, isn't it?"

"You know our leading merchant?" Povenaaa asked expansively.

"Not exactly. I hope to work for him, though."

"Work?" Maggi gulped.

"Did you say work?" Povenaaa gaped.

"Yes. Teuru told me . . ."

Now Povenaaa became all diplomacy. "Do you mean," he probed, "that you have to work?"

"Yes."

"You mean . . . you're broke?"

"That's right. If it hadn't been for Teuru . . ."

This was more than man could bear. Povenaaa became choleric and then spluttered, "Pigs! Dogs! Chickens!" What this meant he did not stop to explain. In majestic outrage he stamped from the hotel and did not show his face in the bar for three days. As for Maggi, she sank back in her chair and studied Teuru. Three times she started to ask questions but each time she shuddered and ended by ordering herself more beer.

By this time Kim Sing had opened his vanilla sheds and the rich smell permeated the bar, so Teuru said, "You'll get used to that smell. We'll go now."

She led Johnny across the road and presented him to the merchant. "An American?" Kim replied. "I couldn't pay an American decent wages."

"Any wages would be decent," Johnny confessed.

So each sunny morning Johnny Roe hauled out into the hot sunlight huge tarpaulins bearing the harvested beans, now five to seven inches long, laden with essence which the heat would tease into condition, so that in time the patiently tended beans became pliable and wonderfully odorous. At night he hauled the tarps in out of the dew, and when the beans were cured, he arranged them upright on big tables.

Then Teuru went to work. Sitting with her eyes at the level of the bean tops, she bundled the licorice-colored beans into the quarter-kilo packages which were shipped to Paris. Forming her left hand in a circle, she would cull from the large assortment a few choice beans to make the outside of the bundle attractive. For the middle she saved the scrubs, being attentive to select each bean so that when the longer outside ones were pulled into position all beans would appear to be of the same length. Kim Sing said that Teuru's deft bundling earned him an extra 20 percent.

These were happy days for Teuru. She watched Johnny thriving under the new regime and saw that he was growing brown and strong. It was fun, too, to have him working with her and she enjoyed watching him spend the money she allowed him at the bar. He drank only beer himself, but he was a great favorite with the young men of Raïatéa, standing them whiskey and gin, beating them at darts. Sometimes Teuru told herself that she had been luckier than most girls, and the more she grew to love Johnny the more clearly she remembered frightened Victor and triumphant Earl Weebles. One night she told Maggi, "I've been lucky."

Maggi leaned back to count up the score. "By and large you have been," she agreed.

Only Povenaaa held out. Each time he saw Johnny he was humiliated anew. Pushing his forlorn mare along the roads, the cruelly betrayed man would dream of that last jeep in Bora Bora. Then he would hammer the mare and imagine it was Johnny Roe.

But when Povenaaa did finally accept Johnny it was completely, said he was the finest American he had ever known. The two men got roaring tight and stopped every stranger on the road to tell them the news. Teuru was going to have a baby!

Yes, Teuru was pregnant. Maggi, of course, had been the first to detect the happy secret and she commissioned Major to dash through the streets informing everyone. When Povenaaa heard, he left the mule right in the vanilla fields and came storming into the shed and informed Kim Sing, "We're going to the bar and get drunk." Then he had a better idea. He whispered to Johnny, "We'll stick the Chinaman for the drinks." Unctuously he said to Kim, "It wouldn't be a celebration without you." So the merchant paid for the bottles and Povenaaa giggled at having made the Chinaman a fool. But Kim Sing had plans of his own and when they were discovered they almost drove Johnny Roe crazy.

It happened one morning when Johnny came to work and found Maggi, Kim Sing, Povenaaa and three other men rolling dice. Teuru stood nearby, watching the game with interest, advising Maggi, "You better try harder! You need three more sixes!"

"What's the game?" Johnny asked.

"Dice," Teuru said.

"I can see that. What's it about?"

Teuru blushed and looked away, so Johnny asked Povenaaa. "Don't bother me now," the excited man cried. Suddenly there were shouts of triumph and Maggi swore the Chinaman had cheated, but Kim Sing grinned happily and picked up the dice.

"The damned Chinaman gets the baby," Povenaaa spat.

"Gets what?" Johnny asked.

"The baby."

"Whose baby?"

"Teuru's."

"I didn't know Teuru had a baby."

"She doesn't . . . yet."

"You mean . . . my baby?" Johnny fell back with his mouth gaping. Then he yelled, "Hey! What's this about my baby?"

"He won it," Maggi said disconsolately.

Grabbing Teuru, the American cried, "What are they talking about?"

"When it's born," Teuru said. "All the people in Raïatéa would like to have it. So we rolled dice."

"But it's your own baby!" he stormed.

"Sure," she said. "But I can't keep it. I'm not married."

"Your own flesh and blood!"

"What's he mean?" Teuru asked Maggi.

Johnny Roe looked beseechingly at the fat woman and asked, "Would you give away your own baby? Would you give away Major?"

The crowd in the vanilla shed burst into laughter and Johnny demanded to know the joke. "It's Major!" Povenaaa roared, punching Johnny in the ribs. "Major's not her baby. She's Hedy's."

"You mean that Hedy. . . ."

"Of course," Maggi explained. "Hedy had to go to Tahiti for a good time before settling down. So she gave me Major."

Johnny Roe had heard enough. He stormed off and bought two bottles of gin, and when Teuru found him he had returned to his Montparnasse days except that now he blubbered, "Our baby! You raffled off our baby with a pair of dice!"

He kept this up for a whole day and Teuru became afraid that it was the start of another epic binge, so she broke the gin bottles and said, "All girls give away their first babies. How else could they get married?"

Johnny sat upright, suddenly sobered. "What do you mean, married?"

"What man in Raïatéa would want a girl who couldn't have babies?"

"You mean . . . the men don't care?"

"Very much! Since people find I'm to have a baby several men who never noticed me before have asked when you were going away."

"What happens then?" Johnny asked suspiciously.

"Then I get married."

Johnny fell back on his pillow and moaned, "It's indecent. By God, it's indecent."

So Teuru consulted Maggi, who said, "I'll talk to him." She puffed into the bedroom and asked, "What are you moaning about?"

"This whole affair. It's indecent."

"What's wrong about it? Tell me, why did you come out here?"

"I was a drunken Papeete wreck, so Teuru brought me here."

"I mean why did you come to Tahiti?"

"Well, in California I was even a worse wreck."

"Why?"

"The war, I guess."

"We had a war, too."

"Mine was different."

"Oh, no. Eighty men from Raïatéa volunteered and went into the desert with the Foreign Legion. We lost many men from Raïatéa."

"They have a statue in Canada which says something about the ones who didn't come back being the lucky ones."

"Don't ever believe it! Is that what you thought, Johnny?"

"Something like that. I got all mixed up."

Maggi started to laugh. "I'll never understand white men."

"How do you mean?" Johnny asked.

"Like you," she said, puffing heavily. "You get sick at heart about something, so you come out here to cure the disease, and when you're cured you despise us for how we manage it. That seems ridiculous to me."

"It's even more ridiculous, how a girl's own father— how Povenaaa can send Teuru to Papeete."

Maggi exploded with laughter. "Povenaaa? Did you say Povenaaa?" She held her fat sides and shook her head hilariously. "Didn't anybody tell you? Povenaaa could have no children. That poor skinny man. We felt sorry for him in Raïatéa so somebody gave him a baby to bring up."

"Who did?"

"I did."

Johnny Roe was stopped dead cold. They were pitching curves at him now and he was stopped cold. He started to laugh and finally kissed fat Maggi on the cheek. Seeing her chance, she grabbed him by the hair and kissed him back.

"You're a smart woman," he cried. "You're about the smartest woman I've ever known."

"I been around," she joked, talking like an American movie.

Johnny finally sat on the bed and asked, "How come you gave up Teuru?"

"I heard the rich Americans were coming to Papeete . . . about the time of Zane Grey. I wanted to see things before I married."

"Did you marry?"

"Oh, yes."

"Where's your husband?"

"He was killed in the war. In the desert."

That was that. Johnny had no more to say, but as she left, Maggi added, "When you get back home . . . Well, if you should ever make any money, send Povenaaa a jeep."

But Povenaaa did not have to wait upon such a miracle, for a more astonishing one took place right on Raïatéa. One morning, about seven, a yacht put into the straits and an expensive launch, manned by men in white, hurried ashore. An elderly gentleman with white mustaches asked many questions at Le Croix du Sud and ended by going to Kim Sing's vanilla shed. He stood in the doorway for a moment until his eyes became accustomed to the shadows. Then he saw what he was seeking.

"Hello, Johnny," he said.

The young American turned, clean, bronzed, solid-looking. "Hello, Mr. Winchester."

"I told your father I'd look you up."

"How is Dad?"

"Fine, fine. I think he'd like to have you back."

That night on the polished yacht Povenaaa and Maggie ate off silver plates, but Teuru was not there.

"I'm too fat," she told Johnny, insisting that he go. After brandy Mr. Winchester said he thought it was about time for Johnny Roehampton to be heading home. Johnny blushed nervously and agreed it was about time.

"He's been here long enough," Maggi said expansively.

"Too long," Povenaaa observed.

Johnny had much to do before shoving off. He thanked Kim Sing for the job. He gave presents to each of the gang at the bar. He bought Maggi a shawl and even promised to send Povenaaa a jeep.

But Povenaaa had been disappointed many times in his life and he was not to be taken in by any more tricks, so while Johnny was packing he rowed out to the yacht and consulted Mrs. Winchester. "I don't ask much," he said. "I'm reasonable, but I've had dreadful bad luck with Teuru."

"Who's Teuru?"

"My daughter."

"Is she sick?"

"No, she's pregnant."

Mrs. Winchester gulped. "You mean . . . she isn't . . . married?"

"Certainly not!" Povenaaa snapped. "It's my bad luck with her men I'm speaking of."

"What do you mean, her men?"

"I don't think she has good sense," Povenaaa explained. "First she brings home a Frenchman. He lives with us eight months and I don't get a sou. Then she brings home an Englishman. Not a sou. Now it's Johnny Roe. Still no money."

Mrs. Winchester grew pale. "You mean . . . you would take money . . . for your daughter?"

"Well, seeing that Johnny is leaving behind a baby that I'll have to feed . . ."

Weakly Mrs. Winchester cried, "Griswold! Griswold!" When her husband appeared she whispered, "Get this creature out of here."

"What's going on?" Mr. Winchester blustered.

"It's unspeakable! This wretched man's daughter has had three lovers. Now she's going to have a baby and her father"—she shuddered—"wants to be paid off."

Mr. Winchester took out his wallet and said, "My dear, I warned you that Tahiti . . ."

"Don't give it to him! Give it to the girl, if she's not some cheap . . ."

"I've seen the girl," Mr. Winchester said. "She's very decent."

He took his wife ashore and led her to the vanilla shed, where she gasped when she saw how lovely Teuru was.

"You're very pretty," Mrs. Winchester said.

"Johnny told me you were an old friend."

"Yes, we've known his family for years."

"What will Johnny do . . . when he gets home, I mean?"

Mrs. Winchester perceived that she had stumbled upon the classic island tragedy: the deserted native girl and the handsome white man. So she said gently, "He'll probably go back to college."

"And get married?" Teuru asked, smiling warmly as she whipped cords about her bundle of beans.

Mrs. Winchester knew that the brave smile masked

the heartbreak of betrayal, so she said consolingly, "And you? What will you do?"

Teuru started a new bundle in her left hand and said thoughtfully, "I guess I'll get married, too. After I get rid of the baby."

Mrs. Winchester swallowed. "What do you mean? Get rid of the baby?"

"Kim Sing won it. After a few weeks I'll give it to Kim Sing."

"He . . . won . . . it?" the American woman asked weakly.

"Yes. He threw eleven sixes."

Mrs. Winchester retreated in a flood of nausea. At the door she bumped into Povenaaa and said to her husband between clenched teeth, "Give this despicable creature some money." Then she stared at Povenaaa and said bitterly, "You had to take care of the baby!"

Yet it was Mr. Winchester's money that finally settled many problems for Teuru. After the yacht left, with redheaded Johnny Roehampton staring at the dock until the headland had been breasted, Povenaaa slipped over to Bora Bora and came home with the last jeep. It was badly battered and carried a garish sign across the front: SHORE PATROL. But it ran and it had a horn. Povenaaa's first use of it was to drive up to Kim Sing's establishment and blow the horn like mad. When the Chinaman appeared Povenaaa stood up and announced to his former employer, "You, M'sieur Kim Sing, can go to hell." Then he drove off down the middle of the road.

Teuru immediately came to apologize. She told Kim he had always been kind to her family and that she appreciated this. "And now what will you do?" Kim asked.

Teuru looked at the bundles she had tied and said, "After the child is born, Maggi wants me to go back to Papeete."

"Papeete is very fine," Kim said.

"But the rooms are so small and dark. I don't want to leave Raïatéa any more."

Kim Sing thought a long time and said, "You should tell your father."

So Teuru sought out Povenaaa at the new pier, where he was hauling rock. "I'm not going back to Tahiti," she announced.

To her surprise Povenaaa said, "Good! We're people of importance now. We still have lots of money left from the yacht." Then, seeing Kim Sing approaching, he shouted, "And no daughter of mine is going to work for a damned Chinaman, either!"

Kim Sing came to the pile of rocks and said haltingly, "I did not come to ask Teuru to work for me again."

"Then get out of the way. Can't you see I'm a busy man?"

"I came to ask . . . since Teuru does not wish to leave . . . since I'm to have the baby anyway . . ."

When the meaning dawned on Povenaaa he slammed the jeep into low gear and tried to murder the Chinaman with it. "My daughter!" he bellowed. "Living with a Chinaman!"

From behind the rocks the merchant said quietly, "I am not asking her to live with me. I am asking her to marry me."

Then Teuru stepped boldly beside Kim Sing and said, "Yes, Povenaaa, we are going to get married." Povenaaa let his hands fall from the steering wheel and started to gulp, but Teuru said softly, "I went to Papeete three times for you. Now I shall stop in Raïatéa."

Povenaaa washed his hands of the whole affair. He announced, at Le Croix du Sud, that if a daughter of his insisted upon such a thing he wished to hear no more about it. Maggi arranged the wedding and exacted from Kim a written pledge that he would not beat Teuru as some of his countrymen did their wives and that he would allow her spending money so long as she continued to wrap bundles of vanilla. But on one point he was adamant. Povenaaa came sniveling around and said that since his only daughter was leaving home he might as well sell the house, but Earl Weebles' big sculptures still cluttered up the place. "Why not move them into the vanilla shed?"

But Kim Sing—even though he had sworn not to beat his wife—was not a complete fool. So years later when hungry collectors from London and Paris reached Raïatéa they uncovered the precious masterpieces in the most unlikely places. The classic bust of Maggi, for example—the one now in the Louvre—it was found propping open the door to the barn where Povenaaa kept his jeep.

The Mynah Birds

*It is interesting to speculate upon
what might have happened had the
American Government accepted
the offer of cession.*

In 1949 the United States closed down its consulate in
Fiji for lack of business. But two years later the in-
flamed Patel case threatened the civil peace of this
colony, and a distinguished young American was hurried back as an official observer. Mr. Louis McGurn was
then thirty-eight, unmarried, trained in the hard schools
of Palestine, South Africa and India. He was reported
to have a very bright future in the State Department.

Unobtrusively he set up quarters in the Grand Pacific
Hotel and let it be known that he had arrived to take a
long vacation. He hired taxicabs and took trips to various parts of the island, stopping overnight at one or
another of the good hotels. He waited for two things:
the arrival in Suva of the well-known British judge,
Sir Charles Jacquemart, and the report of the civil action he had recently started in the courts of Boston,
whose outcome had not yet been determined when he
left hurriedly for Fiji.

To McGurn, the green lands of Fiji were a dream
come true. As a child he had sat with Grandmother
Richardson and listened to horrible accounts of these

Cannibal Isles. A Boston ancestor, one Luke Richardson, had wandered to Fiji with a shipload of trinkets.
Exchanging them for a cargo of sandalwood, he set out
to make his fortune in China. But as he was about to
haul anchor, Fijian savages fell upon his ship.

"Then," said Grandmother Richardson, "the wild men
dragged the crew ashore and tortured 'em. They were
terrible cruel. They ripped the skin off their feet and
jabbed 'em in the belly with torches to make 'em dance
in misery."

Sometimes at night Louis could imagine his feet with
no soles. He would sweat and recall what happened
next. "These cannibals grabbed the tormented men and
dashed their heads against a sacred altar. Then they
cut 'em apart, baked 'em and ate 'em."

Captain Richardson had been saved by three foul-
mouthed Australians, who proceeded to massacre forty-
seven savages for sport. This made the captain feel
better, and three years later he was back with more
trinkets. This time he won his fortune and in later
years spoke well of Australians. He left the city of
Sydney $20,000 when he died.

In his travels about the islands McGurn easily recognized the bloody scenes described by his ancestor in the
latter's book: *Ten Years in the Waters of the South Seas,
Including Pertinent Observations on the State of Our
Trade with China and the East*. Such discoveries gave
him a sense of identification with Fiji.

Yet at the same time, his duties in the Cannibal Isles
occasioned a sense of bitterness, for they reminded him
of the fact that in spite of his regrettable name he was
essentially a Richardson, of Boston. It had been easy,
during the latter years of the preceding century, for

the Richardsons to forget old Cap'n Luke's near piracy and opium trade. On his hundreds of thousands of dollars—nursed into millions—a substantial Boston family had been built.

Then, in 1911, Emily Richardson had revolted against her family and had run off with a dreadful Irishman, Timmy McGurn. He had died in a Monte Carlo brawl, but not before siring a son, Louis, and fixing upon that child the guttural name of McGurn. As soon as he got into Harvard, young McGurn insisted that he be called Louis Richardson McGurn, and when he introduced himself he placed so much emphasis on the second name that strangers often had to ask him to repeat the last.

It was toward the end of February, in the rainy summer season, that Sir Charles Jacquemart and his family finally arrived by plane from the Kenya Colony in Africa. They took rooms at the G.P.H. and that afternoon McGurn reported to Washington. "Sir Charles has appeared on the scene. Both factions, Indians and Fijians, trust him without cavil and the trial should soon begin. I knew of him when I served in Africa and he is a man of absolute probity."

It pleased McGurn that Sir Charles was to have a room next to his own. He liked titles. He was no snob, having seen Palestinian Jews and Australian wharfies knock the spots off snobs, but he did think it appropriate that governments recognize with appropriate titles those of its citizens who lived and worked in such a way as to bring honor upon a nation. In the war, he had known a French baron of incredible bravery, and be felt that the man's actions were inspired partly because he was of noble lineage. He himself had often dreamed of being Sir Louis. So even if titles were forbidden Americans, he intended living his life as Sir Louis. In the war against Japan that determination had won him two decorations. It had also accounted for his rapid advancement in the State Department.

Therefore, when he had finished his confidential report, he selected a neatly pressed suit, shined his shoes once more and put on a sedate tie. Then he sat primly on the veranda outside his room and waited.

He had been sipping gin and tonic for some minutes when the French doors nearby opened. A large woman of fifty-five appeared. She wore a lacy dress favored by British women in the tropics, and after adjusting it carefully, allowed her large bulk to sink into a rattan chair which creaked painfully as it conformed to the bulges of her body. She shifted twice and then sighed.

"We've been coming here for thirty years and those mountains across the bay are finer . . ." She lapsed into a wheezing silence.

McGurn rose and made a little bow. "May I presume?" he began.

"Pshaw!" the plump lady interrupted. "No ceremony with me. I'm Lady Jacquemart. That gin and tonic you're drinkin'?"

McGurn was flustered for a moment and then said, "I'm Louis Richardson McGurn."

"Don't mumble," Lady Jacquemart snapped. "What's that last name?"

"McGurn."

"How'd'ja spell it?"

Painfully, Louis spelled out the ugly name. "My father was born in England," he elaborated. "Surrey."

"Sounds like a boxer's name," Lady Jacquemart said approvingly.

"I used to box," McGurn replied.

"Three minutes ago I asked if that was gin and tonic," Lady Jacquemart laughed. The American blushed and poured her a drink. She produced a small lace handkerchief and wiped the perspiration off her upper lip. When she reached for the drink, McGurn bowed slightly.

"You've got demmed pretty manners for an American," she said. "Where'd'ja learn 'em?"

"Boston," he said proudly.

"Stuffy place," she snorted. "I prefer Carolina. I like hot lands with plenty of niggers."

McGurn winced and peeked about to see if any of the colored servants had heard, but Lady Jacquemart continued sharply. "Don't cringe. They're niggers. In the Empire they are."

The American coughed and said, "We've been carefully taught not to say 'Empire' any longer."

"Empire?" Lady Jacquemart exploded. "What've they been tellin' you? It's a Commonwealth? Fiddle-de-cock! Fiji belongs personally to the King, bless 'im, and if we're not smack in the middle of Empire right now, you can fry me for dinner."

Before he could answer she turned and yelled sharply, "Antonia!" There was no reply and she called again. Then she nudged McGurn in the arm. "'Dja mind pokin' your head in that second door and callin' my daughter?"

McGurn rose, placed his gin carefully on the wicker table, and moved down the veranda to a pair of closely locked French doors. He tapped politely and then shrugged his shoulders at the Englishwoman.

"Give it a good bang," she directed, kicking out with her left foot.

McGurn obeyed and heard a sharp voice inside the room. "What's the row?" Before he could reply, the doors burst open and before him stood a bonny English girl of twenty-two. She had a mop of red hair, a smooth, highly colored face and broad shoulders like her mother. She was barefooted and wore only a slip. Seeing McGurn, she cried, "Hullo, wrong room?"

The American bowed and said with an amused smile, "Your mother."

The girl cried, "O.K., Mums. Be right with you."

"Get some clothes on," her mother commanded without even looking at the door.

"Roger wilco!" the girl laughed. As she pulled the French doors inward, she left her head sticking out so that she could smile at McGurn. "Thanks awfully," she said. "I'll look better in a moment."

Again McGurn smiled his amusement and bowed. When he returned to his chair, he said, "Attractive girl, your daughter."

"She'd go around naked if I didn't watch her," Lady Jacquemart snorted. "She grew up in hot lands."

"Not in England?"

"Heavens, no! We despise England, as a place to live. Too demmed cold. Sir Charles"—she called her husband S'Chalz—"has had a roving commission. Wherever there was trouble, they sent him. He's here now to clean up a notorious case."

"Yes. There's great discussion of it."

"Those wretched Injians!" Lady Jacquemart snapped. She uttered the last word with obvious distaste.

McGurn cleared his throat and said slowly, "If Sir Charles thinks that of the Indians, I'm surprised . . ."

Lady Jacquemart chuckled. "Never impute my thoughts to S'Chalz. I'm really an old gossip. S'Chalz, on the other hand, is the soul of rectitude."

She could have chosen no more fitting word to describe her husband, who now appeared on the veranda. Sir Charles was some six-feet-three and weighed less than a hundred and sixty. He had gray hair and a black mustache, which he dyed. He was rigidly erect and his face had the impersonal glaze of the complete judge.

" 'Lo Chalz," his wife said.

"Evenin', Maud," he grunted.

His wife began, "This is a young American . . ." but Sir Charles totally ignored McGurn. Then followed a long silence as the judge sat down. Lady Jacquemart winked at McGurn and shrugged her shoulders. She said nothing, for it was agreed between the judge and his wife that in company he would set the topics of conversation. In this way, he avoided embarrassment over the trials he might be conducting. Finally he said in a doleful voice, "It's quiet here by the bay."

The subject having been nominated, like trumps at whist, McGurn played one of his small cards. He said, "It's quiet now, but in the morning the birds make a fearful clatter."

At this, Sir Charles noticed the American. "Mynahs," he grunted.

"Those dreadful birds!" Lady Maud exploded.

"They certainly caught on in this land," Sir Charles said.

"Aren't they native?" McGurn asked.

"The Injians brought them along," Lady Maud explained with much contempt, "when they came here to work the sugar."

Sir Charles recalled other years. "When we first came here birds of all kinds clustered on that lawn."

Lady Maud added, "The frightful mynahs have driven them all away."

"Gresham's law of ornithology," the judge reflected. "Sparrows and mynahs drive out the better coin."

"Like everything else, they should have been kept in Injia," Lady Maud announced firmly.

Sir Charles turned crimson. "Really, my dear . . ." he began.

But his wife was not looking at him and added, "The birds are as vicious as the Injians who brought them. Between them, they've ruined Fiji."

Sir Charles rose abruptly and in austere dignity stomped off the veranda. Lady Maud clapped a fat hand over her mouth and mumbled, "Goodness, I've done it again." She struggled to rise from her rattan chair and McGurn helped her. As she stepped through the French doors, the American could hear the acidulous judge protest, "One day you'll ruin me."

And to McGurn's surprise, Lady Maud poked her husband in the ribs and chuckled. "It'll only be because I'm so stupid," she said puckishly, whereupon they both laughed.

At this moment, the French doors farther down the veranda opened and Toni Jacquemart appeared. "Hullo," she said cheerily. "Where's the clan?"

"Inside," McGurn reported, jerking his thumb at the door behind him. "I'm Louis Richardson McGurn."

"What was the last name?" the pink-cheeked girl asked.

"McGurn."

"Oh, Irish!"

He was about to disclose his English ancestry, when he saw a merry twinkle in the girl's eye. He laughed and said, "As Irish as they come."

Toni Jacquemart gripped his hand firmly. "What ya drinking?"

"Gin and tonic," he replied.

"How frightfully British," she laughed. "Any coke?" McGurn winced and said, "I never drink it."

"It's my favorite," Toni said.

"Where'd you meet up with it?"

"Here, during the war. Pops was stationed here and there were scads of Yanks about. You ever hear of the Duchess?"

"No." The servant appeared and, to McGurn's inner satisfaction, said there hadn't been any coke on Fiji for two years. "A lemon squash?" the black man asked.

"If that's all you have," Toni sighed. "This Duchess," she explained, "was an American DC-3. Stationed on the other side of the island."

"At Nadi?" McGurn asked.

"Good old Nadi!" the girl chuckled. "Each Friday, the Yanks flew the Duchess over here to pick up a full cargo of pretty girls. Half-castes, Chinese, white girls! It was a lovely trip. The girls stayed overnight at the BOQ. Big dances. Fine food. There was necking galore."

McGurn shivered. "Did you go?"

"Nope. Mums said I was too young. But once when

the major himself asked Mums to be a chaperone I
tagged along and had a wonderful time. The Americans
got Mums tight and there was a hell of a go!"

The doors behind them opened and Lady Maud appeared. Her daughter leaped up and grabbed her by
the shoulders. "I was telling Mr. McGurn—it's Irish and
very lilting—about the time the Americans got you
spiffo."

Lady Maud laughed. "What a delightful time we
had! The girls of this island wept when that plane was
taken away."

"Mums volunteered to chaperone again," Toni said,
"but Pops put his foot down."

"He takes a very dim view of white men mixing with
colored girls," Lady Maud said sternly. "I must say I do,
too."

"But you were the chaperone!" McGurn said.

"The men were Americans," Lady Maud laughed.
"They don't have to run a thousand colonies."

From within the hotel a musical chime began to
sound and Toni jumped to her feet. "Dinner at last!" she
cried.

Up and down the interior balcony walked an Indian
with his chimes, beating them as if to summon the
spirits of all the notable feasters who had lived in Fiji.
The lovely tones died, and from each room appeared
the Britons who, by their own devious routes, had this
night assembled in the Cannibal Isles.

They were a stately crew. The men were often old
and feeble, but they dressed for evening meal. Their
women occasionally gave evidence of pinching pennies,
but in the lacy shawls of a generation past they ap-

peared to be in formal minuet as they progressed to the spotless linen and shining silver of the dining hall.

The Jacquemarts were led to a corner table where Sir Charles could keep aloof from diners who might otherwise embarrass him by commenting on the trial. Lady Maud, with no such inhibitions, held court and nodded to all the old hands. Toni sat beside her and cried a cheery "Hullo" to everyone. "We won the hockey game," she announced.

"Seems to me," Lady Maud observed icily, "that at your age you'd be giving up hockey."

Toni jabbed a forefinger into her mother's soft arm, " 'Twould do you some good to have a go at it."

"Antonia!" her father interrupted snappishly.

"It would, Pops! You don't appreciate how boys study a girl's mother. They want to see how the girl is going to look in twenty years."

The judge snorted and withdrew into his shell. Lady Maud nodded graciously to friends who greeted her and said out of the corner of her mouth, "That Mr. McGurn seems a right decent sort, Antonia."

Toni screwed her mouth up into a gangster snarl and whispered, "Let me pick me own men, see?" Lady Maud, against her will, broke into a smile and said, "You don't seem to have done very well, so far." But she was pleased to see that Toni, out of the corner of her eye, was looking at the American.

McGurn, seated across the dining room in quarters reserved for Americans and other vagrants, was at the same time studying Toni. She was, he thought, not a beautiful girl. But she had that glowing English complexion which makes any woman attractive, even if she was inclined to plumpness. "She's not fat," he mused. "Not like her mother." Then he looked at Lady Maud sprawling over her chair, and he thought happily of the straight, frail women of his family, the Richardson women. They had been beautiful, his mother loveliest of all. She could have married any man in Boston, and she chose Timmy McGurn. Her son Louis could certainly have arranged her life for her better than that.

His regrets about his mother were interrupted by an Indian messenger, who tapped him respectfully on the shoulder.

"Meestair McGurrrn? A man outside to see you."

Louis put down the forkful of food he was about to stuff into his mouth, English style, and said, "Tell him he must wait."

"He says very important," the Indian persisted.

McGurn had learned never to become impatient—or rather, never to betray that he had become impatient —and he said gently, "You can see I'm eating. Tell him that."

But the messenger said in a low whisper, "This man says it's to do with your mission."

McGurn masked his astonishment and said, "Perhaps I'll see him now." He rose unobtrusively, nodded when Lady Maud smiled, and followed the messenger.

At the curb outside the hotel, a thin and very black figure awaited him. "If you will be so generous as to pardon me," the cadaverous figure apologized unctuously. "Only a matter of gravest importance could justify . . . Permit me, my card."

The funereal face broke into a flashing smile and a

tiny card was thrust into McGurn's hand. By the misty light of a street lamp he read: "Mr. Rancheck Devidas Billimoria. Christian. Dealer in Souvenirs of All Kinds. Cats' Eyes. Tortoise Shell. Fine Indian Ivory."

McGurn had sometimes seen this man about the streets of Suva. The Hindu-turned-Christian carried a small cardboard suitcase, heavily stamped to make it resemble alligator. He appeared to eke out a mean living so that he could wear a threadbare European suit and pointed shoes. His skin was midnight black but he had mastered the trick of looking directly into the eyes of Europeans, whereas most of his countrymen looked away.

"And what did you wish?" McGurn asked cautiously.

"It concerns . . . your mission."

McGurn showed no surprise and asked, "Yes?"

Billimoria had not anticipated this, so he fumbled for a moment. "Your mission for the United States Government," he said.

"I have no mission," McGurn said coldly. "Anyway, I don't deal with informers, Mister . . ." He looked with studied insolence at the preposterous card.

The Indian did not flinch. "Neither do I, normally. After all, there's nothing much lower than an informer, is there, Mister . . ." Here Billimoria appeared to fumble for a name exactly as McGurn had done. "But your man Harvey . . ."

"Who?"

"Joe Harvey. At the airport."

McGurn had met Harvey, but he had no knowledge of his affairs other than that he came from Kansas City and was an airport engineer working on Pacific Air

Transport's base at the new Suva field. "I see no reason why Harvey is any concern of mine."

He started to leave, but the Indian pressed a long index finger into his chest. In a deathly whisper Billimoria asked, "We don't want to see Harvey killed, do we? Not at this time?"

McGurn tried to appear very casual and asked, "Why should a young man like Harvey be killed?"

"Because he's what you Americans call 'running around with' an Indian girl." He paused, then whispered sinisterly, "Our Indian men don't like it."

McGurn smiled. "I understand, Mr. Billimoria. The American has stolen your girl. Why don't you go home and forget about it?"

He turned his back upon the informer and took two steps toward the hotel, only to be caught by the arm and jerked about. "McGurn!" Billimoria threatened, insulting the white man by omitting the "mister," "You're a fool! If Harvey debauches an Indian girl, there will be grave trouble . . . when you want it least." Almost mysteriously, the Indian slipped away into the shadows.

McGurn was disgusted. His food was cold, the Jacquemarts had left the dining room, and he was worried. It was quite probable that Harvey had struck up some kind of acquaintance with an Indian girl. There was a certain type of American man who could be counted on to shack up with absolutely any kind of woman. You couldn't designate the type of female who would be too low for some American to crawl into bed with.

McGurn ate a few spoonfuls of dessert and left the table. "Damn it," he muttered, as he climbed the stairs to his room. "If the young fool has to toy around with

color, why does he do it now? Can't he wait till the
trial's over?"

The pressure of this trial was on everyone that rainy
summer. An Indian had accidentally killed a Fijian with
a taxicab. Then he had fled from the scene and been
reported by a Fijian woman who had subsequently been
beaten up, whereupon some Fijians had caught the
man's brother and thrashed him. Tempers were at an
ugly pitch, and on the very day that Sir Charles
Jacquemart arrived to try to straighten things out
between two warring races who respected him, an
irresponsible American was goading the Indians to new
threats of violence.

His evening ruined, McGurn shifted into a sack coat
and wandered down to the cinema, where a British
comedy of great reputation was playing. But even the
Tawny Pipit was ruined, because at intermission he saw
in the center seats reserved for white people the blond
head of Joe Harvey, and next to him the jet-black hair
of a slim Indian girl. McGurn gasped at the young man's
public folly and noticed that English members of the
audience were outraged. He overheard a woman whispering, "Trust an American! They'll wallow anywhere."
He felt that the censure was merited.

He would have left the cinema in disgust, but Harvey
had already spotted him as a fellow-American and
strode boldly up the aisle with the girl on his arm.
"Hey, Yank!" the young man called. "Don't duck! I
want you to meet my girl." English patrons nearby
moved away in disgust. "This is Pata Cadi," the young
man said.

The slight girl bowed in acknowledgment. She was
twenty, golden-skinned and dark-eyed. McGurn could

do nothing but bow slightly and say, "It's been a good show so far, hasn't it?"

The next minutes were agony for Louis McGurn. He stood conspicuously by his seat while Harvey and the Indian girl blocked the aisle. He recalled the statement an Englishwoman had made in Calcutta: "The Americans are like tomcats, forever on the prowl among the alleys of the world." And here was a prime tomcat hauling his catch into the middle of British society. He blushed and wondered if Americans would ever learn to behave when they were away from home.

As soon as intermission ended, he slipped out of the cinema. When he reached the G.P.H., he found Toni Jacquemart in the lounge surrounded by three young men. As he climbed the stairs, he heard her provocative cry, "Good dreams, Yank." She spoke with the mocking arrogance that English people use when referring to Americans or Australians. McGurn was ashamed of his nationality.

In the morning, his fitful sleep was broken by the mynah birds. They had found a swarm of flies in a tree near the hotel, and their chatter was unbelievable. Like a thousand children at a picnic they screamed and brawled. Back and forth they rioted until McGurn had to rise in desperation.

Wrapped in a conservative robe of dark-blue silk, he rubbed his sandy eyes and stepped onto the veranda to watch the mynahs. They strutted like cabinet ministers in a ducklike waddle. When they ran they placed one yellow foot in front and then brought the other up to match it, producing a grotesque and drunken lurch. They were always hungry, always fighting in scrannel screams. They possessed Fiji. It seemed only a matter of time until they evicted all other birds, as their Indian masters must force out all other races.

"Hang the clatter," McGurn muttered, but his attention was promptly diverted by Sir Charles, who appeared on the veranda fully dressed, combing his mustache with a bony forefinger.

Neither man spoke for at least five minutes; then abruptly the judge pointed to the remarkable trees where the birds were quarreling. "Weeping figs," he said sepulchrally. McGurn looked at the tangled brown parasites that hung from the branches like myriad snakes.

After five more minutes, he asked, "What parasite is that?"

Sir Charles thought for several moments and said, "Part of the tree. Aerial roots." He noticed a Fijian fisherman walking along the quay, carrying four fish and a spear. "Boy!" the judge cried sharply. He added a series of commands in Fijian and the fisherman grinned. Dropping his burdens, he leaped into the air and grasped a tangle of roots. Thus suspended, he jerked his entire weight against the thin wiry strands. They held like cables.

"Good-oh," the judge cried.

"Remarkable," McGurn said approvingly. The judge stood silent for some moments, grunted and went indoors.

In a moment, his wife appeared. She had the servant bring a pot of tea and offered McGurn a cup. "Well," she said slyly. "Hear you entertained an Injian girl at theatre last night."

McGurn sighed audibly. "Where did you hear that?"

"When you've become an old gossip, you hear everything."

"One would think an American might be especially careful right now . . ." McGurn began.

"Yes, an Injian girl, too," Lady Maud said, as she sipped her tea. "I imagine the Injian men are not pleased. You know there's a great shortage of women among the Injians, the beggars."

"She was," McGurn said ruefully, "rather pretty."

"The loveliest girls in the world are colored," Lady Maud said firmly. "That's why it's so difficult to raise sons abroad. If ever I meet God, I shall propose that all white girls of good family be beautiful. All others will be ugly. Unfortunately, it's the other way around. My own girls just escaped being ugly. My oldest was really quite repulsive for years. I couldn't stand her. Then she found she wanted a man, so she did what she could with herself and wound up fairly pretty."

"She took after her mother," McGurn said archly.

"My God," Lady Maud said. "That one creaked. Only the French can get away with a crack like that." She laughed and McGurn said, "I meant that you weren't completely repulsive."

Lady Jacquemart liked this and said, "I take pride in few things. But I am exceptionally pleased that my children escaped color. We were frightfully worried about Teddy. He formed an attachment for a brown girl in Malaya. I think he lived with her, but common sense prevailed. Actually, of course, he married an Irish girl, which wasn't much better. Oh, dear!" she fluttered. "And you're Irish!"

"I'm English," he corrected. "Surrey."

"Of course. You told me before. Well, I'm sure the Irish and the half-castes will inherit the earth one day, but I shall be dead, thank heavens."

The musical gong heralded breakfast, and in the fig trees the mynah birds made new havoc. In that moment by the sea, with the rain just beginning and the Indian gong sounding, Louis McGurn had an overwhelming sensation of being in the tropics. What he had come to observe was a tropic storm fought out by races not his own. There were summer hurricanes afoot that he could not see. He felt quite alone in a strange world. Only the Jacquemarts were his kind. Even that foolish American from Kansas City was an alien. He wanted to cry out to Lady Maud not to leave the veranda.

But at this moment, a mynah bird flew onto the table and snatched up a piece of bread crumb. Lady Maud slapped at the insulting bird with her fan. "Dirty invaders," she cried, retreating to her room.

After a leisurely breakfast, Louis McGurn left the dining room and stood for a moment at the entrance to the G.P.H., rejoicing in a scene he had grown to love. Before him stretched a handsome sports field. To the left were impressive government offices, to the right the high commissioner's mansion. Far to the east, beyond the tennis courts, were flower gardens, and all along the roads were royal palms and bright croton.

McGurn liked this splendid panorama, for it seemed to him to represent those values to whose cultivation he had dedicated his life. The British had ruled the world for some centuries and now it had come time for the Americans to assume the burden. This square of beauty indicated how to govern. Build well. The Brit-

ish could easily have governed a bunch of savage islands
from mean shacks. But if you believed that one day all
the world would know order, you built stately and
pillared mansions, even at the edge of the jungle. To do
so gave an earnest of your intentions.

Louis McGurn was willing that his life should be
spent in building such edifices throughout the world.
But right now he had to talk with young Joe Harvey
and drum some sense into the boy's head. He called a
cab and drove out to the airdrome.

Finding Harvey's office empty, he walked out into
the bright sunlight and looked around. He approached
a group of Fijian laborers, giant barefooted blacks with
kinky hair and glistening torsos, and asked for Harvey.
At the mention of the name every man grinned, and
one big chap waved toward a shack a hundred yards beyond. McGurn found Harvey there, alone.

"Those black boys seem to like you," McGurn said.

"They're my pals," Harvey replied.

"And Miss Cadi?"

Harvey seemed to miss the point of the question. "I
met her down at the Galta Milk Bar. She works there.
A beauty, eh?"

"Very attractive," McGurn said with forced enthusiasm. "But I thought there was a great shortage of Indian women. Don't the Indian men resent . . ."

"Annh!" Harvey sneered. "They don't scare me."
He whipped out his wallet and showed McGurn a
threatening note: *"You'll be sorry if you keep on seeing Pata Cadi."*

"That doesn't worry you?" McGurn asked.

"Nah, those punks make me a little bit sick."

"I used to be stationed in India," McGurn said. "Sometimes those men are jolly tough."

He had used the wrong word. When he said *jolly,* young Harvey froze up. There was a moment of silence and then the youngster asked bluntly, "You come down here to warn me about seeing Pata?"

"What makes you . . ."

"Because last night in the movies you almost wet your pants," Harvey said. "Why in hell do you suppose I stood smack in the middle of the aisle? Because it was eating you so."

"Wait a minute," McGurn said quietly. "You're jumping at a lot of conclusions."

"No, I'm not," Harvey replied, grinning broadly, "Everybody in town's been trying to figure you out. You're here to sort of help out the British, we figure."

"Who is *we?*" McGurn asked patiently.

"Pata and me."

"That was your opinion?"

"Yes. We were right, weren't we?"

"No. I'm dreadfully sorry, but you were totally wrong. I have nothing to do with the British."

"Then why do you try to be more English than they are?"

The conversation had turned into quite an unexpected channel and McGurn was distressed. He said, "I'm simply an American citizen who has lived in India. You're heading for great trouble."

"In the war, I learned how to handle trouble. By the way, what did you do in the war?"

"Just Germany and New Guinea," McGurn replied evenly.

Joe stood back and said in frank approval, "I guess you can claim you saw the war."

A nebulous bond of brotherhood-in-arms thus established, McGurn took advantage of it to say, "I'll admit I came down here to raise the devil about the Indian girl. But what's really important is this trial. Tempers are very tough. The English would . . ."

Again, he had said the wrong word and the fellowship was destroyed. "Mr. McGurn," the young aviator said, "I owe you the respect you earned in the war. But I don't care for the English. You came down here to explain British ways to a dumb hick from Kansas City. You'd be surprised at how much I know. I served with the British in Cairo, and even if they did save the world, I don't want any part of their system."

"It's the best we have in Fiji," McGurn said quietly.

"Then I don't like even the best. I don't like white people in the saddle and everyone else in the gutter. You may get a thrill out of aping the English. I don't."

"Damn it!" McGurn snapped. "You're an arrogant young pup. If you only knew how young you are. All over the world civilizations are crumbling. India, Java, China. It's our duty to help sustain them."

"No," Harvey said abruptly. "Pata and I have talked this out . . ."

"What can she know?"

"In her own way, Mr. McGurn, she knows more than you do."

"I should like to meet this remarkable girl."

"It would do you a lot of good," Harvey said. "How about dinner with us? Tonight?"

"In public? The three of us? Well, hardly!" Instinctively, McGurn cringed.

Joe Harvey was disgusted. "You afraid the British might object? Okay, skip it. Go have a pot of tea and quit worrying. I'm shipping home next week. This job's done."

The diplomat tried not to show his relief. Aloud he reflected, "A week? A lot could happen in a week. I don't suppose you'd promise to stay away from Miss Cadi during that time?"

Harvey slammed open the door. "Why don't you get the hell out of here?" he snapped.

As he left, McGurn said with deep compassion, "I came out here, Joe, to warn you. Don't get hurt."

Harvey laughed. "I'm not the kind that gets hurt," he said.

At the airdrome gate, Louis McGurn rang for a taxi. In a few minutes, a mournful Indian arrived in a new Ford. "Nice car," McGurn said as he climbed in. The Indian said nothing. On the way into the Triangle, the American asked, "What do you think of the new wing to the government buildings?" There was no reply and he repeated the question.

Very cautiously, the Hindu slowed down and said, with no inflection, "Traffic court. Where they fine you for speeding." At the Triangle, McGurn tipped the man a bob. There was no acknowledgment.

The American left the main business streets of Suva and sought out the Galta Milk Bar. Behind the counter, stood slim, neat Pata Cadi.

"Miss Cadi," McGurn began.

"Yes, Mr. Harvey just called and said you'd be in to see me."

Louis McGurn smiled stiffly and nodded. "It would be good if we could talk," he said.

She shrugged her shoulders. "Would you be embarrassed if we talked by the canal?"

"Not at all," he said, waiting until she had gone around the counter and called to her assistant. A very black girl came forward and took command of the bar.

They walked slowly up the main commercial street of Suva, passing countless Indian shops where huddled men sat all day making suits or selling ghee. Finally, they came to where a small canal drained a swamp, and along the southern edge of this canal they entered the green-pillared arcade that led into the Morris Hedstrom South Seas Store. They stood by the wall of this arcade and looked down at the opposite edge of the canal where Fijians and Indians and Chinese and half-castes conducted a noisy market.

"This has always reminded me of Venice," McGurn began.

"It reminds me of something much more precious," the Indian girl replied. "This is where Joe first kissed me." She paused and Louis McGurn studied her sharply. She had the wide forehead and thin nostrils that distinguished the patrician women of his own family. She also used the excellent diction that they had used. He had gone to Galta Milk Bar to lecture a peasant, but this charming gentlewoman was disconcerting. Most disconcerting.

He leaned back against a pillar and stared at the dark canal waters, groping for his next words. Pata continued, "I must put your mind at rest, Mr. McGurn. This is not a casual island romance. I saw too many of them during the war. The white man never marries the colored girl."

"Then you really love this American?" McGurn asked.

"In a hopeless sort of way . . . yes. But not hopeless, either. All the men I've ever known have been tied up in knots. The English are the worst. The Australians are not so bad, but they are so pathologically afraid of anyone with color. Ashamed of owning that great empty continent with so many hungry colored people breathing down their necks. Once we thought the Americans were the world's free men, but you are frightened too, and we poor Indians are the prisoners of fear. Into this mess of futility Joe Harvey . . ." She stopped and blushed. "I don't know why I'm telling you this except that we consider you a very important person . . . I mean, you being a member of the State Department."

McGurn denied this. "I'm only a visitor."

Pata Cadi smiled frankly. "Every interested person in Fiji knows who you are, Mr. McGurn. After all, there are many people in India who respect you very much."

"Very well," McGurn said. "Since you know I served in India you will respect me when I say that your affair with Joe Harvey . . ."

"It is not an affair . . . yet."

"It can end only in tragedy."

"And your mission, Mr. McGurn. You know, of course, that it too can end only in tragedy."

"What do you mean?" McGurn asked abruptly, no longer the diplomat.

"What can happen to this island of Fiji?" the Indian girl asked. "Its tragedy is inevitable. Look! Over there in the shadows! Billimoria, watching us!"

McGurn made no movement except to step closer to the Indian girl, as if he were trying to date her rather than interrogate her. "Is Billimoria in love with you?" he asked bluntly.

"Him? He loves no one! He hates. He hates the British. He hates the Americans. He hates me because I love a white man." She stared into the canal. "Like Hitler he dwells a great deal on foreign men ravishing our women."

"What does he hope to get out of it?" McGurn asked. "Would Indians follow a Christian?"

"He's no Christian!" Pata cried scornfully. "He was a convert only to get a free education. Now he's a Hindu again and most Indians commend his duplicity."

McGurn whipped about and caught sight of Billimoria hiding by the Kuo Min Tang building. "A sinister man like that hates you, and you're not worried?"

"No!" she said firmly. "I will not allow a fanatic to tell me what I must do. I don't care about his dream of a great Indian Empire or the marching soul of Gandhi. I want merely a home where I can live in peace." Her face flushed. "These islands, here, could be the paradise we seek. Free Indians and happy natives and such white men as would work with us."

"Now you sound like Billimoria!"

"I'm willing to wait for time to accomplish these things. But Billimoria . . . He reads wild magazines from India that actually call upon Indians to murder white men who do not stand at attention when the anthem is played! Can you imagine that?" She stamped her foot.

McGurn had to laugh at her tiny anger. "Joe told me I should talk with you. Now I understand why."

Automatically he gave her his professional smile then immediately sensed that here was someone who merited more than conventional gestures. He perceived her as one of that inarticulate group who are always on the verge of making things work. They never do because tragedy—war or pestilence or a new election or death—intervenes. Yet they try.

"Miss Cadi," he said abruptly, "I come to you as a suppliant. If you have no fear of Billimoria, please at least help me. He wants to see something happen to you. He could start a riot. Wreck the trial. Make the British seem . . ."

"You are like a very old man," Pata said quietly. "You want to hold things together as they are . . . a little longer . . . just a little longer."

With intense fervor McGurn said, "I hope you find a better way. Until then, please don't see Joe again . . . at least until the trial's over."

Pata smiled directly at the diplomat. "You're asking me to give up the last few days I have with Harvey?"

"And you refuse?"

"You may be a statesman," the girl said, "but you've a lot to learn about love."

Suddenly Louis McGurn of Boston acknowledged that he had come upon a fresh, hard, honest human being. He bowed before her as he would have done to Lady Jacquemart and said, "I wish that statesmen could put their trust in people like you."

"You don't?" the girl asked in surprise.

"There are not enough of you," McGurn replied.

"Then may God have mercy on you," Pata said.

"I was about to say that to you," McGurn replied, deeply moved.

They shook hands and Louis McGurn returned to
the G.P.H. about as agitated as he had ever been. The
chimes rang for dinner before he gained control of himself, but he had not finished ordering before he felt a
familiar tug at his elbow. It was the mournful Indian
messenger with news: "A man waits outside to see you."

"Oh, not again!" McGurn groaned. He had hoped to
talk with Toni after dinner, but since he had never in
his diplomatic life chosen pleasure before duty, he
turned his back on the Jacequemart table and followed
his dark guide.

In the shadows he found Billimoria, more forlorn and
cadaverous than ever. "Good evening," McGurn said.

"Good evening, sir," the Indian said warmly. He
reached for McGurn's hand and pumped it eagerly. "I
was so relieved to hear that you went to see both Harvey and Miss Cadi. I appreciate your co-operation."

"That's hardly the word," McGurn said with extra
suavity. He had sworn that no matter what Billimoria
said tonight, he would not become ruffled.

"I'm sorry, sir, indeed I am," Billimoria apologized.
"I am aware that like any public servant . . ."

"I'm on vacation," McGurn insisted pleasantly.

"Ah, yes. Well, as the older friend, then, your mission
was a failure. Mr. Harvey has taken Miss Cadi to a
dance. I insist that such behavior is dangerous."

McGurn drew in his breath. "Is there anywhere we
could speak for a moment?"

"Here," Billimoria said.

"You'll excuse me. This smacks of conspiracy, doesn't
it?"

Billimoria smiled. "I have a cab."

"I'll be with you," McGurn said. "Just a moment." He hastened indoors and went boldly to Toni's table. "I had hoped we might have drinks . . . later," he began.

"Why don't we?" she asked disarmingly.

"I've a beastly meeting . . ." Toni laughed at his British affectation and waited. "But would you wait up for me? Please?"

She smiled with tomboy frankness and said, "Sure! I'll play draughts with the old gentlemen."

McGurn bounded back to the cab with unprofessional exuberance, which was dampened when he saw that the driver was the same one he had traveled with that morning. "One of your men?" he asked.

"I have no men," Billimoria reassured him. He spoke to the driver in Hindustani and soon the cab wheeled up in front of a Suva tailor's establishment. A single unshaded light suspended from the ceiling cast an eerie glow upon the bolts of expensive cloth. Four men sat in semidarkness stitching garments for Europeans.

McGurn's wraithlike guide led the way through swinging doors at the rear of the shop. Behind him, the American entered a small room. It was barren. A single chair, a small table, a polychrome portrait of Gandhi and some reading matter in a corner constituted the room's equipment. "You have the chair," Billimoria said unctuously.

"Thank you," McGurn said with a great show of politeness. "Now what are we to talk about?"

"Harvey," Billimoria said menacingly.

"Good!" McGurn said eagerly. "I have very good news to report to you. I spoke with both Harvey and

Miss Cadi and they see the reasonableness of your demands." He sat back to see what effect this irony would have on the Indian. To his surprise, Billimoria nodded his head sagely.

"But they're dancing tonight!" the Indian said.

"Ah, I know. But my friend, we must be patient. Harvey told me he was leaving within the week."

The news was unexpected and Billimoria seemed disappointed. "In that time, much could happen," he whispered hopefully.

"In that time, nothing must happen," McGurn said earnestly. "My friend, the trial starts tomorrow. Tempers will be sharpened. Please let's you and me do nothing to disturb the equilibrium until the trial is ended."

"It depends on what happens in the next fifteen days," Billimoria threatened. "We Indians have watched many white men ogle our girls. And we haven't liked what followed. We are determined that our race shall not be sullied."

"God!" McGurn thought. "Where have I heard that before?" Aloud, he said, "I beg you to be patient, Mr. Billimoria."

"We shall be, up to a point."

"And then?" McGurn asked calmly. He was determined above all not to get angry with this fool.

"England is in retreat all over the world," Billimoria said, standing quiveringly straight. "We threw them out of India. The Boers will throw them out of Africa."

"Aren't you terribly afraid of what the Boers will do to your people . . . then?"

"You started it," Billimoria cried, ignoring the question. "You threw them out of America."

"They throw very hard," McGurn said firmly. It was

then that he conceived the idea that Billimoria was really mad. The thin fanatic's apocalyptic figure in the murky light was one never to be forgotten. McGurn thought, "He is the mad devil whom we all fight."

"And so we do not worry," Billimoria continued softly, "about upsetting one small trial."

McGurn thought, "This is completely crazy! My arguing with a maniac like this! I'm not involved in this madness." He shook his head briefly, as if to cast out evil and proposed, "Let's promise this, Mr. Billimoria: I'll speak to Harvey again. And you will promise not to . . . well, not to disrupt things?"

"A sacred promise," Billimoria said dramatically. "On my word as a Christian."

McGurn let this pass and shook hands solemnly with the madman. When he left the barren and foreboding room, the same taxi was waiting for him. On the desolate ride back through the rain, he spoke twice to the driver and got no reply. Finally, he said, "Your Mr. Billimoria is very brilliant."

Immediately, the driver burst into voluble approval. "He's a wonderful leader. No one puts anything over on him." He said much more, but McGurn had heard enough.

At the hotel, McGurn felt that he had burst from out the darkness of Billimoria's turgid mind into the bright clarity of Toni's. She had drinks waiting on the lower veranda and sat handsomely against the backdrop of rain that strung a hazy veil across the harbor. A ship putting out to Levuka showed fairy lights, and its last crying echoes made the night beautiful.

"Toni!" the American cried with real delight. "You look so . . . refreshing."

"I've always liked talking with Americans," she said bluntly. She was so clean and appealing that McGurn could not possibly hide his feelings.

"I was afraid you might have gone to bed."

"I should have waited considerably longer," she said, and his head throbbed with happiness.

He could not know that Toni wished to talk with him because she remembered Yanks of quite a different sort. Once during the war, she had deceived her mother and flown across the island to the American airbase, where she had met a rollicking fighter pilot. They had, as she expressed it, "necked up a storm," and he had named her his Little Duchess. When he left for Guadal, he informed her that he was married. She still carried an angriness about her heart; but at the same time, she thought that she could have been happy with that Yank. She had enjoyed his clean laugh, his sense of freedom.

In her travels with Sir Charles, she had met many homesick men who had wanted to marry her. This had not turned her head. As Lady Maud said, "If a woman can't marry off her daughters in the tropics, she must have reared a nest of gorgons." But Toni was tired of empire builders. She was tired of the white man's world and the white man's law, administered in mock justice by her austere father. For that very reason Mc-Gurn disturbed her. At the precise time when England was laying down some of the burdens of empire, America was picking hers up; and the type of man to do this work was the same whether English or American. "Mr. McGurn is very tedious," she was thinking. And yet he was not a man to dismiss easily.

"Your family has a fine liberal spirit," he was saying.

"Due mostly to Mums," she replied. "Mums works on the principle that human beings are primarily animals. That sure keeps down neuroses."

"And your father?"

"For him, people are totally damned and always breaking laws established by right-thinking Englishmen."

"And you?" he asked, lighting his pipe.

"I partake of both. Men are animals who must be kept in line."

"You really think that?" he asked, nervously puttering with his pipe so as to keep from reaching for her hand.

"Of course I do!" she said lightly.

"What about man as a divine, aspiring creation?"

"Where have you seen the divinity? What aspiration?"

It was then that he began to realize that he bored her. It was a frightening sensation. Here was a girl he could love. He knew it. Yet he knew that she thought him uninteresting. "What kind of people do you like?" he asked abruptly.

Now it was her turn to feel that this rain-swept evening in Suva was heavy with importance. Here was a man who was cautiously feeling his ground so that he could determine whether she was the kind of girl he wanted to marry. "Oh," she said casually, "in spite of my theory I tend to like men . . ." She stopped. She realized that he had not asked her what kind of men she liked. But she added, "Well, like you. Enough brains to get by on. Maybe a little more daring." She paused and then added with a laugh, "Like most girls. A beast with brains."

"I don't know about the brains," he laughed, "but

as for the beast . . ." Suddenly he took her in his arms and kissed her. Finally, when the hotel lights had been extinguished, when the tropical rain had settled into a throbbing fall, he walked her to her door.

Next morning the mynah birds wakened him long before his usual hour. Reluctantly he pulled himself together and went out on the veranda. Lady Maud was waiting.

"Tea?" she offered brightly.

"Yes," McGurn replied with no enthusiasm.

Lady Maud twisted her head and leered at him. "It'll rain for two more weeks," she said ghoulishly. He sat down with her and started to offer some commonplace about the weather when she stopped him with a bombshell. "I hear you were necking with my daughter last night." Before he could recover she added, "I've got to speak frankly. You won't like this but here goes. If you want to marry Toni, you've got to be less stuffy."

McGurn coughed. He was completely set back; then, as if he were at a disadvantage in a chancellery, he said slowly, "I'll have some more tea, if you please."

"I don't understand it," Lady Maud continued, "but Toni has an affinity for Yanks. She'd like to live in America."

McGurn swallowed very hard. "Is there any chance . . ."

Lady Maud studied him carefully. "You're very tedious. But you would also make a good husband."

The American kept his lips to his teacup for a long time. Then he said carefully, "By those standards I should think Sir Charles a bit—forgive me—stuffy, shall we say?"

"S'Chalz!" Lady Maud exploded hilariously. "My
God, he's so stuffy taxidermists look at him with pride.
Oh, my dear young man, if you think that by pattern-
ing yourself after S'Chalz you'll win Toni . . . Oh,
what a dreadful error!" She laughed merrily and added,
"Find a model as far removed from S'Chalz as possible."

At breakfast he was considerably bucked up when
Toni went out of her way to smile at him. His fears returned, however, when he arrived at the airdrome to
see Harvey. The young man began by being ultrapolite,
but when McGurn finished his warnings, Harvey said,
"Too late, chum. If Billimoria wants to start trouble,
now he's got a reason."

"What do you mean?" McGurn asked nervously.

"Last night Pata and I decided that since we have so
few days . . . Well, she moved in."

McGurn actually fell into a chair. "What utter
folly!" he said in a low, impassioned voice.

"I'll be leaving in a few days," Harvey reassured him.

"A few days may be all they need. Joe, you're asking
for trouble."

"Sometimes a fellow doesn't care," Harvey replied.

Then McGurn became fighting mad. "Listen!" he
commanded. "Less than a hundred years ago one of my
ancestors lost an entire crew on these islands. Roasted
and eaten. People of good will came here and changed
all that through self-sacrifice and devotion. Don't ruin
their work, Joe."

"I'm to give up the one powerful happiness I've
known? For what?"

"To help an island through a time of crisis."

"And when it passes, another crisis comes along."

"All right! Then you try to heal that rupture, too," McGurn pleaded. "Life is a series of crises. Only cowards throw in the sponge."

"Very noble," Harvey sneered. "Very Sunday school. Maybe what you ought to do is let the whole rotten edifice crumble. Start over new."

"You're wrong to throw in the sponge that way, Joe. This mess is no worse than others in the world. You pitch in here and see what can be done. You don't wreck a civilization with irresponsible actions."

"Our actions are terribly responsible, McGurn. Pata and I worked this out last night."

"So you'd ruin her life . . ."

"Ruin? What's your definition of life? The protection of virginity till you're eighty? Wearing stiff white shirts like yours? You be careful, McGurn, that you don't ruin your life!"

There was nothing more to say. For McGurn, Joe Harvey was the new barbarian who would one day desolate the world. Back in his room the diplomat lay down and thought, "It would be so easy to forget the whole mess, as he called it. But you've got to try to hold things together." He was brooding upon the agitated world when he heard Toni's clear voice outside his door.

"Want to go for a boat trip, even if it is raining?"

In the days that followed Louis McGurn lived in a kind of dream. Wherever he went through the wet streets of Suva he saw Indians who resented his presence. He saw Fijians who laughed as if there were no day but now. And he saw thoughtful white men deeply disturbed by the trial. Most of all, he saw Toni.

Wherever they went—these two self-analyzing, debating creatures—they seemed to see Pata Cadi and her white lover. Once Toni noticed them in the cinema and she whispered to McGurn, "I'd like to be in love like that. Just once." To his astonishment he impulsively grasped her hands right there in public and exclaimed, "I am."

Nothing happened to upset the trial, and with great relief McGurn greeted the last day of Harvey's residence in Fiji, but his spirits fell when the young American appeared in the G.P.H. shouting across the lobby, "Well, chum. I'm shoving off tomorrow."

"Considerate of you to stop by," McGurn said icily. "I trust nothing will happen before you get away."

Harvey grinned. "Still the old worry-wart, hey?" McGurn managed a stiff smile and Harvey continued. "My Fijian pals at the airport are throwing me a farewell feast. Pata's coming and I thought you might like to join us and bury the hatchet."

McGurn visibly withdrew into his shell of conventionalism. He was about to refuse the invitation when he saw Toni Jacquemart running down the stairs to join him. "You're Joe Harvey!" she cried, extending her hand.

"I stopped by to invite Mr. McGurn to a native feast," Joe explained.

"Sounds wonderful," Toni exclaimed. "And I'll bet your Indian girl is going, too. Oh, Louis! Can I tag along?"

"I'm not going," McGurn said flatly.

"Oh!" Toni's mouth drooped. "Can't you cancel . . ."

"It's not another engagement," McGurn explained

honestly. "It's just that . . . well . . . it isn't the thing to do. Not now."

Toni flushed and turned away in anger. "Tell me, Mr. Harvey. Would you and your pretty girl take me? Even if Mr. McGurn can't make it?"

"Sure!" Harvey agreed, shaking her hand vigorously. "But you know, this isn't exactly full dress."

"That's why I want to go." Toni laughed.

"But it would be more fun," Harvey said, "if Mr. Mc-Gurn came, too."

The diplomat felt cornered. He knew how dangerous the murky hills of Fiji were, with the winds of hate tearing across them. He knew that as an official observer he had no business getting mixed up in a Fijian feast. And above all he knew that Sir Charles Jacquemart's daughter was almost criminally irresponsible if she meddled in Fijian-Indian affairs. And yet he was in love. If Toni engaged in folly, it was his job to protect her from the consequences. "I'll go along," he said quietly.

Twice during the day he regretted his assent and thought of telling Sir Charles about his daughter's impending indiscretion; but he knew that if he did, he would surrender any chance he might have of marrying this delectable and headstrong girl. Yet his sense of propriety was so ingrained that he had to warn somebody, so he slipped into Lady Jacquemart's room shortly after lunch and blurted out the evening schedule.

For once Lady Maud did not joke. "Will Toni be safe?" she asked soberly.

"Normally I'd say so. But Harvey has been threatened by fanatical Indians."

"So there's a spice of danger?"

"Yes."

"Then," Lady Maud announced firmly, "go ahead. This may convince Toni you're a man and not a mouse." And she slapped him on the seat of his pants.

At dusk, this odd quartet drove fifteen miles into the hills of Fiji. The rain fell mournfully about them and the car lights shone upon great jungle streamers that encroached upon the road. The night was so dark and the feel of the jungle so close upon them that each of the girls huddled against her escort.

And then, suddenly, the car turned into a village square, a horn blew, and giant Fijians tumbled out into murky light. A strong voice shouted, "Joe Harvey come!"

Men of the village who had worked for Joe appeared and carried the girls into a huge native house where many people were gathered. McGurn tried to walk under his own command, but found the footing impossible. "It's soapstone," Joe laughed, as he slipped and sloshed along the village tracks. He had been there before.

Inside the jungle house, three pressure lamps, hung from the roof, made the place bright. Strands of sennit, miles long, had been woven into the roof, and now this roof danced with golden patterns that enchanted the eye. Toni Jacquemart looked about her as the men put her down. The great feel of the tropical night was upon her. "It's glorious," she said. Then, with a sense of what was right, she went to the chief and said, "We are pleased to be your guests."

The natives cheered this felicity and cheered again when Joe Harvey produced four bottles of gin, strictly forbidden to the Fijis. The chief placed the four bottles in a line before him and cried many words in Fijian. Then another old man spoke and dedicated the gin to the guests, and to the night's festivities.

It was apparent that Joe was a great favorite with these men, for they joked at his expense and when he could catch the meaning of their Fiji words, he cussed them soundly, and they drank gin together.

Pata and Toni formed a fast friendship and sat together at the long and beautifully woven frond mat that served as table. Soon, the chief yelled at his women, and they yelled back. Toni said afterwards that there had never been a meal served like that before. One woman ambled in with a pot full of dalo which she slammed on the table. Then for ten minutes nothing happened. The chief yelled some more, and another villager shuffled in with some boiled fish. It took an hour to serve the meal and another hour to eat it. The *pièce de résistance* was a dalo pudding with coconut and brown rice. It was chewy and delicious.

"I've been a pig!" Toni cried, and impulsively she leaned over and embraced Pata's shoulders. The chief applauded and embraced Joe. Then there was much shouting and an old woman brought in a large bowl. She sat cross-legged before it and began to knead a whitish powder into a cloth sack. This she plunged into the water and swished it back and forth many times. Finally, a dirty, pale-white fluid resulted.

"Yaqona!" Joe cried, and the chief ordered him to be served.

A young girl knelt in stately manner before the ceremonial bowl and was handed a dipperful of the whitish liquid. Solemnly, she bore it to Harvey, who solemnly took it. The girl knelt on the ground and clapped her hands twice. Gravely, Joe lifted the dipper to his lips and in a mighty effort put the contents down in one draught.

"Mala!" shouted the Fijians in applause.

The serving maid next attended Pata and then Toni, who also handled hers in one gulp. The chief was impressed. Now it was McGurn's turn. He took the dipper and gingerly tasted the unpleasant-looking liquid. It was slimy to the tongue, earthy-tasting and mildly tingling at the gums. It took him three tries to drain the bowl. He did not like yaqona.

Now the evening was started, and slowly the natives began to hum songs or even to break into words. Harvey, with a gin bottle in one hand and his other upon the chief's arm, reverently began to sing the haunting phrases of *Isa Lei*. "Ahhhhhh!" cried the natives in approval. Toni caught up the immortal phrases of this best of all island songs and for a moment the two alien voices sang the great lament of Fiji. Then, as if the song had been intended for finer powers, the natives began to join in.

When the antiphonal chorus was reached, the hut seemed to explode with grandeur. The mighty, deep-probing voices of the basses carried the aching song far back in time, when suddenly the high, wailing voices of the women would throw it against the present night. When the long chord of conclusion was reached, Joe cried, "Again," and this time one woman sang the melody and all the others in the hut harmonized upon her refrain until the chorus was reached, when the full

power of the basses was let loose. Even Louis McGurn
was deeply moved, and Toni, seeing this, reached down
and kissed his hand.

She became the heroine of the evening a few minutes
later when the next round of yaqona was started, this
time with a chief as server. Joe whispered to her,
"When you finish the drink sing out *Dario.*"

"What's it mean?" Toni asked.

"You'll see!" So when she had gurgled down the last
drop of yaqona, she cried loudly, "Dario!"

McGurn thought a riot had started. The amazed
chief dropped the bowl while six or seven native men
leaped to their feet and started to shout violently.
Soon, the entire Fijian population of the hut had cen-
tered on Toni, screaming imprecations at her.

"What have I done?" she pleaded.

Joe was laughing hilariously. "It's their totem," he
said. "When you use it that way, it means, 'The yaqona
was pretty good, what there was of it.'"

While Joe explained, the senior chief ordered the
whole bowl of liquor brought to Toni's feet. Then,
with a large ladle, he filled a large bowl and personally
thrust it at the white girl.

"You've got to drink it!" Joe assured her.

With misgivings, she put it to her lips and took one
long swig after another. Finally, somewhat dizzy, she
handed back the empty bowl. The chiefs cheered and
the women squealed their delight.

"Is good?" the senior chief demanded.

"Very good!" Toni said.

Then, as Louis was served his portion, she jabbed him
and cried, "I dare you to yell *Dario.*" He looked at her

as if to say, "Don't be foolish," so she nudged him again.

He had a very clear understanding that unless he cried *Dario,* he would never marry Toni Jacquemart. He also knew that if he passed this test, she would apply no others, for she was in no way vicious, so in a half voice, not intending to offend, he whispered *Dario.*

This time, it was no mere woman who had offended the tribe. In an instant, McGurn's coat and shirt had been pulled off, and all the women of the hut were lashing at him with small switches. Then he was handed a huge bowl of the dirty water. He drank until his ears popped, but he did hand back an empty vessel.

The cheers for his performance were loud. The chief himself shook his hand, and the great beauty of that last night started from that moment. The singing became like the sounding of organ music in a strange jungle, and the rain on the roof—incessant rain that seemed to accompany the revelry rather than to depress it—was a lullaby to the senses.

Toward morning, the entire village gathered in a long farewell to their good friend, Joe Harvey. The men were drunk with little gin and much singing. They would sleep all day. And the Indians in the valley would work.

In the car, as they drove to the airport from which Joe would leave this land forever, Toni finally made up her mind. She allowed McGurn to pull her toward him and after a moment of decent hesitation kissed him. Proudly she whispered, "You were quite a man tonight." Then she laughed and confided, "Up to now I've been afraid of you."

"Afraid?" he echoed.

"Yes. Afraid you were a stuffy, dull person."

"I am," he confessed.

"But I thought you were hopelessy dull. You aren't."

Then, as the day broke and the airport loomed ahead, they forgot their own love, for they saw Pata Cadi crying. This was her last hour, as it was their first. Impulsively, Toni broke into tears and clasped the little Indian girl to her while Joe went in to weigh his gear. When he came out, he kissed Toni on the cheek, and said, 'You made the night a real festival." He grasped McGurn's hand and said, "You were a real sport, fellow. I'm glad for both of us that nothing happened."

Then his bravado left him, for he was standing face to face with Pata Cadi. He could remember her as she had lain beside him on his pillow. "May you have all happiness," he began, but his voice broke, and he clutched her tiny body to his.

"And may all that you do prosper," she whispered. The roaring engines warming up drowned out her other words.

Tears in his eyes, blond-headed Joe Harvey climbed aboard the plane that would take him away from Fiji. Rain swept down upon the field, and through his shimmering window he waved good-by to his friends. He watched Pata as long as he could, but by the goodness of God, he had lost sight of her when Ramcheck Devidas Billimoria broke madly from behind a shed and plunged a writhing stiletto deep into her throat.

But Louis McGurn, horrified, was there to see the fanatical knife swirl in the air again. Then, as if driven by a force outside himself, he forgot his stiff white shirt and his diplomat's mission. He lunged furiously at Billimoria, knocking him to the ground. He was pounding his fists at the horrible face when the airport police intervened.

During the useless dash in the ambulance McGurn kept thinking, "I saw it all coming, and I could do nothing." Bitterly he recalled his warning to Harvey and the young man's insolent prophecy, "I'm the kind that doesn't get hurt."

McGurn was sick with fear of what might happen in Fiji because of this morning. Then Pata Cadi coughed. A foam of blood rose to her thin lips and for the second time that day McGurn acted instinctively. He fell on his knees beside her, clutched her frail hands and begged her, in an agonized voice, not to die. She looked at him but could not speak.

When death came, horrible and gurgling, he felt the terror of a strange land closing in upon him. Always before he had considered problems—the Israeli problem, the Indian problem—as subjects for neat intellectual reports to Washington. But now he saw Pata Cadi as a human being, a rare and true person. In a naked humility such as he had never known before, he looked up at Toni Jacquemart with beseeching eyes. "What shall I do?" he mumbled.

It was not until they reached Lady Maud at the G.P.H. that they began to get the murder into perspective. She was firm. She said to Toni, "You've had a dreadful shock, girl. Go to bed and drink several cups of hot Bovril."

With McGurn she was more direct. "You predicted this. You did what you could to prevent it. Now you must dismiss it as an incident. Tragic but inevitable."

"An incident?" McGurn cried.

"As predictable as the tides. I've lived through six of 'em."

"But I might have done something more!" he accused himself.

"More! Don't be an ass!" She poured him a cup of tea and prepared to leave the hotel.

"Where are you going?" he asked pleadingly.

"I'm going to the Governor," she said firmly. "S'Chalz will rant about honor and propriety. He'll surely volunteer to disqualify himself in the Patel case. I've got to get there first and stop such folly. Time comes when a man can be too demmed honorable."

Majestically she swept out of the hotel, and McGurn felt as if the source of his strength had disappeared. He did not even recover his spirits when a messenger appeared with his long-delayed cable from Boston. He sat fingering it and wondered how Joe Harvey would hear of Pata Cadi's death. In a bar some day. A stranger would shout, "Boy, do I know Fiji? Say I heard the damnedest story down there. Seems there was this American . . ." Well, it would serve him right.

He wondered if Americans would ever learn to behave in alien lands. He recalled an arrogant colonel he had known in France. "Hell!" the colonel had boasted, "six energetic Americans could run this place like it ought to be run." Well, he mused firmly, they'll have their chance.

He was interrupted by Lady Maud's return. "The Governor was a dear," she reported. "Very sensible man." Then she asked abruptly, "Have you proposed to Toni?"

"At this time?" McGurn asked.

"Certainly! This is the right time. Marriage is always the child of crisis. When the world is shaking, people marry for security." She collapsed into a chair and shouted for some tea. As she poured it she whispered, "For example, S'Chalz had no intention in the world of marrying me. Had his eye on a French widow. I've never admitted to anyone what I had to do to trap him, but he's been quite happy with me."

At this point the mynah birds discovered a swarm of insects in the weeping figs and there was a furious clatter. "Those wretched birds!" Lady Maud cried. "Everyone of 'em's a murderer." Then she clutched McGurn's arm. "Go in and see Toni. Now."

He walked to the door but found that Toni was sleeping. He started to leave but Lady Maud gave him a firm shove. So he wakened the girl and said. "Will you marry me?"

She blinked several times and then blushed deeply. "I was going to ask you—at lunch." She drew his hand to her lips and kissed it, whispering, "At the airport . . . you were very brave."

Overcome with his love for the girl, he fumbled in his pocket. This was the appropriate moment! Proudly he produced the cable and announced, "Wonderful news! You won't have to be Mrs. McGurn!"

"But I want to be!" she protested.

"Read this!" he cried triumphantly. "The court has changed my name. I'm Louis Richardson now."

Lady Maud, in the doorway, saw her daughter's face grow pale. She knew that Toni was on the point of breaking off the whole engagement with this terribly stuffy man. But with an imperious eye Lady Maud stopped her daughter as if to say, "Marry him. All men are fools, but he's the best we've been able to find."

So Toni Jacquemart reached up and kissed Louis on the ear. "Toni Richardson," she mused. "Well, not exciting, but not bad."

"It's an English name," he explained. "You see, I'm really of English stock. From Surrey."

The Fossickers

✽

*Men in New Guinea say: "We can
probably hold onto our end of the
island another twenty years . . .
at most."*

ALL the way from Honolulu to Sydney I heard about
the Queen Emma. In Tahiti an Australian said, "I guess
I named it."

"How do you mean?" I asked.

"I was serving with the Yanks. Told them about
Queen Emma. She was half Yank herself. Half Samoan.
She became queen of New Guinea. Big, tough woman.
They say she murdered her fourth or fifth husband.
In Monte Carlo."

"What's this got to do with the hotel?"

"I was coming to that," the Aussie said. "This Queen
Emma did the New Guinea Germans out of half a million quid. Oh, she was quite a girl." There was a long
pause, the kind that occurs in tropic bars. Finally he
said, "I told this Yank about her and right away he
painted a big sign for his hut: The Queen Emma. 'It's
me Broadway hotel,' he says, and he gives a coon ten
bob to fix it up nice."

"So that's how the Queen Emma got its name?"

The Australian ignored my question. "Why you goin'
to New Guinea?" he asked abruptly.

"Taking some pictures. I heard about a tribe. Up at

219

the headwaters of the Sepik. But tell me. Is the Queen
Emma as bad as they say?"

"Well," he said thoughtfully, "during the war it was
a good place after a long patrol. In peacetime . . ." He
returned to his spirits and would say no more.

I didn't mind the Queen Emma. Reminded me of the
Hotel De Gink at Guadal. Big sprawling lot of quon-
sets. I didn't mind the beetles or the snakes. And I was
fascinated by those immense bumblebees that bore
holes the size of dimes right through a wooden beam.

I could lie in my bunk and see the towering white
clouds hanging on the Owen Stanley Range, and I enjoyed being back in New Guinea. You know what I
mean. That great hot blast. The heavy smell of jungle.
And over west—the Sepik.

I'd seen it from the air many times during the war,
and I always said, "Some day I'm going up that river!"
Have you ever seen it? One of the world's greatest. A
huge brown mass of ugly water spewing itself out into
the Pacific. Logs, brush, crocodiles, dead natives. Out
they go, as if their brutal land could stomach them no
more. The Sepik was my river, and when I read in a
British magazine about a race of savage pygmies at the
headwaters . . . Well, sometimes you get to do what
you've sworn to do. Breaks, I guess.

On my first afternoon at the Queen Emma the old
hands asked, "What you doin' out here, Yank?" I said
I was trying to hire a boat for the Sepik and they said,
"You must be nuts." But one old codger added, "The
man you want is Shark Eye," and that night I met him.

He was more than seventy, a gnarled, skinny, hard-
drinking Australian with no lower teeth. He was sit-

ting alone at a corner table in the rusted quonset bar.
"Name's Shannon," he said. "Folks call me Shark Eye."
He ran his right forefinger down a gash in his face.
"They say you want to go up the Sepik."

"That's right."

He rose to his full six feet four, pushed back his white
hair and held out his hand. "I'm your man," he said. We
sat down for the first time at that small table and
Shark Eye shouted, "Hey, Monkey!"

A small native boy—couldn't have been more than
ten—appeared with a huge oval tray. Shark Eye leaned
back and studied the lad's blue-black shoulders. Then
he snarled, "You're messy. Fix up your belt." The monkey became greatly embarrassed and tried to adjust the
belt that held up his lap-lap. The tray began to slip
and as it hit the floor Shark Eye gave it a kick so that
it spun across the room. The monkey looked as if he
might cry, but the old man raised his boot and shoved
the boy after the tray. "Keep your belt fixed," Shark
Eye growled. "And bring us some beer."

As the night progressed, that wonderful, quiet,
heavy night, Shark Eye gave me a running account of
his qualifications. "Been in these parts more'n sixty
years. Used to live at Rabaul before there was even a
volcano in the bay. I saw the eruptions, the floods, the
native uprisings. Watched the Germans come and go."
He stopped and eyed me suspiciously, then added
softly, "Did a bit of fossicking, too."

"What?" I asked.

He would tell me no more. "Monkey!" he shouted.
The little boy appeared and stood at attention, his
immense tray under his left arm. "More beer!" The boy

brought them, but I couldn't drink like these Australians. Shark Eye tossed the bottles down and reeled off to bed.

As the bar was closing I asked a stranger, "What's fossicking?"

"You Yanks call it prospecting," he said. "Shark Eye been bashing your ear? He's got a right to. One of the greatest. Made and lost three fortunes."

"Women?'" I asked.

"There's always women," the stranger said, and he too stumbled off.

Next evening, after a fruitless day spent arguing with government officials, I was on my way to dinner when Shark Eye stuck his head out of the bar and called me in. "Sit down!" he said imperiously. He was quite excited and huddled with me in the corner. "I've got me eye on a wonderful craft for this trip," he whispered. "We can coast it right into the Sepik."

"Do you know the river?" I asked.

He stopped cold, deeply insulted. "Monkey!" he screamed. The little boy ran up. "More beer!" We missed dinner that night, and several nights thereafter. We sat in the corner, this old man and I, and he'd tell me about his fossicking days in New Guinea. He'd been everywhere. Could almost smell gold.

"Then why are you broke?" I asked.

"Me? Broke?" He shouted for the monkey and spoke in rapid pidgin, after which he tossed a key onto the big tray. The little boy disappeared into the night and returned with a large box. The old man fumbled with another key for some moments, then hid the box below the table and began to produce papers. There was a bank book, showing some ten thousand pounds in Brisbane, news clippings about a fossicking trip into the heart of Australia, and a parchment citation for his work in rescuing citizens during the volcanic terror at Rabaul.

He fortified these records with verbal accounts of his adventures and I was beginning to be impressed when I recalled his cruel manner toward the monkey. I spoke of this and he guffawed. "Monkey!" he bellowed. "Come 'ere, damn you."

The near-naked little fellow stood before us, his belt straight, his lap-lap tucked in the way Shark Eye had directed. "Who's the best damn man in New Guinea?" the old Australian roared.

A tremendous grin spread over the monkey's face and he said, "You are, mastuh!" Shark Eye looked pleased and dug into his sweaty pocket for five marks.

"Get some bleach for your hair," he said. But he tossed the coins viciously onto the floor, so that the frantic child had to crawl among the table legs to get them.

The bleach had quite an effect on our monkey. He dressed his hair into a ridge, like a rooster's comb, and the top half was bleached a bright red. Shark Eye said the boy looked disgraceful, even for the Queen Emma, and was about to belt him when he stopped and stared at the bar entrance.

There stood a remarkable woman. She was about fifty, sawed-off, dumpy, red-faced and scraggly-haired. She wore men's army shoes and a rucksack. She looked straight at Shark Eye and said, "You still alive?" Several men at the bar stood to say reserved hellos. She ignored them and crossed to our table. Shark Eye remained in his seat and kicked back a chair. Then he said to me, in great disgust, "Meet an anthropologist."

She held out her hand and I thought: "Here's a capable mitt." In a deep voice she said, "I'm Sheila Bancroft."

At this Shannon burst into laughter and said, "In Australia we call our whoors sheila. This here's my sheila."

I paid no attention to him because now I recognized this woman. It was her writing that had brought me to the Sepik. "Aren't you Dame Sheila?" I asked.

"Yes," she said, sitting down and reaching for a glass.

"I studied your report on the Danduras," I said. She was pleased, but as the evening wore on I had the strange feeling that both she and Shark Eye were maneuvering so that the other would have to leave first. I broke the impasse by going to bed, but before I got to sleep the gaunt figure of Shannon loomed in the darkness beside my head. "Don't have anything to do with that crazy woman," he whispered.

"Why?"

He pulled up a chair and hunched up beside my mosquito net. In a low whisper he said, "The most disgusting person you can meet is a woman scientist. They've ruined New Guinea—studyin' natives. They poison the Administration." He could have squeezed no more scorn into the word. "They want to make a coon utopia."

"What you mean is, she spoiled some of your plans?"

"My plans? I never have any. Just wait for what turns up." He lit a hand-rolled cigarette and crossed his long legs. "But this damn fool Sheila . . ."

"Wait a minute!" I protested. "This woman has been honored by the King. And by lots of scientists, too."

I could see Shark Eye's face only dimly. It had frozen into a hard mask. "By God," he snarled, "you're one of 'em too! A coon lover!"

"Go to bed," I laughed. "I'm tired of you Administration haters."

"I won't go until I tell you something. For your own good." He leaned across my bed and whispered through the net. "I found out that this fine lady lived with a native man. Yes, right here in New Guinea. She was in the jungle, studyin' primitive habits—so she said." He filled the night with bitter scorn. Sheila Bancroft must have caused him much hurt to have incurred such hatred.

The old man left my bed and stood in the doorway. "She studied native habits all right. No wonder she fills her books with dirty stuff about sex. She should know!"

At breakfast he winked at me when Dame Sheila arrived. "She should know!" he cried in a whisper she must have heard. When she stopped to look at him, he stuck out his tongue at her and went, "Yannh."

That afternoon she met me going to the toilet, and although she must have known where I was headed, she stood in the pathway and said, "You'd be a fool to risk The Sepik with Shannon."

"I haven't agreed to—yet."

"Be wise," she warned. "Don't." I muttered something, hoping to break away, but she seemed to be weighing ideas. Suddenly she made up her mind and pulled me against the wall where no one could see us.

"What do you know about Shannon?" she asked searchingly.

"What everybody else knows. Rabaul skipper. Some experience with gold. He knows the Sepik."

"I suppose he showed you the parchment from Rabaul. He always does. But did he tell you why he can never return to Rabaul?" She pressed one hand against my chest and told in angry syllables how Shark Eye Shannon had fled the Japs in '42. He had run off with the last boat. Had stranded some fifty men who had fought on to cruel death or even crueler imprisonment and torture. "He got away to Australia. But if he ever went back to Rabaul . . . they would kill him."

I listened and found in her voice a freightage of disgust that was unnatural. "Did he betray a man you loved?" I asked.

"No!" she snapped.

"Then what did you do to Shannon to make you hate him so much?"

The powerful woman stepped back and digested my question. "What do you mean? What did I do to *him?*"

"Look!" I said. "Last night he came to my room to whisper what a monster you were . . ."

"What did he say?" she asked hastily.

"I won't tell you," I said. "But now you report the same about him. What happened between you?"

She was knocked off guard by this approach. Finally she said, as if at confession, "He was put in jail on evidence I gave. He debauched a native tribe. Terribly."

I thought this over for a long time and then said, "Dame Sheila, I like you. How's about us going up the Sepik together?"

"It's very rough terrain, where you want to go."

"I know that. Could we get there without Shannon?"

"No," she said. "I'm here to hire him for my expedition."

This one bowled me over. Even though my bladder was about to burst, I had to get this straight. I said, "Look! You despise the man. You say he's too tough for me. But you're going with him up the Sepik. I don't get it."

The tough little woman laughed. "Sounds silly, doesn't it? But I meant my warning. To my knowledge Shannon has killed two partners and betrayed dozens."

"You're still not afraid of him?"

"No." Then after a moment she added, "Sometimes you reach a point of involvement that insures protection."

That evening I had a further surprise. When I entered the bar Shark Eye and Dame Sheila were sharing a bottle as if they were old friends. Shannon's lean face was extra animated and the Englishwoman's bobbed hair fell about her ears as she leaned forward to hear what he was saying. The Australian kicked a chair back for me and shouted for the monkey to bring more drinks.

"Look!" I said abruptly. "I can't hang around here much longer. Are we going to arrange a deal or not?"

Shannon put down his drink and said, "I bought the boat. We'll be shoving off shortly."

"Good!" Then to Sheila I said, "You coming, too?"

"She is like hell!" Shannon interrupted. "That's what we've been arguin' about."

"You'll take me," the Englishwoman said confidently.

"She thinks we can't get past the Danduras without her," Shark Eye gloated.

Dame Sheila laughed. "Nor can you," she said.

"Why don't we quit this stalling?" I cried. "Let's agree right now. We'll all three go. As soon as possible."

To my surprise Shannon turned almost black in the face and left us for another table. "Monkey!" he bellowed. The boy was slow coming and Shark Eye kicked at him.

"That dirty beast," Sheila gasped.

"More beer!" the old man roared. He drank three bottles—big, black quarts from Antwerp—but he wasn't even staggering when he entered my room late that night.

"American," he said softly, "we've got to come to an understanding. You've almost wrecked things."

"How?" I asked.

He became very confidential. "We mustn't take that busybody."

"What goes on between you two?" I asked. "I know her explanation. About having you arrested . . ."

"And Rabaul. I suppose she told you about Rabaul?"

"Yes." I felt deeply involved with Shannon—for better or worse—and I wanted him to know that I was as tough as he. "She told me about you turning yellow belly. Deserting the ship."

I wasn't prepared for his reply. He laughed heartily, then went "Ssssssh!" as if I were making the noise. "I wasn't the one who deserted the ship," he joked. "I ran off with the bloody thing!"

"She said they'd lynch you if you ever went back."

The tough old coot stopped laughing and said, "You're young. I'm seventy-three. I watched a lot of brave men insist upon committing suicide at Rabaul. They hadn't a chance. I told 'em so."

"They helped to stop the Japs," I said.

"Useless," Shark Eye said in disgust. "A sensible man knows when to fight. The government had betrayed us at Rabaul."

I don't like you, Shannon." I said. "I did my turn against the Japs."

"Look, sonny!" he laughed. "I've done more fighting than all the gallant men in New Guinea. Most of them are dead. I'm alive."

There was nothing I could say to this, and for some moments I could feel his tense face close to mine. Then I let him have it. "Dame Sheila tells me you murder your mates or desert them."

With no embarrassment he explained, "There's always two sides to a story. You've been giving me hell. I know why. You want to test the kind of man you're dealing with. Now I've got to test you. Can I trust you?"

"Why not?" I asked.

Suddenly my left arm was gripped furiously above the elbow. I could feel my skin crinkling. "We're not playing a game now," he said harshly. "Yes or no. Can I trust you?"

I knocked his hand away and said, "Yes."

He pondered a moment, then lit a cigarette. He was afraid to speak, yet he could sense that his match had outlined the scar. He touched it with his finger and said, "It's crazy to call me Shark Eye. A damned native did that."

"On the Sepik?"

"Yes. Up where you want to go."

There was a long silence and I thought: "Well, I can wait." Then abruptly he said, "I'm an old geezer, and I've got to trust someone. I want to get back to them hills because a long time ago . . ."

He stopped and rose. I knew what he had to say, so I finished it. "A long time ago you found gold. Now you need it."

"I need nothing," he boasted.

"Don't kid me, old man. Because I saw the date on the Brisbane bank book. I'll bet you don't have a tanner."

He stood in the deep shadows above me and said, "I know where there's a treasure. But it's inaccessible. The damned rotten stuff is in Dutch New Guinea."

"But you think you can smuggle some out."

"I know I can!" His voice became impassioned. "Yank, I never miss on gold. Forget your pictures," he pleaded. "Come along with me! We'll make a fortune."

"No," I said. "You take me up to the Danduras. I'll pay my share. From then on you do as you wish."

He gripped my arm more violently than before. "A man can't do it alone," he cried. "Last time I had fifty thousand quid worth of metal. Strike me dead. But the cursed savages chopped me up."

"Well," I said, "that winds that up."

"What do you mean?" he cried angrily.

"We could never arrange a trip."

"But I know the Sepik!" he howled.

"You're an old fossicker," I said. "Mad for gold. Now you get any partner you wish. I'll find me a skipper I can trust. Good night."

"But Yank . . ."

"Go to bed. You bore me."

Without another word he left the room, and in the morning I beat up and down the waterfront inquiring after various skippers who knew the Sepik. "That's funny," one of them said. "Short time ago a Dutchman was down here asking the same questions."

I met him that night at the Queen Emma. He was a chap about thirty, slightly bald, handsome and square in the Dutch manner. He was talking earnestly with Shark Eye and Dame Sheila. I was about to pass them when Shannon grabbed me and hauled me down beside him. "Meet Herr van Hoog." Shark Eye laughed with malicious gaiety. "Guess where he wants to go!"

"Up the Sepik," I said, and the four of us sat together and drank beer, as we were to do for three weeks.

The Dutchman took a keen dislike to me and one night finally exploded. "You filthy Americans!" he shouted, and it was apparent that he had been cherishing a grudge until he got safely drunk.

"Take it easy," I said.

"Easy?" he screamed. "When you ruined my country?"

"Oh, hell," I groaned. "Now we get blamed for Java, too."

"It was your fault," he ranted. "If you had stood with us, the Indonesians . . ."

"Take it easy," I said again.

But he raved on about how America had sabotaged the entire Western Pacific. The Dutch were kicked out of Java. Next they'd be run out of Dutch New Guinea. Then hell would start, because pretty soon the Indonesians would overrun all of New Guinea. Australia, with no defenses and no people, would be cut off. "Then," he bellowed in his stubborn Dutch way, "you filthy Yanks with your handsome white teeth will be in the fire."

He had risen from his chair to insult me further, but I'd had enough. I reached over and shoved my hand into his fat square face. I remember that Shark Eye looked pleased at this, as if he prospered on fights, but before van Hoog could do anything I began talking very fast.

"I wasn't going to say this, but you asked for it. So here goes. I agree with you that America was criminally stupid in backing the Indonesians. And we'll pay for that mistake. We'll pay for it in blood. But, van Hoog. I saw the Dutch administration. I saw it good. In a place you never heard of. Tanah Merah. A dump lost in the middle of a swamp fifty thousand square miles wide. Shannon, you've been all over. You ever hear of Tanah Merah? It's got a couple of big, spacious buildings for the Dutch, and a hundred little two-by-fours built of corrugated iron. They're for the Indonesian prisoners. That is, they used to be. I was in one of those iron shacks. Temperature 130 degrees."

The bar at Queen Emma's was deathly quiet, but visions of Tanah Merah came back. I said, "There was an administrator there, a Dutchman. One of the kind we used to hear about in the States. 'The Dutch are the best colonizers in the world.' This one sure was. He beat and starved and baked anyone who opposed the government. You know what the Indonesians from Tanah Merah told us after the Japs had liberated them? They said, 'If we get the Administrator we'll cut his legs off an inch at a time. With rusty knives.' Chickens come home to roost, van Hoog. So do Indonesians."

The Dutchman was very white. He took a drink of beer and said huskily, "All nations make mistakes."

"Yes," I said, "and when we do, we never get another chance."

"Don't say that!" the big, stolid man cried.

The four of us sat around for some time thinking of the nations that had lost their way. Dame Sheila said, "It's inevitable that all subject peoples must rise to the common standard. The Dutch in Java were unfortunate . . ."

Shannon banged down his glass. "You talk like a damned fool. It's you . . . Meddling old-women fools like you who talk savages into believing they can climb to our standards." He was actually quaking with rage.

The party ended dismally, but late that night my room door creaked open. "What the hell do you want, Shannon?" I rasped. I was sick of the old man.

"It's van Hoog."

"Turn on the light."

"Mosquitoes," he replied, and felt his way to my chair.

"I'm sorry about tonight," I said.

"No need. I've been to Tanah Merah."

There was a pause and then it hit me. That white Dutch face over the beer mug. "You were the Administrator!"

"No," he said with deep relief.

"I'm glad," I said.

"I was an assistant." Another silence followed and he said, "Some day tourists will be shown through your Alcatraz. And they won't believe it. All nations make mistakes."

"I said I was sorry."

Bluntly he changed the conversation. "Can I trust Mr. Shannon?"

"He'd cut your throat—if money's involved."

"Money is involved," the Dutchman said. "You must come along with us."

"You find a gold mine near Tanah Merah?" I hazarded.

He whistled slightly and said, "I took some convicts across the swamps. Up into the mountains near the border. That's why . . ." He paused and said in a terrible voice, "That's why I can never go back. It was a bad trip. I had to be harsh. The Indonesian Republic has named me a national enemy."

"Watch out for Shannon," I said.

"Do you suppose he knows about gold? Across the border?"

"No," I said.

"If I paid you, would you come along?" van Hoog begged.

"Nope," I said. My door opened and van Hoog was gone.

Next morning Shannon sailed his boat up to the pier. It was a sturdy craft with two engines, a dirty cowling and a deck house that would sleep four. It smelled of gasoline, and this may sound silly, but it looked a lot like Shannon, barnacled and weatherbeaten.

"She was sunk by the Japs," he said. "But she's worthy, this one."

That night at the corner table he put it up to us. "Now make up your minds. Yank, will you join us?"

I studied the three partners: the Australian adventurer, the Dutch renegade, the English seeker. "All right," I agreed. "As far as the Danduras. You push on by yourselves from there."

"Good. You, Dutchman?"

"All the way."

The nasty old man looked at Dame Sheila. "There's no room for you," he said maliciously.

"I'll be there," she said with no concern. "Because without me you'll not get through. Has he told you, van Hoog, that last time he was nearly killed?"

The fossickers argued late into the night. They were like nations, each hating the other, each needing what the other had.

I thought of Sheila Bancroft's superb essay on sex in ultraprimitive societies, of the furor it had created. It was odd to sit with her in the Queen Emma and to catch a glimmer of what had driven her into the great jungles of the spirit. No man could have loved her. She had been a rejected girl, an unhappy woman. So she'd fled her society to study the ultimate beginnings of sex, the cruel force that had so punished her. Somehow, in some strange way, she had triumphed over those early rejections and had found reassurance in the savage jungles of our first beginnings. She had become a woman loved by the entire world. But the jungle remained her home, and she now proposed to fossick even past the boundaries she had previously reached. Once she told me, "Beyond the mountains you're always sure there will be gold."

Beside her, night after night, sat the stolid Dutchman. When he had boasted of absolute power over miserable brown men, he had pushed them through deadly swamps and up strangling mountains. He had written an arrogant book about it, *Beyond the*

Swamps, and in each line he had signed his own banishment from all he loved. His family had ruled Java for centuries; now Java lusted to crucify him. He was an outcast, a fugitive from everywhere. Yet he felt certain that if he could only get back to that mountain of gold—the mountain beyond the swamp—he could rehabilitate himself. He had executed the only Indonesian who might have deduced the truth about the gold, but he was willing to believe that even such a crime was expiable if one could regain that mountain.

And to my right sat the old man of the islands, hatching his own plots. He had to abide the crazy Englishwoman in order to escape his earlier attackers. It infuriated him to think that a woman so despicable could, by reason of her disinterest, go where his rifle was powerless. He no longer tried to reconcile such absurdities. He'd seen everything: Queen Emma herself, the French settlers who had died like ghosts sensing the dawn, Tiger Lil of the imperial manner, the polite Jap trochus fisherman, the Australian Jew who had found the great gold fields, the whole lot of them. None of them was worth a damn. Men or women. either. Once he'd carried a young married couple from Cairns to Rabaul, and five days after the marriage the girl was sleeping with him. He thought he might have as many as ten black kids, and there wasn't a decent one in the lot. Mewling half-castes, the lot. It was a rum world, but there was gold up the Sepik, and if you played your cards right you'd get your share, and maybe the Dutchman's, too.

It was midnight when we reached our agreement and the jungle was riotous with crickets when we went to bed. The next morning he said good-by to the

Queen Emma while castled clouds began to form upon the mighty mountains.

We were sixty miles off the mouth of the Sepik when Dame Sheila found the monkey. She dragged him from a hole so small you'd have sworn no human could have wedged himself into it. The little fellow bowed his red cockade and produced a remarkable document drawn up by some bush lawyer: "To all men, presents. Know that being of sound mind and body I do depose that my son may go on boat along Capt. Shannin. My mark."

"Well," Dame Sheila sniffed. "A fine thing."

"What do you mean?" Shark Eye demanded.

"We've got to put him ashore. That's obvious."

"We've not!" Shannon roared.

I was surprised when the Englishwoman backed down. "Very well," she said. "You're the captain." Further, she took the legal document and endorsed it: "There was no way to put him ashore among his own people. We kept him with us."

The monkey was a tremendous help. I often talked with him and found that he considered Shannon the greatest man who ever lived. It was beyond me. Sheila and I treated the boy with respect, while Shannon bullied him, made him work like a slave. Yet the monkey had run away to be near the man who abused him. "Mastuh good man. Me like go ship."

I mentioned this to Sheila and she said, "I'd be stupid not to admit it. Many natives prefer brutal white men."

"Why?"

"Because such men conform to the stereotype of what a white man should be. The way Hitler, whether

we like it or not, is most people's ideal of what a
political leader should be."

"Then you can't educate people?" I asked snidely,
meaning: "You admit Shark Eye is right about women
scientists?"

She laughed. She knew what I was driving at. "No,"
she protested. "Look over there at tragic van Hoog.
People who were once stupid caught up with him."

As we neared the Sepik—even the name haunts me,
the great savage river, my Congo—I watched van
Hoog with increasing pity. I could not even approxi-
mate the feelings of a man whose world had been
washed away. For instance, I get terribly fed up with
Chicago. It's one hell of a place. But no matter where I
go, Chicago's always waiting, between Gary and Joliet.
I would hate to think it wasn't there. Or that the
enemy held it. Or that I couldn't go home.

I tried talking with the steel-brained Dutchman but
there was nothing I could say. He never even laughed
at the monkey. He was a man impossible to like.

Then we hit the Sepik. I remember the scene. I
could never forget it. It was about dusk and we heard
a shout far to starboard. The water was muddy and we
couldn't see a thing. Then the glasses picked out a
native riding a raft of logs. He was being swept out to
sea. We tried to reach him, but it was no use. Drifting
logs cut us off, and finally a wave washed him into the
turgid waters. We heard him yelling. Something got
him. Crocs. Sharks. Something snapped him in two.

"That's that," Shannon said, swinging our craft into
the great river.

We went upstream about three hundred miles,
moored the boat, and hired some canoes. Above us.

around us, even growing from the bottom of the river, the jungle muffled all we did. Immense lianas twisted down like snakes, and pythons writhed away like drooping lianas. Parrots, birds of paradise and monster pigeons swept in and out of shadows. We caught strange fish and van Hoog predicted they'd all be poisonous, but no one died. The monkey sat in my canoe and chattered across the water to Shannon, who told him to shut up.

Natives skulked along the banks to watch us pass. White kiaps, who governed the disciplined tribes, stopped us and took legal notice of the monkey's presence. Soon we were beyond the places where white men dared to live.

This was the upper Sepik, one of the most fatal areas in the world. Headhunters still lurked here. Murders still went unpunished, and natives lived in deathly fear of voodoo, night mists and strange diseases that swept through villages like mountain floods.

I was ready to call it quits. I wondered if Amundsen and Scott had ever thought: "What a mess! Why did I come here?" Then I'd see Dame Sheila taking notes. She observed things I never even guessed at. And I came to the conclusion that the great explorers were like her. They pursued facts until they uncovered ideas.

When I watched Shark Eye shoot crocodiles and smack his lips after each good shot, it occurred to me that this man, too, had escaped fear. He hadn't scrammed out of Rabaul because he was afraid of Japs. He wanted a more even fight. He said, "You draw stumps and wait for a better pitch."

On the thirty-eighth day we approached the Danduras, and Dame Sheila's nose dilated as if she were a race horse. I commented on this, and to my surprise she grew quite sober. "Everyone recalls that portion of earth where he grew up. When he finally discovered there was no cause to be afraid. It was in these mountains that I grew up." She pointed to where Shannon now led us. We climbed two days on that trail and each of us must have lost five pounds. I sweated until my fingers were a pale white. Then we hit the kunai plateau, and before us on the broad plain was the village of Lagui, close to the Dutch border. I fancied that van Hoog, staring across at the distant hills, was biting his lip.

Certainly Dame Sheila wasn't. A runner from the village had recognized her and now jumped up and down in giggling delight. He shouted some words which Shark Eye translated with mocking scorn: "Lady doctor come back!"

"Are you a doctor?" I asked.

"No. I used horse sense and cured some of them."

The villagers crowded out to meet us, and presently the Paramount Luluwai—a handsome brute—came toward us in stately measure. Behind him walked a girl of about sixteen. She was naked except for a small apron and was curiously appealing. Her nose was not broad. Her hair was curly instead of kinky. And I remember that she kept her feet one before the other.

She watched us carefully and it amused me that even a girl who had never seen white people before took only a quick survey of the woman and the old man. She divided her attention between van Hoog and me.

In the days that followed, while Dame Sheila assembled a crew for me and Shannon collected his, this girl Alwi spent more and more time watching van Hoog.

The Dutchman was aware of this, and so was Shark Eye. He finally took us aside and laid down the law. "There's one rule up here. Learn by the gash on my face. Never fool with women if you've got to come back through their village."

Van Hoog showed great interest. "What happened?"

"I came back through the village," old Shark Eye laughed, "and the villagers came through me."

But van Hoog would not be warned. He shared a frond hut with me and one night I heard the monkey creep in and shake him. "Mastuh! Mastuh!" the little boy whispered. "Alwi say, 'You come 'long now.'" And the little conspirator led the Dutchman away.

I said nothing to Shannon, but after three nights van Hoog no longer pretended that he was living in my hut. What really surprised me was that the Paramount Luluwai made no complaint.

But I still had to come back through this village, and I had a bit of wind up. I spoke to Dame Sheila. "Will this mean trouble later on?"

The Englishwoman never batted an eye. She perched on a box of gear and said slowly, "You're young."

"I know. That's what Shannon said when he had dirty business to explain."

"You might call this dirty business," she said quietly. I recall that sweat stood at the roots of her bobbed hair. "But it's also essential business. The Luluwai knows that. Herr van Hoog is a sick man. His life has been cut away. You wouldn't understand."

"But I do!" And I told her about my sick feeling when I thought about Chicago lost.

"You do comprehend," she said with some surprise. "The moment often comes in a life when the world is lost. God doesn't exist. There's no good, no bad, no hope, no past. You're the basic animal, bewildered. You're dead." She now spoke with terrible intensity. "That's the moment I hope you will never know."

After a moment she unclenched her hands and said, "When such a time hits you, if it ever does, let the basic animal take control. There's a great cure in nature. The girl Alwi is that cure, and she's going with us. Van Hoog won't find his gold, and if he does Shannon will probably steal it. But he'll be cured."

And Alwi did go with them. This strange party set off one morning for the distant hills. Shannon led the way, with a rifle on his arm. Then came the bearers and Dame Sheila. The monkey ran up and down the line, swinging a machete. And behind them all trailed van Hoog and the naked girl.

Then like a flash of light, I saw it all! Dame Sheila let the monkey come along to tie down Shannon's suspiring emotions. This way the old devil wouldn't bother the girl. And Alwi was going along so that if trouble came, van Hoog wouldn't have to face it alone. But where did Dame Sheila herself come in?

Then I understood. As the train disappeared toward the mountains—beyond the swamp—this naked girl Alwi walked in a strange way that I had seen before. I rushed like crazy into the Paramount Luluwai's hut and cried, "This girl Alwi! Whose daughter is she?"

"Mine," the big man said proudly.

This stopped me for a moment and I started to leave. But suddenly I began to laugh very loud. The Luluwai joined in, so I said, "Sure. She's your daughter. And who else's?"

He would not reply, so I took a long chance: "The lady doctor's?"

The Paramount Luluwai never stopped laughing, but he did say, "You savvy too much."

from

THE
VOICE OF
ASIA

The Proconsul

❋

It was a dark wintry day in Tokyo and friends in the
Press Club said, "If you've never seen General Mac-
Arthur leave the Dai Ichi building, today would be a
good time."

We bundled up and walked down Shimbun Alley to a
cross street which we followed to the Emperor's palace
grounds. Then we walked briskly down to the Dai
Ichi building, where a small crowd had already gathered.

It was a pregnant day, for the New York *Herald
Tribune* had just run its famous editorial pointing out
that General MacArthur should perhaps be displaced
as military leader in Korea. Among the men at the
Press Club it was generally known that the great debacle on the right flank near the Yalu River was somebody's fault and most of the up-front men felt that
ultimately the blame would have to fall on Mac-
Arthur.

At the Dai Ichi building very tall and handsome
military guards stood at brisk attention, symbols of
our Pacific empire. At the curb a long automobile
waited. In the streets traffic came to a halt. Japanese
on bicycles were directed to place at least one foot on
the ground. The crowd pressed forward.

Suddenly from the central doors a running guard
appeared. Others leaped forward to hold open doors,
and the erect guards snapped to an even more dramatic

247

pose. The running guard hastened across the broad side-walk and held the car door.

Then, from the Dai Ichi doors, the general appeared. He was erect, his stride was long, his large coat was tight about his waist, his belt ends hung sedately and his famous cap was precisely straight. He looked straight ahead and gave the appearance of a man not hurried but bearing a considerable burden.

In profound silence he entered the car and rapidly disappeared into the growing darkness. A Japanese policeman blew his whistle and traffic was allowed to resume. My guide said, "It's sort of pathetic to see a great general end his career in disgrace this way."

"What do you mean?" I asked.

"This Korea business. If the story is ever released back home it'll mean public disgrace."

We returned to the Press Club in deep gloom. These were the bad days. Our troops were getting kicked about in Korea and there was already talk that the Navy would have to pull some kind of miracle to save the right-flank army that had been so badly mauled. Many correspondents thought we might have to evac-uate Pusan as well and surrender all Korea. There was serious talk of a Russian invasion of Japan. MacArthur had rarely been in a tougher spot.

I felt additionally sorry that these evil days had come upon the general, for I had known him—not personally—in many weathers, and I wondered what would be the effect on America of the stories coming out of Korea. Our men had done badly. One British correspondent who had seen a lot of fighting in lots of wars summarized it this way: "American troops are

fleeing southward before untold hordes of Chinese bar-
barians—in company strength." We also knew that a
tremendous and probably unjustified military gamble
had been taken, without adequate preparation, for at
times our Marines had marched into the teeth of a
half-million Chinese, with no mechanical support, with
our men spaced sometimes fifty yards apart. We hoped
that Americans back home would not become panicky over the news, for of course we did not then know
that Americans were not to be told the full gravity
of the debacle.

When I got back to my room I thought of this
great provocative character. Through a strange series
of events I had developed a vast admiration for Mac-
Arthur's military genius. It happened in this round-
about way.

On Espiritu Santo, south of Guadalcanal, I was with
a squadron of Marine fighting planes when our pilots
limped back to base after having plastered Jap shipping.
The flyers were already jittery and bushed when they
heard over the radio General MacArthur's latest flamboyant communiqué from Australia. He announced
that his planes had sunk the Jap ships which had
actually been destroyed by our Marines a thousand
miles away.

There was a horrified silence, for this was the fourth
or fifth time the general's flaming communiqués had
stolen the show. That night his picture happened to
appear in a newsreel, and the Marines wrecked the
joint. Thereafter it was a rule that all newsreels had to
be inspected before being shown to the troops, so that
any pictures of General MacArthur could be elimi-

nated. Otherwise so many coconuts would be thrown through the screen that it would become impossible to continue showing films.

Later, in 1944, I happened to be traveling through all the islands from Manus through Bougainville and on down to Guadalcanal. The announcement had just been released that those islands were to be transferred from Admiral Halsey's old command to General Mac-Arthur's enlarged area. Since I traveled on headquarters business it was mistakenly assumed that I might have some pull with the admiral.

On every island, eleven of them, Army, Navy and Marine officers came to me and begged me, sometimes with tears in their eyes, to get them transferred either back to Nouméa or right up to Iwo Jima—anywhere, so long as they would not have to serve under Mac-Arthur. This was not a mass hysteria. It was the result of factual stories about the ridiculous military nonsense not only tolerated by MacArthur's command, but actually sponsored by it.

Men who had fought a free and honorable war in the South Pacific shuddered at the prospect of becoming a part of the MacArthur fancy-dress hoop-la and bally-hoo. I myself helped one young fellow escape a perfectly safe desk job with MacArthur. He volunteered to swim underwater to explode Jap mines at places like Okinawa.

For a short period after that I was in a position to compare the general's flamboyant communiqués with what appeared to be the sober truth, and in late 1944 I would rather have been assigned to a small-boat invasion of Truk than take a job in the MacArthur system. It is a matter of record that when I was threatened with such a transfer, I too volunteered for underwater demolition off the coast of Borneo. I believe that most of my fellow Navy and Marine officers felt the same way.

It was with these preconceptions that I went to Australia some time later, where I witnessed one of the most terrific fist fights of my life. An American Marine had observed, in a saloon, that he didn't think General MacArthur was so hot. A big, rangy Australian knocked him into the sawdust. "No bloody man livin' can speak that way about the general!" the Australian bellowed. And he proceeded, with the help of a few murdering bushrangers, to clean us all up.

The love for General MacArthur in Australia—up to 1949—was unbelievable. It makes any subsequent American professions of gratitude seem rather puny. For in 1942 Australia lay totally at the mercy of Japan. The finest Australian troops were in Africa and England. The British Navy, on which Australia obviously relied, was engaged elsewhere. There were no munitions. Already the Japs had penetrated almost to Port Moresby and their planes had started the reduction of Darwin. It was beyond compare the darkest day in Australia's history.

Into this terrifying void stepped General MacArthur. Resolutely he said that he would not only save Australia, but would recapture the Philippines, too. For three years he never once wavered in this determination. In ringing phrases he conveyed to the Australian people his iron confidence in his and their destiny.

Then, almost as if he were constructing the timetable, he moved from Melbourne to Brisbane to Hol-

landia to Manila to Tokyo. His long assault on the
Japanese Empire was one of the most brilliant in military history, and I have heard Australian military men
describe it as "the impeccable campaign." This is an
opinion in which I concur. MacArthur's subjection of
Japan was a campaign without blemish.

But when I returned to Australia in 1949 I did not
find the same hushed reverence for MacArthur, the
savior of the nation. Instead I encountered an embarrassed confusion. There were many Australians who
muttered through their teeth, "Who in hell does he
think he is, sitting up there in Tokyo? God?" There
was a prevalent feeling that the one American who
best understood Australia had failed her.

What accounted for this change? General Mac-
Arthur in 1949 was faced by the frightful problem
that will ultimately face every American leader in
the years to come: "Japan has 83,000,000 people; Australia has 8,000,000. Which country shall we make con-
cessions to in order to have that nation as a strong
ally?"

General MacArthur, facing this inevitable problem,
had suggested that perhaps Japanese food and population pressures might be relieved by permitting Japanese emigrants to occupy New Guinea. It is difficult to
convey the shudder that passed over Australia when
this proposal was announced. The savior of the nation
had somehow forgotten the nation. Henceforth the
name of MacArthur would be linked with that of
Woodrow Wilson. They were two well-meaning Americans who understood the Pacific so imperfectly that
they had advocated placing Japanese on New Guinea,
a scant ninety miles from Australia.

A very learned Australian asked me, "What can Mac-Arthur mean? Suppose the Japs had held New Guinea on December 7, 1941? They could have invaded us with no trouble. That would have meant evil for Australia but it would have been disastrous for the United States. What bases would MacArthur have used for the reconquest of the Philippines? Where would he have staged his great drive north? Tell me, has Mac-Arthur been so worshiped by the grinning Japs that he's gone balmy? Does he think he is the arbiter of the Pacific?"

I replied that the general had been forced to face one of the great problems of the Pacific—Japan or Australia—and without turning his back upon the latter had seen that he simply had to acknowledge the priority of the former. I added furthermore that no one else seems to have a solution to the question of New Guinea, this vast and wildly wealthy island. Australians can neither populate it nor develop it. Indonesia, which will soon own the western end of the island, can populate it but not develop it. America, which could develop it but not populate it, was in effect thrown out of the area by Australia's childish insistence that we abandon the great base of Manus in 1945. That leaves only Japan, which has the facilities both to populate and to develop. "In fact," I concluded, "an Australian in New Guinea who knows the island better than either of us has come to just that conclusion. Bring the Japs in. Treat them decently. And pray that in time of trouble they will remain loyal."

The Australian wiped his lips and asked, "Then you agree with MacArthur?"

"Yes."

"May God help your nation on the day it happens."

"The decision was made a long time ago," I replied.

"What do you mean?"

"When you decided that no one but white people could settle your empty continent."

"That was one of those difficult national decisions that all countries have to make," the Australian replied.

"Our choice of supporting Japan or Australia is exactly the same kind of choice," I said.

"If MacArthur forces this through, his name will live in infamy," the Australian cried. And he spoke for many of his countrymen.

Some time later I worked with a distingushed woman who was writing a book about Asia, and she told me of General MacArthur. Her story was so deeply moving that from time to time she had to pause to gain control of her tears. She said, "I was in Santo Tomas prison. For more than a year we heard nothing about the progress of the war except what the Japanese told us. Singapore had fallen. Australia was gone. Seattle had been invaded.

"My former houseboy used to smuggle food into the prison, although he risked his life doing so, and sometimes he added bits of news he had picked up from the outside. Hong Kong had fallen. New Zealand was gone. The Japs held Honolulu.

"In despair we thought of our future and the most we could hope for was that some kind of Japanese-dictated peace would permit us to work as their underlings.

"Then one day my houseboy smuggled in a bar of chocolate. I . . ."

She broke down completely. In prison she had lost fifty pounds and had been mortally shaken by her experience. Then she resumed. "This bar of candy bore a wrapper which read, 'I shall return. General Douglas MacArthur.' "

Again the woman broke down and it was some time before she could continue. Then she said, "We were famished for sweets but we could not break that wrapper. It passed from hand to hand, the first substantial news we had heard. From that day we never doubted."

For this woman General MacArthur was beyond reproach.

Yet at the time MacArthur was accomplishing these miracles it was reported that a young naval officer had been court-martialed and sent home in disgrace for merely writing on his hut where enlisted men could see it:

> *"With the help of God*
> *And a few Marines,*
> *I have returned*
> *To the Philippines."*

When I tried to track down this rumor I was told that it was not only true but that the charge against the young man was sacrilege.

It was with these conflicting emotions that I arrived in Tokyo in late 1950. I met at least thirty-six famous and reasonably honest correspondents, of whom thirty-two detested General MacArthur. Some of them had personal reasons. They had released the flash that the general had said the boys would be home by Christmas. Subsequently the story was denied and they were branded as liars. Others had been at the Yalu River and had witnessed what they called a wanton waste of American life on a precarious military gamble. Others, while supporting the gamble as one of those calculated risks which characterize all war, were nevertheless outraged at the militarily inept way it had been carried out. All of them said that MacArthur's conduct of the occupation of Japan was excellent, but that his own imperious aloofness from the Japanese people as well as from his own homeland was insufferably arrogant.

Only four correspondents would agree with me when I argued that this original conquest of Japan had been a military classic. In view of this thirty-two-to-four vote of "No Confidence" I was astonished at America's news reporting when General MacArthur returned to the United States in April, 1951. I happened to be traveling in an automobile through the West and was able to listen sixteen hours a day to the radio and read ten or twelve newspapers. Not once did I catch a hint that those Tokyo newspapermen who knew MacArthur best had grave doubts as to his divinity. I therefore concluded that one of three things had happened: (1) either all the newsmen I had met in Tokyo were liars; or (2) they had forgotten to send reports home; or (3) most unlikely of all, every report had been lost in the otherwise reliable mail. It was unthinkable that the Tokyo news reports had been suppressed.

In shivering disbelief I listened through those fateful days for one dispassionate review of the controversy. Instead, I heard a great network report that their man in Tokyo had come upon a sergeant on the Ginza with tears in his eyes who muttered between clenched teeth, "Why did they have to do this to my commander?" At this point I nearly threw up. The average enlisted man I knew on the Ginza usually called MacArthur just what the average enlisted man had called Halsey or Eisenhower: "Old fat mouth." And when the general did return I felt the old sick feeling all over again when I heard the breathless announcement that the first thing he had ordered was a chocolate milk shake and a hot dog; for in at least a dozen Japanese PX's and especially at Haneda Airport, they serve the best milk shakes in the world—and have for the past five years.

I have reported my varied and shifting attitudes toward this controversial figure in such detail for one reason only. MacArthur has become, understandably, the most listened-to American spokesman on Asia. It is critically urgent to evaluate what he and everyone else says about Asia, for so very few of us know anything about this enormous continent—and we must learn.

The first nineteen paragraphs of General MacArthur's speech to Congress on April 19, 1951, are among the soundest, clearest and most substantial words ever uttered by an American statesman regarding Asia. They constitute an epitome.

Nor can anyone reasonably doubt that his short-range policies in Japan were superb. His factual knowledge of Asia is enviable. I wish we were going to have, for the next two generations, men in charge of our Asia policies who know as much.

I do think, however, that several of General MacArthur's basic attitudes toward Asia warrant inquiry. We must remember that he is merely one human being. The policy of 150,000,000 other Americans toward the 1,300,000,000 people of Asia cannot possibly or properly be based upon the opinions of any one man.

First question: What does General MacArthur mean when he says to Clyde A. Lewis, Commander of the Veterans of Foreign Wars, in his letter released on August 28, 1950, ". . . it is in the pattern of the Oriental psychology to respect and follow aggressive, resolute and dynamic leadership"? Until Thanksgiving Day of 1950, General MacArthur consistently suggested that he knows Asians and that they will buckle down if white men show a little force. That idea is completely discredited and defunct. The French have shown a lot of force in Indo-China, and there are few signs of benighted Asians buckling down. In fact, it is the white men who duck when peasants hurl hand grenades among them. The Dutch mustered considerable force against the Indonesians and so frightened them that all the Indonesians did was throw the Dutch right out of every island. General MacArthur himself, shortly after his Formosa letter, threw at North Koreans and Chinese communists the greatest relative superiority of airplanes and naval gunfire in history, and the Asiatic peasants were so impressed they marched right on and tossed our best troops into the ocean at Hungnam. The fact is that General MacArthur wrote his letter in the palmy days when his troops were having easy pickings and seemed destined to attain the Yalu River. It must have seemed as if the old order in Asia was being restored; Asiatic forces were then wilting before a show of arms. Those old days are not coming back. We must absolutely erase from our national memory the ancient idea that a little show of force is going to scare hell out of quaking

Asians, after which we can make them do what we want. That day is past. Anyone who tries to revive it is doing both America and Asia a disservice. I prefer to believe that General MacArthur meant that if Asia ran wild against us it was useless to counter such aggression without real force. Asians, led by Russians, ran wild in Korea and it was necessary to use substantial force to discipline such willful aggression. But I dispute whether in the long run we could either dominate Asia by force or support our policies and our friends by war. And even if by a miracle we could do those things, I still don't think we should. I think that identifying the legitimate desires of Asians and helping them to attain those desires peacefully will be the far better policy.

Second question: What does General MacArthur mean when he says, in his address to the Congress, that from our Pacific islands chain extending in an arc from the Aleutians to the Marianas, "we can dominate with sea and air power every Asiatic port from Vladivostok to Singapore . . . and prevent any hostile movement into the Pacific"? Does he mean that we shall forever be at enmity with Asia? If he means that then he means that the United States is permanently at war for the next fifty years. We had better batten down the hatches and prepare for a long and terrible siege. For in such an implacable enmity we shall not be besieging Asia. Asia-Europe-Africa will be besieging us. If we are resolutely determined to oppose Asia's self-determination, then the Asia-Europe-Africa coalition will become a reality, possibly led by Russia but just as possibly led by some Asiatic power in the 1980's or 1990's. More likely General MacArthur meant that during the present impasse, when China threatens to run wild, it is prudent to keep bases in Formosa and the Philippines from which to forestall aggression eastward, especially against Japan but also Australia. But the ultimate purpose of bases anywhere—Japan, Philippines, Formosa or Australia—must be to serve as bridges rather than as bastions. We must ultimately co-operate with Asia and Asia with us, otherwise island fortresses are of no use. In the last war when our relations with Asia deteriorated to the crumbling point, our bastions fell like overripe plums. Our great hope with Asia lies in our establishment of common interests and mutually respected aims.

Third question: What does General MacArthur mean when he says, "The Philippines stand as a mighty bulwark of Christianity in the Far East, and its capacity for high moral leadership in Asia is unlimited"? This is an alluring but dangerous idea. It takes us back to the 1850's when it was believed that time and missionary effort would convert all the world to Christianity. It perpetuates the belief, which arose before the other great religions of the world were studied comparatively, that only Christianity can solve the world's problems—and all other religions will then retire to the darkness from which they sprang. That idea no longer bears inspection. I happen to believe strongly in the Christian faith and I think it one well suited to the spiritual leadership of our democracy; but I also suspect that in the long run it may well be some Oriental religion infinitely older than Christianity that will provide the spiritual leadership for that part of the world. No one can overlook the fact that Asians happen to be totally committed to their religions, which in certain respects serve them even better than Christianity serves us. (Care of the old would be an example.) But I am not attempting to compare and evaluate religions on a basis of merit. I am satisfied with the one I have and believe that in its finest manifestations it is a supreme expression of man's longings. In fact, if I had never known Asia I would be content to believe that my religion was incomparably the finest in the world. But having experienced the passionate devotion with which Asians are committed to their religions, having heard the anger that rises when Christianity tries to force its way into their lives, displacing a religion they prefer, I am no longer willing to stipulate that my religion is automatically bound to conquer the world. And as for finding in the insecure and confused Philippines a moral bastion from which to do the conquering, that seems ridiculous. In fact, I should rather think there was a danger that it might work the other way around, especially if Islam should become a great solidifying force in Asia pulling naturally toward the many Muslims in the Philippines. That is not likely, but what is likely is that each of the great religions of Asia will retain authority in its allotted geographic area and that in each religion the many good points will triumph over the obvious weaknesses: Christianity in the Philippines; Judaism in Israel; Buddhism in most of Southeast Asia; Islam in Indonesia, Pakistan, Iran and westward; Confucianism in China; and Shintoism in Japan. I would dread to see a religious war set aflame amid that collection of diverse faiths.

Final question: What do the supporters of General MacArthur mean when they insist that he knows Asia better than any other living American? Does he know

Indonesia (population 80,000,000)? Not that I know of. He probably knew something of the Dutch East Indies, but I believe he has never been to Indonesia. Does he know India (population 346,000,000)? He may have visited British India but I don't think he has even been in free India, and there is a vast difference. Does he know Pakistan (population 74,000,000)? I don't know of any visits to Pakistan. Does he know at first hand modern Iran, free Burma, the dominion of Ceylon, French Indo-China, Thailand? I think that to establish his credentials we should be given a list of his visits to these places, and their dates, for a visit twenty years ago hardly warrants life-and-death modern generalizations. As a matter of fact, how well does General MacArthur know modern China? How often has he traveled there? How far inland and to what districts? Actually, there must be a great deal about Asia that General MacArthur does not know at first hand. On the other hand, his constant wartime briefings and postwar considerations of policy have undoubtedly built up in his mind a fund of knowledge that is unequaled. He has shown himself to be able to master an infinite amount of information supplied him by others. Furthermore, he probably knows the Philippines far better than most Filipinos. He knows Australia intimately, New Guinea and the islands, and Japan (although many Americans in Japan would deny that he knows much of Japan at first hand). I ask these questions about his personal knowledge of Asia because great new nations have arisen in the postwar period. It worries me when leaders in Congress repeat that he alone understands this new Asia. If we don't have a half-dozen men who understand vast parts of Asia better than he does, we are doomed.

I want to make it perfectly clear that General Mac-Arthur knows ten times more about this continent than I will ever know. But it is not the knowledge of one man or a score of men which will bring us to a better accord with Asia and the Asians. It is, rather, a new orientation of mind and heart to a culture and a religious history and a political, social and economic transformation to which all Americans will have to accommodate themselves.

Boy-san

Most American military men serving in Korea despised the Koreans. I am sorry to report this but it is the truth. The causes of this feeling were many. Koreans are vengefully proud. In long years of Japanese occupation they kept their spirits alive solely by their intransigent will. They were subdued but they were never bought off. Furthermore, even though the Americans were their helpful allies the Koreans never kowtowed to them. Third, we met them in time of war when their old suspicions of the foreigner were revived. Fourth, being near starvation they stole much American food, and being impoverished they stole our equipment. Fifth, their untrained troops had the bad luck to be found out consistently by attacking communists, so that time and again the Korean front gave way and permitted attacks against the American flanks.

So the average Yank had little time for the Korean. The men of B-Company were good examples. They invented new profanity to describe Koreans, but at the same time they watched out for Boy-san.

Everywhere in the company you could hear the exasperated cry, "Boy-san! Where the hell are you?" The plaintive wail was usually followed by shattering oaths, whereupon a ten-year-old Korean boy would appear dressed in a jet-black schoolboy's uniform with

264

white buttons and a celluloid edging which formed a dummy collar.

His face was mostly round, his cheeks were russet red, and he was always smiling. There were several thousand like him with our troops and they presented a special problem.

It was rather difficult to talk with Boy-san because if the question was embarrassing he grinned apologetically and said, "No got English," while if he ever did reply he always lied. In what follows, the truth as I was able to discern it from the men of B-Company appears in parentheses.

"I born Chonju where my father he own large farm." (His old man was the town drunk.) "I go school do berry good." (He was always a juvenile delinquent.) "When dirty communist come Chonju I much scared. I run away and hide in hills." (He collaborated famously and ate lots of their rice.)

"Then American come back. Berry strong. Berry fine men, Americans. I get job in mess B-Company. All soldiers say I best mess boy they ever damn well see." (During the first week Boy-san copped every available fountain pen and sold them all to a Seoul hock shop.) "Americans like me berry much, put me in school." (The captain of B-Company said flatly Boy-san was to get out of camp and stay out. The sergeant finagled it for the kid to be accepted by a Presbyterian orphanage.)

"Presbyterians fine people. I like berry much." (He ducked out the second night and rejoined B-Company.) "Pretty soon sergeant come for me and say he need me right away B-Company. This time I work berry hard pick up all things for men." (That's true. He

picked up everything and sold it. The captain personally had the kid put in reform school. Two weeks later
he was back with B-Company.)

"I like war. Berry much fun ride in jeep, shoot gun.
Best of all I like American men. They good to me, I
good to them." (The little racketeer nosed out bottles of bootleg hooch for them, terrible stuff that led
to courts-martial.)

"I help all soldiers. I do all things for them. Keep
camp berry clean." (He became the best boy-san in
Korea for going into a village and asking girls if they'd
like to come out to camp.)

"These pants I got on. Sergeant make them for me."
(This is correct and rather difficult to explain. The
sergeant despises Koreans, can never speak of them
without the vilest adjectives to describe their thiev-
ery, knavery and general worthlessness. His opinion is
shared by 95 percent of enlisted men and most officers.
Yet this same sergeant risked a court-martial by steal-
ing an officer's pants and cutting them down to Boy-
san's size. At home the sergeant never even mended
his socks, yet now he was a tailor.) "Pretty good pants,
huh? He make me shirt, too." (Boy-san stole the shirt
when he scrammed from the reform school.)

"Big days! We ride into Seoul. Into Pyongyang.
B-Company say I good luck. They take me along to
Yalu River." (Not quite true. At Pyongyang the captain
tried once more to jam his problem case into a reform
school. Boy-san didn't care for it. He went up to the
Yalu on his own and overtook his company right before
the debacle.)

"Then bad days. Dirty communist come out of
mountains. B-Company fight berry hard. Four night

we fight communist. I always right up front." (Boy-san wanted to stay up front but the sergeant kept him in the rear. Said he didn't want the kid to get hurt.)

"So we walk back the same road we ride up. Fight, fight, fight. One day we catch truck. Then everything pretty good. I ride in front." (The captain said they better keep the kid up front where they could watch him. He didn't want the kid to get hurt.)

"In Pyongyang I leave B-Company. I go back to school." (The company took up a purse and gave it to an LST skipper and told him to see to it that the kid was kept in the Presbyterian school down in Pusan.)

"But I not like school. Pretty soon I back with B-Company." (The captain told me, "One day I looked up and cripes, there was Boy-san. He'd run away from school again and had ridden north with a truck convoy.")

"Now everybody in B-Company berry good to me. I think they glad to see me back." (This is curiously true. Everyone in the defeated company looked with deep tenderness at their little crook. They talked with him at night, cursed him with real affection and taught him to wash his face. Something had happened at Pyongyang which had made Boy-san terribly important. In the long and humiliating retreat the kid became a symbol, a focal point of human love.)

"Each night the captain say, 'We hold here,' but each day we move farther back. Pretty soon we get on train and come all way back to Pusan. Now we can't go no more. But anyway we got to have one damn fine Christmas." (The men of B-Company spent a good deal of money to send home for a complete outfit of cloth-

ing for their boy-san. The stuff arrived in Christmas
wrappings and two men went into the hills near
Pusan and chopped down a tree. There was a terrific
Christmas.)

"Now B-Company don't try no more to send me to
school. I stay with them." (The captain of B-Company
said, "That kid stays with us.")

"So I think that even maybe when Americans leave
Korea I go along." (Yes, the captain of B-Company
said, "I don't want to hear any more discussion. When
we leave, he leaves. And if Truman and Acheson and
Ridgway don't like it, they know what they can do.")

The same problem exists in almost every unit. If
Americans ever do evacuate Korea there will have to be
a rule that no boy-sans may accompany our troops, but
since what happened at Pyongyang there will be a
mutiny if the rule is enforced.

What has Pyongyang to do with Boy-san? At
Pyongyang the communists caught some boy-sans who
had helped the Americans. They broke their backs and
shot them.

The Hard Way

※

DURING this year perhaps 200,000 American students will work their way through college. If they ever feel sorry for themselves they should consider Liu Ping, a bright, cocky student of political science at Taiwan (Formosa) University.

"My father was a doctor and had thirteen sons. Ten of them died. Don't ask me why. Before I could finish my degree at Chungking University the communists gained control of China. I was now faced with a most difficult decision."

It's fun to talk with keen-eyed Liu Ping because in the classical Chinese manner he moves logically from point to point, introducing each with a rhetorical question which he immediately answers, thus anticipating almost every query.

"Why was my decision difficult? I had to get my degree but I was under suspicion of the communists. I had been a student of political science, I spoke English, and my oldest brother was a major general in Chiang Kai-shek's armies. I was in a bad spot.

"What was I to do? I argued with myself for a long time and concluded that what I had studied in political science was true. Man is supposed to be free. A nation is supposed to have a decent government. I decided to run away to Formosa where other people believed these things.

"How was I to get there? My father gave me two

ounces of gold and I walked through China for two months. When the gold gave out I went four days without food. I arrived at the port of Amoy with nothing, no clothes, no money, no friends. But there I met other students who had made the same decision, and that gave me strength.

"What were we to do? We formed a committee and went to see a ship's captain. We pointed out that since he was going to Formosa we would go along.

"Did he agree? He did not. So we went anyway. We landed at last in Free China. The first days were truly terrible. We starved and had no place to sleep. Then the Kuomintang organized a shelter and the screening process began.

"We were so many and the university was so small that we were told most of us would have to go into the Army. But a few would be permitted to enter the university.

"How did they select us? By the classical method of examinations. For three weeks I lived on one bowl of rice a day and read every book I could find, memorizing whole passages. Then I asked a friend for a bowl of hot soup and took the examination.

"How did I stand? Very near the top. It was glorious. I was a student again. The Government said that as long as I did well I would get $4 a month and thirty katis of rice. That's enough. I have two shirts, two pairs of socks, one pair of shoes and one suit. I study very hard.

"Where do I live? I am shamed for to say I live nowhere. At night I sleep where I can. The shirts and socks come from my friends. I own no books, but this good American fountain pen is a help.

"Am I happy? I am very happy. For I study with excellent teachers and I know I am helping to build the new China. But one thing amuses me. I the student ran away from communism because my brother was a major general for Chiang Kai-shek, but my brother the major general stayed behind and joined the communists. Why I do not know. I have often had the idea that my brother is not very smart.

"My father and other brother stayed behind, too. In fact, I am the only one of all the friends I had in China who came to Formosa, but I hear that intellectuals are being killed when they can't be converted and I am glad I came.

"I hear from my family but they never write anything I want to know about. My younger brother works for the communists and I think he will be pretty happy because he was never interested in politics. I am sorry to say I am beginning to forget about my family. I may never see them again.

"Now what do I think of my new home? I see here in Formosa a new way of life. Things are healthy in Formosa. Justice prevails.

"Will there be war? Of course there will be. Very shortly. I shall be graduated by then and I'll take part. Everyone on Formosa is loyal to Chiang Kai-shek. Not long ago they shot four generals who weren't and one of them was a four-star job. They also investigated the Chinese who served as translators for American newspapermen. They were found to be communist spies, telling the Americans what Mao Tse-tung wanted them to believe. The translators were shot.

"But there is one thing perhaps you can explain. In American universities were many Chinese students.

Why did more than 80 percent choose to go back to Red China? What did they learn in your universities to make them do that? It is we, on this island, who stand for democracy and freedom."

When it came time to leave Liu Ping I did a regrettable thing. I have known many students in my time, the fine young men on whom the world depends, but I had never before known one who lived on a bowl of rice a day with only two shirts. So I offered Liu Ping some money, and in flashing anger he rejected it. "We need your ships and your tanks and your ammunition. But not your charity." And he stalked away in his worn and battered shoes.

The Old China Hand

For two reasons Bill Downs doesn't belong in this series. First, he's not a real person. He's eight people. He runs an air line, heads a major news bureau, is a world-famous writer, runs a big store, is an adviser to governments.

Second, Bill is not an Asian. He is a white American citizen and a registered Republican, a fact which is very important to remember as you listen to what Bill has to say.

For he is a real Asian. He was born in China, speaks the language, worked there for years. Educated in America, he went back willingly to a land he loves. And when he talks about Asia he really lays it on the line.

"Let's face it like men. The white sahib is through in Asia. Absolutely through. I don't mean he's going to be asked to leave. He's going to be kicked out. Out of Korea, Hong Kong, Indo-China, Singapore, Indonesia. And if he doesn't scram he's going to be murdered.

"The white man is absolutely through. He's done Asia a world of good, and much evil. But any careful balancing of good and evil is past. He's getting the bum's rush.

"And if he insists upon fighting his way back in he's going to be massacred. He's out and he's got to stay out for at least a dozen years while Asians rearrange the furniture in what we often forgot was their home.

"The compradore who encouraged serfdom while piling up profits is out. The missionary who did his pitiful best is out. The arrogant fools who lounged in the exclusive clubs and shouted to grown Chinese men with five children, 'Damn it, boy! Bring me that drink, you filthy dog!'—they're out. And the businessmen who were going to show the Orientals how to live and make 18 percent profits a year. They're all out.

"Along the entire coast of Asia a KEEP OUT sign has been posted. And it's going to stay there for a generation. When some Admiral Perry's black ships come back this time to reopen Asia, they'll beg permission to land and there will be a lot of discussion about terms. And the discussion will be between equals."

Bill Downs is cautious about explaining how it all happened. "I don't go for this simple barefoot-boy, agrarian-reformer line. Of course every uprising is communist now. But it's a stubborn fact that all the trouble did start over land and general reform. The people wanted land and food. They wanted the insolent whites to get out. That's how it started.

"Then, by one of those lousy tricks of fate, their vague determination on reform happened to coincide with the rise of communism. The Asians had failed to make Englishmen or Frenchmen or Americans take them seriously. So they allied themselves with Russia, which made believe its heart bled for them.

"In the face of what's happening in Asia now, old clichés of thought are useless. Nobody out here admires General MacArthur more than I, but it's a fact that less than six weeks after his Formosa speech, when he said all you had to do with Asians was ruffle them with a show of force and they'd back down, he threw some of the mightiest air power ever seen in the Pacific at

them in North Korea, and they kept right on coming
at us. We've got to give up the old ideas.

"What should take their place? Humility. The honest-to-God acknowledgment of the fact that all men
are brothers. An acceptance of the idea that there is
no 'way to handle the Asian.' The Asian is a full-grown
man with all of a man's aspirations and potentials. If
we could honestly accept such a program we might
some day get back into Asia."

Here Bill Downs disagrees with himself for the first
time. Six of him are abjectly pessimistic. They say,
"The simple reformers who could have been on our side
are now hopelessly communistic. They will absorb all
of Asia and then back up Russia as she absorbs all of Europe. Then America is totally cut off, for South America will wither on the vine and tag along with Russia.
We'll hold Mexico and Canada but in fifty years of such
a life we will subtly modify our nation into Russia's pattern. So in fifty years it won't matter much."

The other two Bill Downses say, "No need to commit
suicide over this. It's merely a historical fact. We had a
great chance in Asia and we muffed it. We're out in the
cold for a dozen years while Asia adjusts itself to a communist life. But Asia needs what we have, our technical
skill, our sense of brotherhood. We need what they
have.

"Never believe that Asia is completely lost to Russia.
We have many friends among the billion enemies. When
they remember us, how we actually tried to treat them
decently, they'll invite us back. I'll go. I like Asia, and I
think I'd like it even better on their terms."

Then the eight Bill Downses join ranks in their opinions about what to do now. "Fight our way back to the mainland? Impossible. We haven't enough men. We haven't enough money.

"Use Chiang Kai-shek? Absolutely fatal. We lost Asia through this tactic. To try it again would merely mean losing Asia forever.

"Drop the atomic bomb? Completely useless. The first bomb would inflame Asia against us for as long as memory persisted. I've been telling you, Asians despise us today. Now you want to make them hate us, too. When you talk about the atomic bomb you're speaking of mechanical weapons. Long ago we won the war of mechanical ideas. We have superior planes, machinery, bombs, stores. What we lost was the moral war. We didn't have the idealism, the brotherhood, the sense of participation in actual daily life. Well, you can't win moral wars with atom bombs.

"What do you do? You retreat from Asia, leave it alone, allow it to stew in its own juices and then settle down. Then you come back in with a new program. A mature program of equals meeting to discuss mutual problems. And the first white man who shouts, 'Damn your filthy hide, boy, bring me that drink,' you shoot him."

On one final point Bill Downs speaks with fervor. "As we leave we should bow out gracefully. Leave behind memories of a decent crowd of people. Remind everyone of our essential honor. There's going to be rotten days in Asia, and if they remember us as we were they'll want us back. What I mean is, let's sow a little love as we leave. We can never tell what it might grow into while we're gone."

The Marginal Man

I MET Hugh Channing in Singapore and he will haunt my conscience forever. He was taller than I, better-looking, better-educated and more gifted in the correct use of language. His skin was whiter and his smile more gracious. In fact, there was only one thing wrong with him. His grandmother had been a native woman.

"Therefore I am nothing. I am not a European. The white people see to that. Nor am I an Asian. Because the white people insist that I never push a rickshaw or clean gutters. I can neither go up nor down. I am the man ordained by God always to be a clerk in some English shop. They don't have to pay me much, for I can't leave. There's no other job I could get. And they don't have to promote me because everyone knows I'm not really to be trusted.

"What am I? I'm a Eurasian. I can never be a European as long as Englishmen despise anyone with even a drop of color. I can never be an Asian as long as my parents bring me up to imitate the white man.

"This was proved in the recent riots. On Saturday night there was dancing at the Tanglin Club. I could never hope to enter such a club. White Englishwomen see to that. They never had a servant at home, but out here they can rule the world.

"On Monday the riots began and a gang of infuriated Malays saw me in my car. With huge bamboo flails they

277

smashed the glass and hauled me into the street. They set fire to the car and destroyed it. They were going to beat me to death but a fearless Sikh rescued me. Eurasians took terrible punishment that night because the Malays looked upon us as traitors.

"This riot was most difficult to understand. We had a fine police force, all Malays, all armed. Four of them watched casually as I was being beaten nearly to death. They stood by with their arms folded. A white priest was almost killed but managed to crawl to a police station where the officers slammed the door in his face. They said that otherwise it might look as if they were taking sides.

"At the investigation the Malay police were astonished that anyone had expected them to interfere with the mob. 'They were all Muslims,' the police protested. 'How could we fire upon our own religion?' A newspaperman explained that in New York if there's a riot, Negro cops will fire on Negro criminals or Irish cops upon fellow Catholics. The Malay police thought this very strange and said the Irish cops must not take their religion very seriously.

"I myself am a Catholic, and this has been a great solace to me. This was the only church that really welcomed Eurasians and I have always felt myself a brother with all Catholics across the world.

"But recently I have begun to wonder if I ought not turn my back upon Christianity, confess my sins and become a complete Malay Muslim. I believe now that my future lies with the Malays."

For many years social scientists have studied the tragic problems of the man who stands astride two societies belonging spiritually to neither but inheriting the prime evils of each. Such men are known as marginal men and in all societies their life has been hell. In Canada, America and India the half-breed has been an object of bitter hatred. Only in chance places like Mexico or Tahiti has he gained a decent home.

"But in British colonies he inherits a special hell. For some curious reason the Englishman has a pathological contempt for the Eurasian. It took my mother two years of daily pleading to get me into a school. I was prohibited from social contact with white children.

"As I became older they treated me with politeness but also with contempt. Then when I reached courtship age the real misery began.

"Of course I couldn't speak to any white girl. But at the same time all the prettiest Eurasian girls were chased by white men. I had two feelings. I was enraged when I thought of myself, but I was also amused when I saw how terrified the white fathers and mothers became when they thought their son might actually marry a Eurasian girl.

"They tried everything. Women wept and men threatened to shoot somebody. I had a sense of revenge when the Eurasian girl went right ahead and married the boy. They were usually driven out of Singapore, but lots of them established good lives elsewhere.

"The case we Eurasians enjoyed most was the recent one when an army officer announced that he was going to marry a Eurasian. His commander huffed and chumped and said he damned well would never marry the girl while he was in uniform. So the officer waited until he got leave and popped out of uniform. The

Army countered by ordering him to another post on four hours' notice. He deliberately missed the plane and got married. So they court-martialed him, but a brilliant Eurasian lawyer proved that the Army had no right to send him to another station until they first canceled his leave. This outraged the Army lawyer so that he screamed, 'Everyone knows that all Eurasian girls are whores!' Then the court began to sweat, because they knew that if this were published there would be riots, so the commanding officer ordered the lawyer to apologize. But they saw to it that the man who had married the Eurasian girl was ruined.

"Usually, however, the Eurasian harbors no desire for vengeance. He is a playboy. He gives enormous parties and has a good time and never worries about business because he knows he can never get promoted. Sometimes white men come to our parties, but always looking for pretty girls. And the girls don't mind, because if they can catch a white man they may escape to a better life.

"One thing that has happened in Singapore has given us all hope. Today for the first time in history there's one club which any man with a clean shirt and the initiation dues can join. The American Club. We also now have a free library to which anyone, regardless of color, can belong. The United States Information Library. These things are important.

"I think that if enough such things happened in Asia there might be some chance of avoiding communism." But things are happening with terrible swiftness in Asia today, and even as Hugh Channing spoke, one of the most brilliant, handsome and gifted Eurasian law-

yers in Singapore was being arrested. He was a leader
of the communist underground. When Hugh Channing
saw the headlines he shrugged his shoulders. "What
could you expect?" he asked.

A Grand Old Man at Thirty-six

THE single most astonishing thing about Indonesia is the youth of its rulers. Every leading official is under forty-nine. The oldest man in the cabinet is forty-seven. The premier is thirty-eight. And the grand old man of the independence movement led the government when he was thirty-six.

Sutan Sjahrir is a handsome, slightly potbellied intellectual whose brilliant mind has provided the philosophical structure of the new nation. Today, at forty-one, he is the lodestar for most of the best young men in the country, and his spiritual power is enormous.

"I am somewhat different from the other leaders and therefore somewhat under suspicion. I alone did not collaborate with the Japanese. I alone have never called for the complete explusion of the Dutch. I owe my education and even my mental processes to them, for they picked me out as a promising student and sent me to their university at Leyden.

"But when I came back and they saw that I had developed a mind of my own they promptly threw me into jail. The charge? 'Sutan Sjahrir has conducted himself so that if other Indonesians did the same they might end by contesting Dutch rule.'

"Have you ever heard of Tanah Merah prison in New Guinea? Perhaps the worst in the world, surrounded by jungle and swamps. They sent me there for nine years, along with criminals and murderers of every description.

"Fortunately I was there only a year when out of common decency they moved me to Banda, where I had little to complain of. From Banda I even sent the government long reports predicting exactly what has since happened. It was in Banda that I formulated my philosophy of social advance.

"It is this. In a new country where 80 percent of the population were never allowed to read or write one must start first with a few basic things. Education. A workable system of government. Health. The rise of capable leaders. Development of a sense of responsibility. Those are the first requirements and basic to them is a philosophical understanding of men.

"That's why I left the government. I knew I could do more good on the outside, stressing these fundamentals. If I were enmeshed in actual governing I would be bowed down by too many immediate decisions.

"I would explain our country this way. Under Dutch rule any promising young man found himself in jail. This was not too bad because in jail he found all the other young men who would one day rule Indonesia. Why are there no old men in our government? None of the old men got into the jails while the big plans were being formulated.

"When the Japanese came, Indonesia had an astonishing awakening. The Japs used all the jail men in setting up a puppet government. This was a very good thing because it taught us how to establish the forms of government which the Dutch had kept secret from us.

"I believe I alone stood out against the Japs. I was sure they would be defeated within three years, but men like Sukarno and Hatta thought they would last for at least ten, maybe forever. Therefore somebody had to co-operate with them.

"So this puppet government was established and for two years the future leaders of Indonesia went through the motions of governing a state. They were given a constitution, which later became the constitution of Indonesia. They had a system of governmental organization, which we kept for our own use. The effect of Japanese occupation must never be underestimated. It showed us we did not need the Dutch.

"When the Japs were defeated we swung their puppet government right into the full arena of Indonesian life, but we expanded it, for it was a structure that could have continued to exist only if the Japanese held all the real power.

"For example, there was no provision for a cabinet or a parliament. Worst of all, there was no responsible premier to execute the laws. So we made Mr. Sukarno a president in the French style, the figure about whom the entire nation rallies. And to my surprise the leaders asked me to become the first premier, in whom the power of the government would actually reside. We made many other necessary changes. I would say that now we are a real democracy.

"The question then arose as to our freedom from Holland. I was sent to the United Nations to plead our case. We were victorious for two reasons. In prison I had learned patience and I worked hard to present my ideas simply, without intellectual or nationalistic arrogance. But even so I would have accomplished little if the

Dutch had not sent some of the most stupid, aloof and arrogant men I have ever known. We kept our mouths shut and let the Dutch talk. They argued themselves to death. No one could hear their stupidities without knowing they had no moral right to govern any colony.

"After that I served only as ambassador-at-large, a post I still hold but about which I do nothing. My job is to teach young men what efficient government means, what a good police force is, the relationship between an army and the state. I tell them how free men should live within a free community."

Sutan Sjahrir lives in a modest, slightly broken-down house in a noisy street far from the palatial residences of other government officials. The most memorable furniture in the house is the young men who come there day after day. They make it distinguished.

"We have three parties. The Nationalist led by Hatta is first in power. The Muslim led by Hatsir is first in numbers. The Socialist led by me is first in brains. When I became premier I was embarrassed by communist support but later on the Marshall Plan split them off and I wasn't sorry to see them go. Now they don't carry much weight.

"But I'm afraid that if China captures all of Asia we are doomed. The one thing we pray for in Indonesia is time. If we have time the young men you saw leaving my office will have a chance to provide the country with a good government. It has been said that Indonesia is a nation with lots of generals and many foot soldiers, but no captains. How could this be otherwise when the five-star generals are in their forties? If we have time, I shall provide some of the captains.

"That is why I never mention New Guinea or Malaya.

And I think politicians who do simply divert the attention of the people from jobs that need to be done here at home. What Indonesia needs is not more land in New Guinea, but a better land here at home. Right now we need men with low voices and high ideals."

I told Sjahrir that nevertheless I was worried about Indonesia's determination to get control of Western New Guinea. I said that I could foresee the day when possession of Western New Guinea would lead to an attack on Eastern New Guinea and ultimately upon Australia. At that time, I reasoned, America would side with Australia and there would be war.

Sjahrir did not avoid the problem. "I realize the possibility of such dynamics. But I absolutely believe that before such a time comes to pass the entire world will have seen the stupidity of any more conquest. There will be one government, one common interest. That is what I work for. For the day when Australia need have no fear of Indonesia and we need have no fear of China. It is my job to see to it that when such a day comes, Indonesia will be mature enough to find a respectable place in that world government."

Sutan Sjahrir talked for some time, a quiet man with enormous force and enviable good humor. He was interested in all sorts of things and as he spoke I kept thinking of Thomas Jefferson.

The Buddhist Monk

❦

I MET Par Anake Angkanarlong one hot midnight in Bangkok. The Buddhist temple near where I was trying to sleep was conducting a whale of a carnival, so I slipped into some old clothes and went out to join the fun. I had been there only a few minutes when this little man in thick glasses and saffron robes accosted me and said, "You speak English? Never mind."

He took my arm and led me to a row of a hundred and thirty-five gold Buddhas, each about two feet high, depicting Buddha in all the traditional poses remembered by his followers. The great religious leader who lived half a thousand years before Christ was shown blessing the poor, entering Nirvana, seeking protection from a mighty snake, and in more than a hundred other poses.

"What day you born?" Par Anake demanded abruptly. He led me to a Buddha standing with outstretched hand. "This your Buddha. Two ticals, please." He handed me a slip of paper written in Sanskrit. "This your fortune. You can't read? Never mind." And he tore up the paper.

Then he led me to the temple and said, "Shoes off! Follow me! Never mind." He took me to the high priest, who rubbed charcoal on my face and gold leaf on my tongue. Then he blessed me and Par Anake said, "Twenty ticals, please. Never mind."

We had a fine time that night, the little monk and I.

He led me to the tree where thousands of bits of paper were tied to branches. For three ticals I grabbed the one he suggested and won a bottle of indelible purple ink. He looked at it in disgust and said, "No damn good. Never mind." And he gave it back to the monk who tended the tree.

He took me to the dance where lively couples did the ram-wong, a processional dance in which partners never touch. A Chinese hot-dog man offered us a mess of that wonderfully jumbled and delightful food cooked on the spot, but Par Anake refused. "Monk eats only twice a day. Five in the morning. Twelve at noon. But I can have soda water. Never mind."

Par Anake had only a little English and I had no Siamese, but we knocked about Bangkok together for several days. For some months I had been arguing about politics and wars and economics, and it was a great relief to see this little man in saffron robes come swaying down the street with a bright hello.

"We go my room. You see how monk lives." He led me down a very dark and dirty alley to a row of dormitories in back of the temple. Some of the rooms were pretty bad but he led me at last to a fine, clean platform at the top of which he lived. It was spacious and had fifteen gold Buddhas. "I worked hard to get this room. Very nice." He hired a servant who kept it clean.

He slept on a mat one-sixteenth of an inch thick placed on polished boards. At the head of this bed he had a vase of rush tapers which he lighted from time to time to the accompaniment of brief prayers.

Par Anake was popular with the younger monks, many of whom clustered about him to borrow books or to argue. While they talked I peered down from the platform and saw on one of the porches a remarkably pretty girl of twenty sitting with a monk playing gin rummy.

"Very bad!" Par Anake said. "Monks not touch girls. Not talk lovely-lovely to girls. Not play cards." He sent a young monk, not yet ten years old, to tell the girl to go away. But the gin-rummy game continued.

Next door to the monastery there was a Chinese theater and the younger monks had ripped down some of the corrugated-iron wall so they could watch the plays. Par Anake did not approve of this, but from his platform I watched the performances. They were noisy and a lot of fun. Sometimes as many as forty monks would be crowded about this broken wall.

Par Anake said, "I thirty-five years old. I a monk now for one year. I stay two more years. No money, no clothing. Anything I need my younger brother give to me. Suppose I break my tooth, he pay dentist."

He took me to see his brother, a collar-ad young fellow with a beautiful wife and two children. Par Anake said, "My fine brother do all things for me. Give me much money." I noticed that the younger brother's wife took a rather dim view of Par Anake and we soon left.

I rose early one morning and watched the monks go out to beg their daily rice. It was a moving and colorful sight. From all over Bangkok appeared the saffron robes, the rice bowls, and the good women of the city who appeared with huge buckets of rice from their kitchens. The monks ate copiously and did not say thank you, it having been directed by Buddha himself that religious people feed the monks each morning.

At midday the monks went out again, this time for

more substantial food. Par Anake said, "I allowed to smoke cigarettes. Good thing. Most Siamese men be monks for three months some time in their lives. Shave their heads. Put on robes. Beg for food. Very good for all men to know this."

I told him I had heard that criminals habitually flee to monkhood when the police are hot after them. Par Anake said, "Some bad monks. Never mind. We all pray to one god. You good Catholic maybe? Ave Maria Gloria Plenis. O.K. Or maybe you say Father, Son, Holy Ghost. O.K. Never mind. I pray to Buddha. All means same thing. Never mind."

I tried in vain to discover why Par Anake had become a monk at thirty-four. He explained sorrowfully, "My father died. I very sad. Heavy heart. I become a monk." I was impressed and asked when his father had died. "Twenty-two years ago. But my aunt die, too. I very sad. Heavy heart." She had passed on twelve years ago. "Other things, too," he added. "I tired of working at custom house."

I grew to like and respect Par Anake's gentle religion. It had done much for Asia in providing a substantial, matter-of-fact moral code without morbid qualities. Every statue of Buddha must show the saint smiling with benign compassion.

Then one day to my surprise Par Anake said, "All right, we go see my family." He led me along the interminable winding footpaths that probe into the interior of Bangkok city and we came at last to his home. I was astonished to find that he had a wife, two children, a living room with an immense colored photograph of June Allyson, and a Buddhist shrine with five gold Buddhas. He was annoyed to find that his wife had won a naked kewpie doll at a fair and that she had placed it among the Buddhas. He made her take it away.

When she brought us drinks he made her put them on the floor, from which his servant lifted them to his hands. "I not touch anything my wife hold in her hand. I not live here while I am a monk. I never talk lovely-lovely to my wife. One year I not talk lovely-lovely. Two more years. My brother he pay all bills but my wife she work too when she can."

His children were delighted to see him and he banged his son up and down on his knee, but his daughter he would not touch. On his way back to the temple he said, "Buddhism very gentle religion. Everybody kind. Buddhism make the heart pure." Then he frowned. "But if communists capture Siam they destroy Buddhism. Laugh at our religion. That very bad thing, I think."

The Patriot

❧

I HAD finished my work in Burma and had gone to the airport when a long black government car sped into the enclosure and a worried man of sixty hurried out to speak with me.

I had talked with this man several times in Rangoon, and while he had said nothing that I considered startling he had made much sense. I thought of him with respect and affection, for he was a dedicated and intelligent public servant.

But now he was distraught. He said, "Last night I reviewed what I had told you, and I talked it over with my wife. We agreed that I had been imprudent. May I implore you to tear up your notes? And promise me you will not use my photograph."

"You said nothing disloyal to Burma," I protested.

"You don't understand." His hands moved nervously and he began to perspire. "You might not think it dangerous, what I said, but if it appears in American papers it will surely be spotted by our embassy official in Washington, who will report it back to Rangoon. Then I might get shot."

I promised him that I would use neither his name nor his photograph, for as we talked there at the airport I had to acknowledge that, harmless as were the things he had said, they still might cause him to be shot. In this respect he represented 80 percent of the intelligent men I had met in Asia. They knew the various disasters that threatened to overtake their countries and they knew that this time they simply had to guess right. They had to guess which side was going to win, because if they backed the loser they would get shot.

This likable Burmese official said, "I have a wife and three children, all girls. I cannot afford to have the communists angry at me. For we don't know who is going to win in Burma. Or in Asia, for that matter. And I have already been through too much hardship.

"What do you think? Will America start a war in Asia? If she does, then Burma is doomed to another terrible disruption. The communists will invade us from the outside and terrorize us from within. America will be too occupied elsewhere to give us help, and China will occupy us within a few weeks.

"You asked me why we don't face this problem now. Why don't we do something? All right, I ask you: What can we do? We are a little country. More than any land in the world we have been devastated by war. We will not listen to any policy that might lead us into another war.

"You Americans cannot understand this. Look at Rangoon! A tired, dirty, frightened city. Before every main building a barricade of barbed wire to give us a little time if another revolution starts.

"Our main roads are barricaded, too. In the northern hills it's unsafe to walk about. And on all sides rebels threaten our national security."

In the hot sunlight this man spoke like a person who cherished the land in which he was born. He spoke like the hero in one of Robert Sherwood's plays, his back to the wall, his mind agonized by the insuperable problems he must face.

"Burma is one of the loveliest countries on earth. It is one of the richest, too. Our teak is the world's best. We have mines that produce essential metals. We produce an abundant surplus of rice. Famine does not strike our land. And you yourself said the Burmans are delightful.

"Then why is so favored a land so impoverished now? Because when the Japanese invaded us they set in motion forces that no one has been able to stop. Eight different rebel armies have attacked the government at one time or another. For what? For nothing. Some of the leaders say they want freedom. Others say they want a petty state to be a sovereign nation. Some fight for a communist state. Others fight because they have the guns.

"Here in Burma you can see the true terrors of war. A magnificent country devastated. Civil life at a standstill. You must remember this when we say we want no more war. Especially not if we have to choose sides between America which is very far away, and China which is on our border."

I asked this nervous man, "Then you do not fear communism?"

"Yes! The government does, too. Perhaps even a majority of the Burmese people do, too. But as between communism and another war, they'll take communism."

"But don't you realize that communism will be worse than the Japs?"

"There you are wrong. I was in Jap hands. This scar came from them because I was known as a democratic liberal. When I refused to work with them they slapped me in the face and took everything I had. Believe me, my family knew what true poverty was. We could not stand that again."

"Communism will inevitably be worse. Communists don't slap liberal democrats in the face. They shoot them."

"That I know," the government man said. "That's why I hurried out here to make you stop that story about me. Because if the communists arrive I don't want to be shot."

"Do you think they will arrive?"

I have no idea what this man really thought, but he said, "No, I do not think they will come this far. For one thing, Burma has no large Chinese colony to cause trouble. For another, Rangoon has no large slums to breed a communist movement. For a third, we are Buddhist and that means spiritual opposition to communism. Most important, we side with India in international affairs, and Pandit Nehru says India will not be overrun by the Chinese."

"You believe that?"

"Yes, I do. In this respect we must believe Nehru. Burma will go along with India in foreign affairs. We live or die with India and can have no separate life of our own."

"You agree with Nehru when he says there is no danger from Red China?"

"Yes."

"Then why do so many people in Burma fear communism—as you yourself have been saying?"

There was a long pause and the government man said, "We have got to weigh various possibilities. Remember that the rebels were in Rangoon itself not long ago. We drove them out that time. Who knows? Who can foresee what will happen by this time next year?"

This sensible man—he spoke English fluently and said that the British had been the salvation of Burma, starting her on the path to freedom—could have been speaking for 500,000,000 Asians: "We prefer democracy. We cherish national freedom. But the American Navy and the British Army are a long way off. We had better not make the communists too angry. Because who knows? Maybe this time they'll be the winners."

The Grace of Asia

I AM always amazed when Americans ask, "How did you manage to get along in Asia? Can you speak Asiatic?" Or, "Were you able to eat that funny food? Did it make you sick?" Or, "I suppose you know they're all crooks out there. They'll steal the gold fillings out of your teeth."

To all such questioners I can express only one wish: that they could spend some time with Sohan Lal, of Delhi, India. He is a little fellow forty-four years old, a brilliant, darting, handsome hummingbird of a man. He stands five feet one, moves with compulsive energy and talks with brilliance, spicing his observations with inviting wit.

Like most educated Asians, he speaks excellent English, for he was specially tutored in the language for many years. It is, in fact, his native tongue. But he apologizes. "I am not really so good in English because my education was interrupted. I should have gone on to Oxford but my father died prematurely. I had to stay home and start assuming control of some of the family interests."

Who's Who states that by the time Lal was thirty-six he was chairman of six companies (including electricity, wool, trade, banking); director of three (in manufacturing and farm products); guiding hand in a private high school, a public college and a religious movement;

chairman of his chamber of commerce, member of his city corporation and state legislator in Punjab.

The word Punjab is important. For when partition came Sohan Lal lost his wealth, his titles and his positions. He was a Hindu in Muslim Lahore, one of the great cities of Asia. His voice chokes when he speaks of Lahore.

"Finest city in India. One of the oldest. A superb center of civilization for more than two thousand years. The gateway to India. Now it's gone.

"I had to flee. I left everything behind. Printing presses. Woolen mills. All my life. But above all I had to leave Lahore."

How does he live now? He has set up a printing press in Delhi and some woolen mills in Bombay. His Delhi Press has been in the news recently, for from it Lal has issued a series of pamphlets written by himself which suggest to the government of India means whereby it could govern better. His first pronouncement dealt with the refugee problem. His second contained suggestions for a better foreign policy. And his third dealt with economics.

"I feel a citizen has an obligation to share with the government any ideas he might have. I take government seriously. I'm like a lot of Indians in that respect. I flee my homeland without a shirt but pretty soon I'm telling my new government how it ought to behave."

Lal himself behaves with extraordinary grace. I met him one night at the sedate and vaulted Gymkhana Club. To the strains of a military band he danced waltzes and polkas energetically with slim dark ladies in shimmering saris.

I shall never forget the Gymkhana Club. Once no Indian would have been allowed within its formal portals. A few subservient rajahs or chinless princes might have squeezed in but the white men would have resented them. Now with the white men gone, Indians control the club. Across its stately floor dance turbaned and bearded Sikhs, officers in bright uniform, handsome men in full dress and Sohan Lal in his bejeweled achkan.

Lal never looks better than when he wears this traditional suit: ankle-hugging white chudithar pajamas and black-silk tight-collared achkan. "It's a wonderful costume," he explains enthusiastically. "Very cool in hot weather. The cloth is so thin." You notice that instead of buttons or links he wears large rubies studded with diamonds. The effect is dazzling.

The dance continues and sprightly Mr. Lal insists that each lady dance with him at least once. And now you watch not this handsome little man but the graceful women of India as they go by in their diaphanous saris. It is an unforgettable delight to see a dimly lit room filled with beautiful women in flowing saris. For this must be one of the finest gowns ever devised, especially for waltzing.

At intermission Lal fans himself energetically—he never does anything halfway—and jumps up and down with pleasure when food is announced. He personally escorts three women to the table, fixes their silverware, talks with everyone and whispers, "I have three sons and two daughters. They'd love this dance."

To see Sohan Lal at his best, however, you must visit him at home. It is a modest apartment in one of Delhi's hotels near the Kashmiri Gate. "I'm re-establishing myself," Lal says brightly, jumping up to meet you. "In Lahore we had a fine home, I can tell you. Here it is work and starting a new life that is important."

His guests include members of the Turkish, Canadian, Burmese and French delegations to India. Lal says, "I like to have people from all over the world in my house. Listen to them talk!"

Then as if motivated by sheer joy he claps his hands and cries, "Now we give the Americans our specialty. They must guess what these are!" He brings a silver tray containing a biting sauce and a towering mound of little brown balls. With a swoosh he dips one into the sauce and pops it into your mouth. "What is it?" he demands. There is no clue except that the taste is delightful.

"Chicken shami kebabs," Lal cries. "Chopped chicken and special spices and flour made from a pulse which we call channa. Very tasty, yes?"

You try two more and he becomes impatient. "More, more! I always have eight or nine."

Then from the other side of the room someone asks about America and Lal stops clowning. "I've been there several times," he explains. "From New York to California and back. It's a fairyland. Even the magic lamp of Aladdin could not reproduce the wonders of America. The marvelous limits of human enterprise in material things have been reached there. To those of you who have not been to America I cannot do justice in general terms. But when I am in America I always think of India. Because Americans are very healthy. They enjoy many comforts. India and America must make strong efforts to remain friends, for we can learn from one another."

Then his irrepressible buoyancy takes over and he cries, "But what I liked best in America was that wonderful Waldorf-Astoria. Oh, what a heavenly place! You push a button and order anything you want. You push another button and the newspaper arrives. I was in the Waldorf-Astoria many times and never ate one meal except in bed. I thought, 'This is what people mean when they talk about living like an Indian rajah!' No rajah lives half as well."

There are other Indians who do not share Sohan Lal's enthusiasm for America. I recall a brilliant dinner party Lal gave when he introduced me to a group of his Lahore expatriates. He pointed at them laughing and joking. "You'd never think they were refugees! Ah, we Indians forget misery in a hurry."

One of his guests was a famous Indian editor. I had better call him Bahadur. He was extremely handsome and spectacularly brilliant in conversation. I had barely got into my chair when he let fly about the Korean war. How did any American justify such behavior? I started to explain but he was absolutely too much for me. He shotgunned me with facts, figures, fragments of American history and the latest scandal from Texas. It was an overwhelming performance and Lal whispered, "You think his manner of arguing too agressive?"

"No, I can take it. I'm interested in what such a man thinks."

"Perhaps this will explain him," Lal said. "He's been invited to visit Moscow. A special trip arranged for by the Russian Government."

Americans ought to know that men like Bahadur are common in Asia. Brilliantly educated, gifted in debate and politically alert, they feel no identification whatever with America. Having fought England all their lives they consider us merely an extension of their old enemy.

I read Bahadur's paper carefully and could find no apparent pro-Russian bias. True, it printed scare headlines about Negroes receiving injustice in America. True, it took a crack at us whenever our communiqués from Korea tallied up the newest number of Asian dead, but it was neither pro-Russian nor anti-American. It merely illustrated that classic Burmese phrase: "America or Russia? I couldn't care less!" But in the case of this brilliant leader, Russia is taking careful pains to get him to commit himself. When he returns from Russia he may have made up his mind.

Bahadur had to leave Sohan Lal's party early and a beautiful young woman at my side said, "He talks very well. But his ideas aren't always clear." Hers were particularly clear. She said, "All of us tonight are old Lahore people. We have all lost our old way of life. But now we have a nation we can call our own. That's worth whatever price we had to pay.

"When I was a girl my family had a summer home in Simla. It was lovely and cool in the hills but suddenly that home became an insult. For the English chose Simla as their summer capital. And we Indians were forbidden even to walk on certain streets."

The beautiful refugee makes no effort to hide her unforgiving bitterness. She turns to watch a well-behaved party of Englishmen rise and start to dance. "Look at them!" she whispers impishly. "Surely they are the most clumsy people on earth." Then she confides, "Don't you worry about what the editor said. If Americans will only avoid the mistakes of the English you will find India your lasting friend. Any time I see a white man in Delhi dance well or show courtesy or appear to be interested in India I know he's an American."

Another of Lal's guests has other ideas. He takes me to Parliament where I witness the finest, most dignified and intellectual governing body I have ever seen in action. It's been my good luck to watch most of the world's great parliamentary bodies—Congress, parliaments in Australia, Great Britain, France—but I have never seen one that surpasses the Indian for attention to business, brilliance of debate, responsibility to the nation, and average caliber of the membership.

The reason for its excellence is at the same time a castigation of its insecure foundations. For the Indian Parliament is appointive, as perforce it must be, since India is a vast oligarchy which for the present must appoint its senior officials. If the American Congress were made up of the 531 men and women best equipped to govern our land, it would be a pretty dazzling spectacle. But no appointive body is ever superior in ultimate political good. At best it is a stopgap until the people learn enough to elect their own officials. When this happens it is inevitable that some pots and crocks will get elected along with sagacious men. It is curious, therefore, that the Indian Parliament will be a better body when it includes a lesser breed of man thrown into office by the will of the people.

Lal's friend whispers, "You have observed, I'm sure, that our Parliament is based on English procedure.

India owes England an enormous debt. Our law is English. Our language. Our universities. Our medicine. Many Indians hate England for the wrongs she did us. But we must all acknowledge the good, too."

I spent about a week in Parliament listening to the birth cries of a new nation. It was an inspiring experience to hear Ambedkar cry that everyone wanted the Indian princes put in their places, but that there was in the world something larger than mere revenge. The spirit of law. And even if it was tempting to pass recriminatory legislation against the arrogant princes, it was better not to do so.

But it was terribly disturbing to hear Pandit Nehru address this Parliament. He spoke for forty minutes on the Kashmir problem, and although I followed each word he said, and although Parliament approved his arguments with a hurricane of banged desk tops, I did not comprehend a word of his reasoning. Nehru had pled law and justice when Hindu Hyderabad was forcibly taken into Pakistan by its chance Muslim ruler. Quite properly Nehru pointed out that this was a gross betrayal and he used arms to correct it. But when Kashmir, which is predominantly Muslim, was brought into India by a chance Hindu ruler, Nehru said that was all right. He argued that there was a higher law, but I could not understand his logic.

Sohan Lal prays for a peaceful solution to Indian-Pakistan relations. More than most he has suffered from the great troubles. He says, "All of us in India must work on our immediate problems. Our illiteracy is appalling. If we want to catch up with the world we must have more technical schools."

Of caste he says, "I am a Hindu and I understand the old bases for caste organization. It grew out of our belief in rebirth, which implies that at each successive birth the soul comes equipped with certain inherent mental abilities. Therefore each newborn individual is best able to perform certain jobs. This placed our caste system into a philosophical, metaphysical, social and religious framework. It was like the guild system in England or the specialization by family in Europe. But now the system is crumbling and outmoded.

"Mahatma Gandhi speeded its death by maintaining that so long as Hindu society was stratified no one could attain political maturity. I myself have long had the opinion that caste does not deserve to continue. Look at our Constitution. All distinctions of caste have been abolished. And great efforts are being made to bring the backward classes up to the level of the rest. Of course, the same thing is happening all over the world so we are merely part of a universal movement."

To be with Sohan Lal is a rare privilege. He is intelligent and charming. He owed me nothing yet he put his car and chauffeur at my disposal, he arranged meetings for me, he fed me, he answered some very prying questions, and he introduced me to his friends. He said he did these things because when he was in America, people had gone out of their way to help him.

Men like Sohan Lal know what is wrong with India. They recognize the immense poverty, the illiteracy, the oligarchy, the wrongs of partition and the scars of ancient social customs. But in his bouncing eager way Lal tries to do something about them.

Oh, yes. About everyone in India's being a crook. I crossed all of Asia with nine scattered pieces of luggage and never lost an item. But when I returned to America I found that thieves had completely ransacked my home.

The New Mem-sahibs

NOEL COWARD, who can be extremely cruel when in the mood, made the wry comment after meeting the British matrons of Singapore that now he understood why it was so difficult to hire upstairs maids in London.

I could not agree to this libel, for I found the matrons of Singapore both intelligent and attractive, and one night at the super-posh Tanglin Club I saw several who were downright beautiful.

But I would agree heartily with the French cavalry officer who said that in his lifetime only three things had really terrified him, a tiger in the Malay jungles, a cobra in Mysore and almost any Englishwoman in the tropics.

What happens to perfectly decent women after they live in India or Java or Malaya is impossible to explain. At home they were not the sort to lord it over servants, for most of them had none. Nor were they self-appointed paragons of social virtue, for many English towns have an enviable freedom in social relations. But once put them in the tropics, and these same gentle girls become unbearable.

It would be unreasonable to expect women suddenly surrounded by twenty servants, when they had none before, to retain their balance, and few do. Quickly they succumb to delusions of grandeur and consider it inevitable that white women should order about almost any of the 1,500,000,000 yellow and brown and

black men of Asia. As one French priest-sociologist
explained it, only the lowest-caste natives would hire
out as servants because the others bitterly resented
being kicked by white women.

It would also be unreasonable to expect that white
women in the tropics should remember much about
the democracy they knew at home. Almost alone and
submerged in an alien sea of strange colors, strange
foods and strange inhabitants, it is instinctive for
them to clutch at the silliest rules for protecting
their cherished social life. For real, archaic and oppres-
sive social patterns you have got to go to the tropics
and watch white societies protecting themselves from
brown.

But it is not unreasonable to demand that from now
on the mem-sahibs accept the citizens of Asia as human
beings or stop coming to Asia. Proud Indians and
Indonesians and Filipinos will no longer tolerate the
social nonsense of past generations, for they know that
the white man and his mem-sahib are no longer gods.

It must be quickly admitted that Englishwomen
were not the only offenders in establishing insufferable
social systems which ridiculed and insulted Asians. The
Dutch in Java were as bad. Australians in Rabaul were
worse. And although the French behave a little better,
they made up for it by excessively harsh economic
exploitation. All the Europeans were alike.

But it was reserved for the Englishwomen to lead
the pack. All across Asia you meet local citizens who
speak with venomous hatred of the British social system as it affected them. Today many Indians frankly
acknowledge the debt they owe to England, but they
add that the social persecutions they experienced in

English society were unbearable. Usually they place
the blame for this upon the women, holding that
Englishmen were often prepared to accept Asians as
human beings, but that their women would never
relent.

The desire for revenge that such behavior generated
in Asia is incalculable, yet it must be taken into con-
sideration when judging Asia's future. There is a memory of social ignominy that this crop of political leaders
will never forgive, and many of their actions are obviously motivated by a desire to prove that Asian
society will no longer accept white domination in any
particular.

Although Englishwomen were largely responsible for
the hateful policy of arrogant supremacy, it was left
to their men to express this policy in its most ridiculous form. A recent letter from such a gentleman has
had wide circulation in Asia, always to the accompaniment of hoots of ribald laughter. A last-gasp Englishman explains to the public how white people should
govern Asia. The letter was written, believe it or not,
in 1951.

"Psychological propaganda and an outward show of
authority are worth dozens of committee meetings.
Leading officials should wear colorful uniforms as often
as possible.

"When the High Commissioner leaves King's House
in his Rolls-Royce, fine example of the world's finest
motor car, he should be preceded and followed by
traffic police outriders on motorcycles.

"The traffic police all over town should be warned
of his journey and should control and direct traffic
accordingly to allow him free and swift passage.

"His convoy should be ostentatious so that people will know when it passes that it is the High Commissioner.

"All major officials should conduct themselves in the same way, so as to impress the population. A suitable uniform should also be designed for soldiers who are on leave, so that their presence will invariably be noted.

"Lesser officials should be officials. When the secretariat empties itself at tiffin time you cannot tell if the people coming out are officials or junior assistants in a commercial undertaking.

"Newspapers, too, should give prominent display to the photographs of highly respected citizens and accompany the photographs with suitable captions.

"High officials should also address the population frequently by radio to remind the country that it is being well governed."

Such a letter, accompanied by the mem-sahib point of view, represents such a discredited theory of colonial government as to be tragic in the light of today's events. One might grudgingly admit that in governing a totally ignorant and savage land such pompous nonsense might be necessary for a few decades. But the poison of such empty forms is that they remain as pleasant games long after their usefulness is past. And into the emptiness someone like Ho Chi Minh or Sukarno or Mao Tse-tung injects a real, life-size revolution.

Contrast this bankruptcy of ideas with what Russia offers Asian people today. Leadership of their own lands. Increased crops. More food. Ownership by local people of local industries. It is true that most of the Russian promises are not fulfilled, but when opposed to

Rolls-Royces and uniforms and police on motorcycles the Russian theory is going to win every time.

It is disturbing, therefore, to find that today in the first flush of America's world responsibilities, many American women fresh from two-room apartments have picked up the mem-sahib racket right where the Englishwomen left off. I have heard half a dozen American women sipping tea say, in self-pity, "If we Americans pulled out of here tomorrow, within six months these characters would be back in trees."

I am sure Englishwomen thought the same way right up to the minute they were being kicked out of one establishment after another. Surely the Dutchwomen were convinced that without them Java would collapse. And if Americans persist in such ideas, if they persist in playing the role of great white father and mem-sahib, our efforts to win Asia to our side are absolutely doomed.

All American firms sending employees to Asia, all governmental agencies having business there, and all friends seeing vacationists off should see to it that the women who go along are given a pamphlet explaining what happened to the English and Dutch and French and Australian societies that were built upon the tacit assumption that all people who are not white are feeble-minded.

There is much that is wrong with Asia. Some things are terribly wrong. And by and large sensible Asians want our help in correcting them. But they will not tolerate our ridicule.

It is good, therefore, to remark that in numerous instances white women have done great things in creating friendly respect between Americans and

Asians. I think they have done a better job, sometimes, than their husbands, and it is such women who should represent America.

This is terribly important because Red China and Communist Russia are sending extremely powerful and impressive women to other parts of Asia. The results are impressive, for they are undoing the damages done by the mem-sahib. We must not leave the field of social victories entirely to the enemy. Let some other nation become the new mem-sahibs. Let us be the nation of democratic equality.

The Sheik's Women

THE word *sheik* has been so misused that I am going to describe Sheik Sadiq Hasan with unusual care. He is a distinguished-looking man in his mid-fifties, about five feet six, of slight build and military carriage. His hair is graying and he covers it with an expensive caracul Jinnah cap, named after the founder of his native Pakistan.

Sheik Hasan wears Muslim clothes, a trim long coat with stiff buttoned collar. His white cotton trousers fit snugly about the ankles but bag enormously at the knees so that they appear to be a skirt. English shoes complete the outfit.

Hasan's face is unforgettable. His nose is big and sharp. His lips are finely drawn and his mustache is closely clipped. His eyes are the distinguishing characteristic of his face. Normally they are cold and competent, yet they often light up with sparkling fun when something witty is said. He has a habit of fixing you with his eyes, so that you see they are dark brown rimmed with blue.

His very good English is marked by two phrases which he uses almost as punctuation marks. "Well, you see . . ." and "I may say . . . ."

In addition to English the sheik speaks Urdu, Hindustani, Kashmiri and Persian. He tells you, in his clipped way, that like the sheiks of fiction he has just

ridden in from the desert. On a stallion shod with fire?
No, in a jeep.

But nothing Sheik Hasan says is quite so surprising
as his offhand remark that he has been to New York
seven times. Before partition he lived in Hindu India,
where he owned five choice carpet factories. His entire
product was sold to a swanky New York store and he
handled the contracts. Hasan says he liked New York.

"But I won't be going there again. When partition
came I stuck by my Muslim religion. My five factories
were lost, my family fortune, and even my clothes.

"I was wealthy in the old days, for we made the
finest Kashmiri carpets, but now I get along with a
small income. I don't weep about my losses. For Pakistan to have been born as a Muslim state is worth whatever we have had to suffer. I've forgotten my other
days and gone to work. I was economic adviser to the
government and a member of Parliament. I've helped
start a college and I serve on a high-school board. I've
also launched an orphanage. I keep busy.

"My reward is to see Pakistan flourishing. I may say
we're a surplus state in everything. Very rich. Very
promising."

He laughs and this is a good time to ask him what a
sheik really is. "A sheik? To tell you the truth, I don't
know. I'm one. But the man who sweeps my gutter is,
too. I think it was an old honorary title, but now
everyone uses it. If you wanted to, you could be a
sheik, too."

But there is one thing about which Sheik Sadiq
Hasan never jokes. He spends most of his time now
trying to find the thousands of women who were

abducted during the riots and who are now kept as brothel slaves in remote districts.

"Americans don't understand the terrible things that accompanied the birth of Pakistan. More than 500,000 people were massacred. Hundreds of trains were ambushed by maniacs with swords and guns. More than 12,000,000 people became refugees.

"I may say that no part of this terror was worse than the way women were abducted. Gangs of men would swoop down on refugee trains, shoot the men and drag away the young women. I may say most of the girls were used for immoral purposes and now live hidden away in dark cellars, absolute slaves. I may say there were thousands of them, many thousands. On both sides.

"Four years have now passed and most of these girls are still held in slavery. There was a girl we found in Pakistan. She refused our efforts of help. Refused to go home. I may say she was afraid her family would revile her. Almost no girl wants to go home, and they'll hide from the committee. But I talked with her and sent her back to India. Her family was blessed when she returned. She sent word that she had never been so happy and that life was starting over again.

"Not all stories end so well. We track down some girls who have been so tortured and misused that they cannot remember home. We can't make them go back.

"I've been working on this problem for three years. It is a blot on the reputation of both Pakistan and India that these girls have not been exchanged. I don't insist upon this for the sake of good government, however. I don't even do the work for the sake of the girls,

I insist upon it for what the Muslim calls God and the Hindu, Kharma. God would will that strong nations do the right thing.

"Four tasks remain. First, every girl must be returned or the man holding her must be jailed. Second, police must be given extraordinary powers and bonuses for recovering these girls. Third, we must double or treble the number of hired searchers. Fourth, as a gesture of humility let Pandit Nehru himself seek out one of the slaves held in India. Let Liaquat Ali Khan do the same and let there be a ceremonial exchange to symbolize how ashamed of ourselves we are."

Sheik Hasan, with the aid of his committee, has already located 7,175 Hindu girls in Pakistan, while the Indian Government has returned 14,070. But on one point Hasan grows violently angry. Indian newspapers claim that every one of the two thousand Pakistani Army officers has a Hindu girl locked up in his barracks.

"By heaven, if a single such case is brought to my attention I'll haunt that man out of Pakistan. I'll ruin his honor and destroy his reputation. I may say that I've investigated this charge and up to now have not found it to be true."

When his anger subsides Sheik Hasan asks that one point be made clear. "Pakistan and India broke away from one another with the greatest violence. I may say the tragedies of partition will never even be recorded in our generation. But today the two countries have forgotten the terror and look forward to years of friendship. You might ask how two countries can forget 500,000 murders. We have to forget. That's why, when I go to India today, I move about without police escorts. I get hearty co-operation from the Indian Government. On this small problem of enslaved women we've been able to co-operate. That's why I have hope for the future."

THE
BRIDGES
AT
TOKO-RI

Sea

THE sea was bitter cold. From the vast empty plains of Siberia howling winds roared down to lash the mountains of Korea, where American soldiers lost on patrol froze into stiff and awkward forms. Then with furious intensity the arctic wind swept out to sea, freezing even the salt spray that leaped into the air from crests of falling waves.

Through these turbulent seas, not far from the trenches of Korea, plowed a considerable formation of American warships. A battleship and two cruisers, accompanied by fourteen destroyers to shield against Russian submarines, held steady course as their icy decks rose and fell and shivered in the gale. They were the ships of Task Force 77 and they had been sent to destroy the communist-held bridges at Toko-ri.

Toward the center of this powerful assembly rode two fast carriers, the cause of the task force and its mighty arm. Their massive decks pitched at crazy angles, which for the present made take-offs or landings impossible. Their planes stood useless, huddled together in the wind, lashed down by steel cables.

It was strange, and in some perverse way resolutely American, that these two carriers wallowing in the dusk bore names which memorialized not stirring victories but humiliating defeats, as if by thus publishing her indifference to catastrophe and her willingness to

surmount it, the United States were defying her enemies. To the east, and farther out to sea, rode the
Hornet, whose predecessor of that name had absorbed
a multitude of Japanese bombs and torpedoes, going
down off Guadalacanal, while the inboard carrier, the
Savo, would forever remind the Navy of its most
shameful defeat in history, when four cruisers sank
helpless at Savo Island, caught sleeping by the auda-
cious Japanese.

Now, as night approached the freezing task force,
the bull horn on the *Savo* rasped out, "Prepare to
launch aircraft!" And it was obvious from the way her
deck was arranged that the carrier already had some
planes in the skies over Korea, and every man who
watched the heaving sea wondered how those planes
could possibly get back aboard.

The bull horn, ignoring such problems, roared, "Prepare to launch helicopter!" and although the deck
pitched in abandon, rotors began to turn, slowly at
first and then with lumbering speed.

Now the great carrier struck a sea trough and slid
away, her deck lurching, but relentlessly the bull horn
cried, "Move jets into position for launching," and the
catapult crew, fighting for footing on the sliding deck,
sprang swiftly into action, inching two heavy Banshees
onto the catapults, taking painful care not to allow
the jets to get rolling, lest they plunge overboard with
some sudden shifting of the deck.

"Start jet engines," roared the insistent bull horn.

The doctor, who had to be on deck in case of crash,
looked at the heaving sea and yelled to the crane oper-
ator, "They may launch these jets, but they'll never
get 'em back aboard."

The craneman looked down from his giant machine, which could lift a burning plane and toss it into the sea, and shouted, "Maybe they're planning to spend the night at some air force field in Korea. Along with the ones that are already up."

But at this instant all ships of the task force swung in tight circles and headed away from the open sea, straight for the nearby cliffs of Korea, and when the turn was completed, the deck of the *Savo* mysteriously stabilized. The effects of wind and sea neutralized each other, and planes returning from the bombardment of Korea now had a safe place to land.

But before they could do so the bull horn cried eerily into the dusk, "Launch helicopter!" and the crazy bird, its two rotors spinning so slowly the blades could be seen, stumbled into the air, and the horn cried, "Launch jets!"

Then, as the great carrier rode serenely amid the storms, the catapult officer whirled one finger above his head and a tremendous, almost unbearable roar arose and twin blasts of heat leaped from each Banshee, burning the icy air more than a hundred feet aft. Now the officer whirled two fingers and the roar increased and white heat scorched the deck of the carrier and the twin engines whipped to a meaningless speed of 13,000 revolutions a minute and the Banshee pilot, forcing his head back against a cushion, saluted and the catapult officer's right hand whipped down and the catapult fired.

Nine tons of jet aircraft were swept down the deck at a speed of more than 135 miles an hour. Within less than 150 feet the immense Banshee was airborne, and by the time it reached the forward edge of the carrier, it was headed toward its mission. Four times the catapults fired and four times heavy jets leaped into the darkening sky and headed for the coastline of Korea.

As soon as they had left, the bull horn wailed, "Respot planes. On the double. We must recover the Korea jets immediately."

When this announcement was made thirty old-fashioned propeller planes were already lashed down on the after part of the flight deck in precisely that area needed for landing the jets which now appeared overhead. The prop planes had been stowed there to permit catapult take-offs, and now they must be moved forward. So on the wooden deck, swept by icy winds, hundreds of young men in varicolored uniforms sped to the task of clearing the landing space. Men in green stowed the catapult gear so that no remnant of the powerful machine was visible. Other men in yellow leaped upon the deck and began to indicate the course each plane must follow on its way to forward stowage. Dozens of tough young men in blue leaned their shoulders against the planes, swung them laboriously into position and pushed them slowly into the biting wind. In blazing red uniforms other men checked guns or fueled empty craft while plane captains in brown sat in cockpits and worked the brakes to prevent accident. Darting about through the milling, pushing, shouting deck hands three-wheeled jeeps of vivid yellow and lumbering tractors in somber gray hurried to their jobs, while over all towered the mighty arms of the enormous black and sinister crane. Behind it lurked two weird men in fantastic suits of ashen gray asbestos, their faces peering from huge glassine boxes, ready to save the pilot if a crashed plane should burn, while in back of them, clothed in snowy white, the doctor waited, for death was always close upon the carrier deck.

So in an age of flight, in the jet age of incredible speed, these men pushed and pulled and slipped upon the icy deck and ordered the heavy planes with their bare hands. Upon trailing edges burdened with ice they pushed, their faces open to the freezing wind, their eyes heavy with frozen salt and the knuckles of their hands covered long since with protecting scars. And as they moved, their bright colors formed the pattern of a dance and after they had swarmed upon the deck for some minutes the *Savo* was transformed and from the lowering shadows the jets prepared to land.

This intricate operation was guided by one man. From the admiral's country he had directed the task force to run toward the communist coast. The last four jets had been dispatched at his command. He had placed the ships so that the operations of one would not trespass the allotted space of the other, and it was his responsibility to see that his carriers faced the wind in such position that smoke trailed off to one side rather than directly aft and into the faces of incoming pilots. Now he stood upon his bridge and watched the mountains of Korea moving perilously close.

Admiral George Tarrant was a tall narrow man with a sharp face that was sour and withdrawing like those of his Maine ancestors. Battle-wizened, he had fought the Japanese with his own carrier at Saipan, at Iwo Jima and at Okinawa, where his austere and lonely presence had brought almost as much terror to his own fliers as it had to the enemy.

He was known through the Navy as George the Tyrant, and any aviator who wanted to fetch a big laugh would grab a saucer in his left hand, a coffee cup in his right, lean back in his chair and survey the audience sourly, snorting, "Rubbish." Then the mimic would stare piercingly at some one pilot, jab the coffee cup at him and growl, "You, son. What do you think?"

But men who served with Tarrant soon forgot his tyranny and remembered his fantastic skill in operating a task force. His men said flatly, "He can do it better than anyone else in the world." He knew the motion of the sea and could estimate whether a morning swell would rise to prevent recovery of afternoon planes or subside so that even jets could land freely. He was able to guess when new gales of bitter Siberian air would rush the line of snowstorms out to sea and when the snow would come creeping softly back and throw a blizzard about the task force as it slept at night. And he had a most curious ability to foresee what might trouble the tin-can sailors serving in the remote destroyers.

He fought upon the surface of the sea and in the sky. He sent his planes inland to support ground troops or far out to sea to spot Russian submarines. His was the most complex combat command of which one man's mind was capable and on him alone depended decisions of the gravest moment.

For example, the position he was now in, with mountains closing down upon him, was his responsibility. Early that morning his aerologist had warned, "Wind's coming up, sir. You might run out of ocean by late afternoon."

He studied the charts and growled, "We'll make it."

Now his navigator warned, "We can't hold this course more than sixteen minutes, sir." The young officer looked at the looming coastline as if to add, "After that we'll have to turn back and abandon the planes."

"We'll make it," Tarrant grumbled as his ships plowed resolutely on toward the crucial hundred fathom curve which he dare not penetrate for fear of shoals, mines and submarines. But he turned his back upon this problem, for he could do nothing about it now. Instead, he checked to be sure the *Savo's* deck was ready and in doing so he saw something which reassured him. Far aft, standing upon a tiny platform that jutted out over the side of the carrier, stood a hulking giant, muffled in fur and holding two landing-signal paddles in his huge hands. It was Beer Barrel, and if any man could bring jets surely and swiftly home, it was Beer Barrel.

He was an enormous man, six feet three, more than 250 pounds, and his heavy suit, stitched with strips of fluorescent cloth to make his arms and legs easier to read, added to his bulk. He was a farmer from Texas who before the perilous days of 1943 had never seen the ocean, but he possessed a fabulous ability to sense the motion of the sea and what position the carrier deck would take. He could judge the speed of jets as they whirled down upon him, but most of all he could imagine himself in the cockpit of every incoming plane and he seemed to know what tired and jittery pilots would do next and he saved their lives. He was a fearfully bad naval officer and in some ways a disgrace to his uniform, but everyone felt better when he came aboard a carrier, for he could do one thing. He could land planes.

He could reach out with his great hands and bring them safely home the way falconers used to bring back birds they loved. In the Pentagon they knew he broke rules and smuggled beer aboard each ship he served upon. Carrier captains knew it, and even Admiral Tarrant, who was a terror on Navy rules, looked the other way when Beer Barrel staggered back after each drunken liberty, lugging his two ridiculous golf bags. The huge Texan had never once played golf and the two clubs sticking out were dummies. Once a deck hand, fearful that drunken Beer Barrel might slide back down the gangplank, had grabbed one of the outsize golf bags to help, but the surprising weight of it had crumpled him to the deck. Beer Barrel, barely able to heft the bag himself, had got it onto his massive shoulder, whispering beerily to the boy, "Thanks, Junior, but this is man's work." And he had carried the bags full of beer into his quarters.

For he believed that if he had a can of cold beer in his belly it formed a kind of gyroscope which made him unusually sensitive to the sea and that when this beer sloshed about it harmonized with the elements and he became one with the sea and the sky and the heaving deck and the heart of the incoming pilot.

"Land jets!" moaned the bull horn.

"Let's hear the checks," Beer Barrel said to his spotters, staring aft to catch the first jet as it made its 180° turn for the cross leg and the sharp final turn into the landing run. Now the jet appeared and Beer Barrel thought, "They're always pretty comin' home at night."

"All down!" the first watcher cried as he checked the wheels, the flaps and the stout hook which now dangled lower than the wheels.

"All down," Beer Barrel echoed unemotionally.

"Clear deck!" the second watcher shouted as he checked the nylon barriers and the thirteen heavy steel wires riding a few inches off the deck, waiting to engage the hook.

"Clear deck," Beer Barrel grunted phlegmatically.

He extended his paddles out sideways from his shoulders, standing like an imperturbable rock, and willed the plane onto the deck. "Come on, Junior," he growled. "Keep your nose up so's your hook'll catch. Good boy!" Satisfied that all was well, he snapped his right paddle dramatically across his heart and dropped his left arm as if it had been severed clean away from his body. Instantly the jet pilot cut his flaming speed and slammed his Banshee onto the deck. With violent grasp the protruding hook engaged one of the slightly elevated wires and dragged the massive plane to a shuddering stop.

Beer Barrel, watching from his platform, called to the clerk who kept records on each plane, "1593. Junior done real good. Number three wire." Never did Beer Barrel feel so content, not even when guzzling lager, as when one of his boys caught number three wire. "Heaven," he explained once, "is where everybody gets number three wire. Hell is where they fly wrong and catch number thirteen and crash into the barrier and burn. And every one of you's goin' straight to hell if you don't follow me better."

From his own bridge, Admiral Tarrant watched the jets come home. In his life he had seen many fine and

stirring things: his wife at the altar, Japanese battle-
ships going down, ducks rising from Virginia marshes
and his sons in uniform. But nothing he knew sur-
passed the sight of Beer Barrel bringing home the jets
at dusk.

There always came that exquisite moment of human judgment when one man—a man standing alone
on the remotest corner of the ship, lashed by foul
wind and storm—had to decide that the jet roaring
down upon him could make it. This solitary man had
to judge the speed and height and the pitching of the
deck and the wallowing of the sea and the oddities of
this particular pilot and those additional imponder-
ables that no man can explain. Then, at the last
screaming second he had to make his decision and
flash it to the pilot. He had only two choices. He
could land the plane and risk the life of the pilot and
the plane and the ship if he had judged wrong. Or he
could wave-off and delay his decision until next time
around. But he could defer his job to no one. It was
his, and if he did judge wrong, carnage on the carrier
deck could be fearful. That was why Admiral Tarrant
never bothered about the bags of beer.

On they came, the slim and beautiful jets. As they
roared upwind the admiral could see their stacks flaming. When they made their far turn and roared down-
wind he could see the pilots as human beings, tensed
up and ready for the landing that was never twice the
same. Finally, when these mighty jets hit the deck
they weighed well over seven tons and their speed
exceeded 135 miles an hour, yet within 120 feet they
were completely stopped and this miracle was accomplished in several ways. First, Tarrant kept his carriers

headed into the wind, which on this day stormed in at nearly 40 miles an hour, which cut the plane's relative speed to about 95 miles. Then, too, the carrier was running away from the plane at 11 miles an hour, which further cut the plane's speed to 84, and it was this actual speed that the wires had to arrest. They did so with brutal strength, but should they miss, two slim nylon barriers waited to drag the plane onto the deck and chop its impetus, halting it so that it could not proceed forward to damage other planes. And finally, should a runaway jet miss both the wires and the barriers, it would plunge into a stout nylon barricade which would entwine itself about the wings and wheels and tear the jet apart as if it were a helpless insect.

But it was Beer Barrel's job to see that the barriers and the barricade were not needed and he would shout curses at his pilots and cry, "Don't fly the deck, Junior. Don't fly the sea. Fly me." An air force colonel watching Beer Barrel land jets exclaimed, "Why, it isn't a landing at all! It's a controlled crash." And the big Texan replied in his beery voice, "Difference is that when I crash 'em they're safe in the arms of God."

Now he brought in three more, swiftly and surely, and Admiral Tarrant, watching the looming mountains of Korea as they moved in upon his ships, muttered, "Well, we'll make it again."

But as he said these words his squawk box sounded, and from deep within the *Savo* the combat intelligence director reported coolly, "1591 has been hit. Serious damage. May have to ditch."

"What's his position?"

"Thirty-five miles away."

"Who's with him?"

"His wingman, 1592."

"Direct him to come on in and attempt landing."

The squawk box clicked off and Admiral Tarrant looked straight ahead at the looming coast. Long ago he had learned never to panic, but he had trained himself to look at situations in their gloomiest aspects so as to be prepared for ill turns of luck. "If this jet limps in we may have to hold this course for ten or fifteen more minutes. Well, we probably can do it."

He studied the radar screen to estimate his probable position in fifteen minutes. "Too close," he muttered. Then into the squawk box which led to the air officer of the *Savo* he said, "Recovery operations must end in ten minutes. Get all planes aboard."

"The admiral knows there's one in trouble?"

"Yes. I've ordered him to try to land."

"Yes, sir."

The bull horn sounded. "All hands. We must stop operations within ten minutes. Get those barriers cleared faster. Bring the planes in faster."

The telephone talker at the landing platform told Beer Barrel, "We got to get 'em all aboard in ten minutes."

"What's a matter?" Beer Barrel growled. "Admiral running hisself out of ocean?"

"Looks like it," the talker said.

"You tell him to get the planes up here and I'll get 'em aboard."

So the nineteen dark ships of the task force sped on toward the coastline and suddenly the squawk box rasped, "Admiral, 1591 says he will have to ditch."

"Can he ditch near the destroyers?"

"Negative."

"Is his wingman still with him?"

"Affirmative."

"How much fuel?"

"Six hundred pounds."

"Have you a fix on their positions?"

"Affirmative."

"Dispatch helicopter and tell wingman to land immediately."

There was a long silence and the voice said, "Wingman 1592 requests permission stay with downed plane till copter arrives."

The admiral was now faced with a decision no man should have to make. If the wingman stayed on, he would surely run out of fuel and lose his own plane and probably his life as well. But to command him to leave a downed companion was inhuman and any pilot aboard the *Savo* would prefer to risk his own life and his plane rather than to leave a man adrift in the freezing sea before the helicopter had spotted him.

For in the seas off Korea a downed airman had twenty minutes to live. That was all. The water was so bitterly cold that within five minutes the hands were frozen and the face. In twelve minutes of immersion in these fearful waters the arms became unable to function and by the twentieth minute the pilot was frozen to death.

The decision could not be deferred, for the squawk box repeated, "Wingman 1592 requests permission to stay."

The admiral asked, "What is the absolute minimum of gas with which the wingman can make a straight-in landing?"

There was a moment's computation. "Assuming he finds the carrier promptly, about four hundred pounds."

"Tell him to stay with the downed man . . ."

The voice interrupted, "Admiral, 1591 has just ditched. Wingman says the plane sank immediately."

There was a moment's silence and the admiral asked, "Where's the helicopter?"

"About three more minutes away from the ditching."

"Advise the helicopter . . ."

"Admiral, the wingman reports downed pilot afloat."

"Tell the wingman to orbit until helicopter arrives. Then back for a straight-in landing."

The bull horn echoed in the gathering dusk and mournful sounds spread over the flight deck, speaking of disaster. "Get those last two jets down immediately. Then prepare for emergency straight-in landing. A plane has been lost at sea. Wingman coming in short of fuel."

For a moment the many-colored figures stopped their furious motions. The frozen hands stopped pushing jets and the yellow jeeps stayed where they were. No matter how often you heard the news it always stopped you. No matter how frozen your face was, the bull horn made you a little bit colder. And far out to sea, in a buffeted helicopter, two enlisted men were coldest of all.

At the controls was Mike Forney, a tough twenty-seven-year-old Irishman from Chicago. In a Navy where enlisted men hadn't much chance of flying, Mike had made it. He had bullied his way through to flight school and his arrival aboard his first ship, the

Savo, would be remembered as long as the ship stayed afloat. It was March 17 when he flew his copter onto the flight deck, wearing an opera hat painted green, a Baron von Richthofen scarf of kelly green, and a clay pipe jammed into his big teeth. He had his earphones wrapped around the back of his neck and when the captain of the *Savo* started to chew him out Forney said, "When I appear anywhere I want the regular pilots to know it, because if they listen to me, I'll save 'em." Now, as he sped toward the ditched pilot, he was wearing his green stovepipe and his World War I kelly-green scarf, for he had found that when those astonishing symbols appeared at a scene of catastrophe everyone relaxed, and he had already saved three pilots.

But the man flying directly behind Mike Forney's hat wasn't relaxed. Nestor Gamidge, in charge of the actual rescue gear, was a sad-faced inconsequential young man from Kentucky, where his unmarried schoolteacher mother had named him Nestor after the wisest man in history, hoping that he would justify everything. But Nestor had not lived up to his name and was in fact rather stupid, yet, as the copter flew low over the bitter waves to find the ditched plane, he was bright enough to know that if anyone were to save the airman pitching about in the freezing water below it would be he. In this spot the admiral didn't count nor the wingman who was orbiting upstairs nor even Mike Forney. In a few minutes he would lean out of the helicopter and lower a steel hoisting sling for the pilot to climb into. But from cold experience he knew that the man below would probably be too fro-

zen even to lift his arms, so he, Nestor Gamidge, who
hated the sea and who was dragged into the Navy by
his draft board, would have to jump into the icy waves
and try to shove the inert body of the pilot into the
sling. And if he failed—if his own hands froze before
he could accomplish this—the pilot must die. That's
why they gave Nestor the job. He was dumb and he
was undersized but he was strong.

"I see him," Nestor said.

Mike immediately called to the wingman: "1592.
Go on home. This is Mike Forney and everything's
under control."

"Mike!" the wingman called. "Save that guy."

"We always save 'em. Scram."

"That guy down there is Harry Brubaker. The one
whose wife and kids are waiting for him in Yokosuka.
But he don't know it. Save him!"

Mike said to Nestor, "You hear that? He's the one
whose wife and kids came out to surprise him."

"He looks froze," Nestor said, lowering the sling.

Suddenly Mike's voice lost its brashness. "Nestor,"
he said quietly, "If you have to jump in . . . I'll stay
here till the other copter gets you."

In dismay, Nestor watched the sling drift past the
downed pilot and saw that the man was too frozen to
catch hold. So he hauled the sling back up and said,
"I'll have to go down."

Voluntarily, he fastened the sling about him and
dropped into the icy waves.

"Am I glad to see you!" the pilot cried.

"He's OK," Nestor signaled.

"Lash him in," Mike signaled back.

"Is that Mike? With the green hat?"

"Yep."

"My hands won't . . ."

They tried four times to do so simple a thing as force the sling down over the pilot's head and arms but the enormous weight of watersoaked clothing made him an inert lump. There was a sickening moment when Nestor thought he might fail. Then, with desperate effort, he jammed his right foot into the pilot's back and shoved. The sling caught.

Nestor lashed it fast and signaled Mike to haul away. Slowly the pilot was pulled clear of the clutching sea and was borne aloft. Nestor, wallowing below, thought, "There goes another."

Then he was alone. On the bosom of the great sea he was alone and unless the second helicopter arrived immediately, he would die. Already, overpowering cold tore at the seams of his clothing and crept in to get him. He could feel it numb his powerful hands and attack his strong legs. It was the engulfing sea, the icy and deadly sea that he despised and he was deep into it and his arms were growing heavy.

Then, out of the gathering darkness, came the *Hornet's* copter.

So Mike called the *Savo* and reported, "Two copters comin' home with two frozen mackerel."

"What was that?" the *Savo* asked gruffly.

"What I said," Mike replied, and the two whirly birds headed from home, each dangling below it the freezing body of a man too stiff to crawl inside.

Meanwhile Admiral Tarrant was faced with a new problem. The downed pilot had been rescued but the incoming wingman had fuel sufficient for only one pass, and if that pass were waved off the pilot would have to crash land into the sea and hope for a destroyer pickup, unless one of the copters could find him in the gathering dusk.

But far more important than the fate of one Banshee were the nineteen ships of the task force which were now closing the hundred fathom mark. For them to proceed farther would be to invite the most serious trouble. Therefore the admiral judged that he had at most two minutes more on course, after which he would be forced to run with the wind, and then no jet could land, for the combined speed of jet and wind would be more than 175 miles, which would tear out any landing hook and probably the barriers as well. But the same motive that had impelled the wingman to stay at the scene of the crash, the motive that forced Nestor Gamidge to plunge into the icy sea, was at work upon the admiral and he said, "We'll hold the wind a little longer. Move a little closer to shore."

Nevertheless, he directed the four destroyers on the forward edge of the screen to turn back toward the open sea, and he checked them on the radar as they moved off. For the life of one pilot he was willing to gamble his command that there were no mines and that Russia had no submarines lurking between him and the shore.

"1592 approaching," the squawk box rasped.

"Warn him to come straight in."

Outside the bull horn growled, "Prepare to land last jet, straight in."

Now it was the lead cruiser's turn to leave the formation but the *Savo* rode solemnly on, lingering to catch this last plane. On the landing platform Beer Barrel's watcher cried, "Hook down, wheels down. Can't see flaps."

The telephone talker shouted, "Pilot reports his flaps down."

"All down," Beer Barrel droned.

"Clear deck!"

"Clear deck."

Now even the carrier *Hornet* turned away from the hundred fathom line and steamed parallel to it while the jet bore in low across her path. Beer Barrel, on his wooden platform, watched it come straight and low and slowing down.

"Don't watch the sea, Junior," he chanted. "Watch me. Hit me in the kisser with your left wing tank and you'll be all right, Junior." His massive arms were outstretched with the paddles parallel to the deck and the jet screamed in, trying to adjust its altitude to the shifting carrier's.

"Don't fly the deck, Junior!" roared Beer Barrel and for one fearful instant it looked as if the onrushing jet had put itself too high. In that millionth of a second Beer Barrel thought he would have to wave the plane off but then his judgment cried that there was a chance the plane could make it. So Beer Barrel shouted, "Keep comin', Junior!" and at the last moment he whipped the right paddle across his heart and dropped the left.

The plane was indeed high and for one devastating moment seemed to be floating down the deck and into the parked jets. Then, when a crash seemed inevitable, it settled fast and caught number nine. The jet screamed ahead and finally stopped with its slim nose peering into the webs of the barrier.

"You fly real good, Junior," Beer Barrel said, tucking the paddles under his arm, but when the pilot climbed down his face was ashen and he shouted, "They rescue Brubaker?"

"They got him."

The pilot seemed to slump and his plane captain ran up and caught him by the arm and led him to the ladder, but as they reached for the first step they stumbled and pitched forward, so swift was the *Savo's* groaning turn back out to sea.

As soon as the copters appeared with little Gamidge and the unconscious body of the pilot dangling through the icy air, Admiral Tarrant sent his personal aide down to sick bay to tell the helicopter men he would like to see them after the flight doctor had taken care of them. In a few minutes they arrived in flag plot, Forney in trim aviator's flight jacket and Gamidge in a fatigue suit some sizes too large.

The admiral poured them coffee and said, "Sit down." Forney grabbed the comfortable corner of the leather davenport on which the admiral slept when he did not wish to leave this darkened room of radar screens, repeating compasses and charts, but Gamidge fumbled about until the admiral indicated where he was to sit. Pointing at the squat Kentuckian with his coffee cup, the admiral said, "It must have been cold in the water."

"It was!" Forney assured him. "Bitter."

"I hope the doctor gave you something to warm you up."

"Nestor's too young to drink," Forney said, "but I had some."

"You weren't in the water."

"No, sir, but I had the canopy open."

"How's the pilot?"

"When me and Gamidge go out for them we bring them back in good shape."

"They tell me he wasn't able to climb into the sling."

"That pilot was a real man, sir. Couldn't move his hands or arms but he never whimpered."

"Because he fainted," Nestor explained.

The admiral invariably insisted upon interviewing all men who did outstanding work and now he pointed his cup at Gamidge again. "Son, do you know any way we could improve the rescue sling?"

The little Kentuckian thought a long time and then said slowly, "Nope. If their hands freeze somebody's got to go into the water to get them."

The admiral put his cup down and said brusquely, "Keep bringing them back. Navy's proud of men like you."

"Yes, sir!" Forney said. He always pronounced *sir* with an insinuating leer, as if he wished to put commissioned officers at ease. Then he added, "There is one thing we could do to make the chopper better."

"What's that?"

"I got to operate that sling quicker. Because it seems like Nestor goes into the sea almost every time."

"You know what changes to make?"

"Yes, sir."

"Then make them."

The two enlisted men thanked the admiral and as

they went down the ladder Tarrant heard Forney ask, "Nestor, why'd you stand there with your mouth shut, like a moron? Suppose he is a mean old bastard. No reason to be scared of him."

"By the way," the admiral called. "Who was the pilot?"

"Brubaker, sir," Forney cried, unabashed.

The name struck Tarrant with visible force. He backed into the darkened flag plot and steadied himself for a moment. "Brubaker!" he repeated quietly. "How strange that it should have been Brubaker!"

Shaken, he slumped onto the leather davenport and reached for some papers which had been delivered aboard ship by dispatch plane that afternoon. "Brubaker!" He scanned the papers and called sick bay.

"Doctor," he asked, "any chance I could talk with Brubaker?"

A crisp voice snapped back, "Admiral, you know the man's suffered exposure."

"I know that, but there's an urgent matter and I thought that when he found himself in good shape . . ." He left it at that.

Then he thought of Brubaker, a twenty-nine-year-old civilian who had been called back into service against his will. At the start of the cruise he had been something of a problem, griping ceaselessly about the raw deal the Navy had given him, but gradually he had become one of the two or three finest pilots. He still griped, he still damned the Navy, but he did his job. The admiral respected men like that.

But Brubaker had a special significance, for on recent cruises Admiral Tarrant had adopted the trick of selecting some young man of about the age and rank his older son would have attained had the Japs not shot him down while he was trying to launch a Navy fighter plane on the morning of Pearl Harbor. Tarrant found satisfaction in watching the behavior of such pilots, for they added meaning to his otherwise lonely life. But in the case of Harry Brubaker the trick had come close to reality. The Banshee pilot had the quick temper of his sons, the abiding resentments, the courage.

Admiral Tarrant therefore desperately wanted to leave flag plot and go down into the ship and talk with Brubaker, but custom of the sea forbade this, for the captain of any ship must be supreme upon that ship, and even the flag admiral who chances to make his quarters aboard is a guest. So Admiral Tarrant was cooped up in flag plot, a tiny bedroom and a special bridge reserved for his use. That was his country and there he must stay.

There was a knock upon the door and the aide said, "Sir, it's Brubaker!"

The good-looking young man who stuck his head in was obviously a civilian. He wore two big bathrobes and heavy woolen socks but even if he had worn dress uniform he would have been a civilian. He was a little overweight, his hair was a bit too long and he wasn't scared enough of the admiral. Indelibly, he was a young lawyer from Denver, Colorado, and the quicker he got out of the Navy and back into a courtroom, the happier he'd be.

"You can scram now," he told the medical corpsman who had brought him up to the admiral's country.

"Come in, Brubaker," the admiral said stiffly. "Cup of coffee?" As he reached for the cup Brubaker didn't exactly stand at attention but the admiral said quickly, "Sit down, son. How's the Banshee take the water?"

"All right, if you fly her in."

"You keep the tail down?"

"I tried to. But as you approach the water every inclination is to land nose first. Then from way back in the past I remembered an October night when our family was burning leaves and at the end my mother pitched a bucket of water on the bonfire. I can still recall the ugly smell. Came back to me tonight. I said, 'If I let water get into the engines I'll smell it again.' So I edged the plane lower and lower. Kept the engines up and the tail way down. When the nose finally hit I was nearly stopped. But I was right. There was that same ugly smell."

"How was the helicopter?"

"That kid in back deserves a medal."

"They handle the rescue OK?"

"This man Forney. When I looked up and saw that crazy hat I knew I had it knocked."

Admiral Tarrant took a deep gulp of coffee and studied Brubaker across the rim of his cup. He knew he oughtn't to duscuss this next point with a junior officer but he had to talk with someone. "You say the green hat gave you a little extra fight?"

"You're scared. Then you see an opera hat coming at you out of nowhere. You relax."

"I would. Forney was in here a few minutes ago. Put me right at ease. Implied I was doing a fair job. You've got to respect a character like that. But the funny thing is . . ." He looked into his cup and said casually, "Captain of the ship's going to get rid of Forney. Says the hat's an outrage."

Brubaker knew the admiral was out of line so he didn't want to press for more details but he did say, "The pilots'd be unhappy."

The admiral, far back in his corner of the davenport, studied the bundled-up young man and jabbed his coffee cup at him. "Harry, you're one of the finest pilots we have. You go in low, you do the job."

Brubaker grinned. He had a generous mouth and even teeth. His grin was attractive. "From you, sir, I appreciate that."

"Then why don't you stay in the Navy? Great future here for you."

The grin vanished. "You know what I think of the Navy, sir."

"Still bitter?"

"Still. I was unattached. The organized units were drawing pay. They were left home. I was called. Sometimes I'm so bitter I could bitch up the works on purpose."

"Why don't you?" Tarrant asked evenly.

"You know why I don't, sir. The catapult fires. There's that terrific moment and you're out front. On your way to Korea. So you say, 'What the heck? I'm here. Might as well do the job.'"

"Exactly. The President once rebuked me publicly. I'd had that big fight with the battleship boys because they didn't think aviation was important. Then the brawl with the air force who thought it too important. I know I'll never get promoted again. But you're here and you do the job."

"It would be easier to take if people back home

were helping. But in Denver nobody even knew there was a war except my wife. Nobody supports this war."

At the mention of Brubaker's wife the admiral unconsciously reached for the file of papers, but he stopped because what the young pilot said interested him. "Every war's the wrong one," he said. "Could anything have been stupider than choosing Guadalcanal for a battleground? And look at us today!" With his cup he indicated on the chart where the permanent snow line, heavy with blizzards and sleet, hung a few miles to the east, while to the west the mountains of Korea hemmed in the ships. "Imagine the United States Navy tied down to a few square miles of ocean. The marines are worse. Dug into permanent trenches. And the poor air force is the most misued of all. Bombers flying close air support. Militarily this war is a tragedy."

"Then why don't we pull out?" Harry asked bluntly.

Admiral Tarrant put his cup and saucer down firmly. "That's rubbish, son, and you know it. All through history free men have had to fight the wrong war in the wrong place. But that's the one they're stuck with. That's why, one of these days, we'll knock out those bridges at Toko-ri."

Flag plot grew silent. The two men stared at each other. For in every war there is one target whose name stops conversation. You say that name and the men who must fly against that target sit mute and stare ahead. In Europe, during World War II it was Ploesti or Peenemunde. In the Pacific it was Truk or the Yawata steel works. Now, to the Navy off Korea, it was the deadly concentration of mountains and narrow passes and festering gun emplacements that hemmed the vital bridges at Toko-ri. Here all communist supplies to the central and eastern front assembled. Here the communists were vulnerable.

Finally Brubaker asked, "Do we have to knock out those particular bridges?"

"Yes, we must. I believe without question that some morning a bunch of communist generals and commissars will be holding a meeting to discuss the future of the war. And a messenger will run in with news that the Americans have knocked out even the bridges at Toko-ri. And that little thing will convince the Reds that we'll never stop . . . never give in . . . never weaken in our purpose."

Again the two men studied each other and the admiral asked, "More coffee?" As Brubaker held his cup the old man said gruffly, "But I didn't call you here to discuss strategy. I'm supposed to chew you out." With the coffee pot he indicated the file of papers.

"They crying because I wrecked that wheel?"

"No. Because of your wife."

The astonishment on Brubaker's face was so real that Tarrant was convinced the young man was unaware his wife and two daughters were in Japan. Nevertheless he had a job to do so he asked, "You knew she was in Japan?"

"She made it!" A look of such triumph and love captured Brubaker's face that the admiral felt he ought to look away. Then quietly the young man said, "This is more than a guy dares hope for, sir."

"You better hope you don't get a court-martial."

"I didn't tell her to come," Brubaker protested, but such a huge grin captured his face that he proved himself a liar.

Tarrant kept on being tough. "How'd she get here without your help?"

"Politics. Her father used to be senator from Wyoming."

Brubaker closed his eyes. He didn't care what happened. Nancy had made it. In the jet ready rooms he had known many pilots and their women troubles but he kept out of the bull sessions. He loved one girl. He had loved her with letters all through the last war in New Guinea and Okinawa. The day he got home he married her and she'd never given him any trouble. Now she was in Japan. Quietly he said to the admiral, "If she's broken a dozen rules to get here it's all right by me."

The old man didn't know what to say. "War's no place for women," he grunted.

Then Brubaker explained. "If my wife really is in Japan, I know why. She couldn't take America any longer. Watching people go on as if there were no war. We gave up our home, my job, the kids. Nobody else in Denver gave up anything."

This made the admiral angry. "Rubbish," he growled. "Burdens always fall on a few. You know that. Look at this ship. Every man aboard thinks he's a hero because he's in Korea. But only a few of you ever really bomb the bridges."

"But why my wife and me?"

"Nobody ever knows why he gets the dirty job. But any society is held together by the efforts . . . yes, and the sacrifices of only a few."

Brubaker couldn't accept this, Tarrant realized, and he was getting mad in the way that had characterized the admiral's sons. The old man had learned to respect this attitude, so he waited for the young pilot to speak but Brubaker happened to think of his wife waiting in Japan and his anger left. "Look," he said. "It's sleeting." The two men went to the dark window and looked down upon the silent carrier, her decks fast with ice, her planes locked down by sleet.

"It'll be all right by dawn," the old man said.

"You ever hear what the pilots say about you and the weather? 'At midnight he runs into storms but at take-off the deck's always clear, damn him.'"

The admiral laughed and said, "Three days you'll be in Japan. No more worry about take-offs for a while." He slapped the papers into a basket. "I'll tell Tokyo you had nothing to do with bringing your wife out here."

"Thank you, sir."

Quickly the admiral resumed his austere ways. Shaking Brubaker's hand he said stiffly, "Mighty glad you were rescued promptly. Why don't you see if the surgeon can spare a little extra nightcap."

As soon as Brubaker left, Tarrant thought, "His wife did right. If mine had come to Hawaii when our oldest son was killed, maybe things would have been different." But she had stayed home, as Navy wives are expected to, and somewhere between the bombing of Pearl Harbor, where she lost one son, and the battle of Midway, where her second was killed trying to torpedo a Japanese carrier, her mind lost focus and she started to drink a lot and forget people's names until slowly, like petals of apple blossoms in spring, fragments of her gentle personality fell away and she would sit for hours staring at a wall.

Therefore it angered Tarrant when civilians like Brubaker suggested that he, a professional military man, could not understand war. Quite the contrary, he knew no civilian who understood war as thoroughly as he. Two sons and a home he had given to war. He had sacrificed the promotion of his career by insisting that America have the right weapons in case war came. And now in Korea, of the 272 pilots who had initially served with him in his task force, 31 had been killed by communist gunfire. Tonight he had come within two minutes of losing Brubaker, the best of the lot. No one need tell him what war was.

He was therefore doubly distressed when the people of the United States reacted like Brubaker: "Hold back the enemy but let someone else do it." He felt that his nation did not realize it was engaged in an unending war of many generations against resolute foes who were determined to pull it down. Some of the phases of this war would no doubt be fought without military battles. Whole decades might pass in some kind of peace but more likely the desultory battles would stagger on and from each community some young men would be summoned to do the fighting. They would be like Brubaker, unwilling to join up but tough adversaries when there was no alternative. And no matter where they might be sent to serve, Tarrant was positive that they would hate that spot the way he and Brubaker hated Korea. It would always be the wrong place.

As if to demonstrate afresh how ridiculous Korea was, the aerologist appeared with the midnight weather reports from Siberia and China. Since these nations were not officially at war, their weather stations were required to broadcast their customary summaries, just as American and Japanese stations broadcast theirs. But since Korean weather was determined by what had happened in Siberia and China two days before, the admiral always had the tip-off and the enemy gained nothing.

"All wars are stupid," the old man grunted as he filed the Siberian reports. "But we'd better learn to handle the stupidity." He recalled England and France, dragging through their Korean wars for more than two hundred years. They had avoided panicky general mobilization and millions of citizens must have spent their lives without worrying about war until something flared up like Crimea, South Africa or Khartoum.

"And their wars weren't even forced upon them," he growled. Secretly he was frightened. Could America stick it out when dangers multiplied? If Englishmen and Frenchmen, and before them Athenians and the men of Spain, had been willing to support their civilizations through centuries of difficulty when often those difficulties were self-generated, what would happen to the United States if her citizenry abandoned the honorable responsibilities forced upon her by the relentless press of history?

He went up on the bridge to check the rolling sea for the last time. "What would they have us abandon to the enemy?" he asked. "Korea? Then Japan and the Philippines? Sooner or later Hawaii?" He walked back and forth pondering this problem of where abandonment would end, and as the sleet howled upon him he could not fix that line: "Maybe California, Colorado. Perhaps we'd stabilize at the Mississippi." He could not say. Instead he held to one unwavering conviction: "A messenger will run in and tell the commissars, 'They even knocked out the bridges at Toko-ri.' And that's the day they'll quit." Then reason might come into the world.

Upon that hope he ended the long day. He had checked the wind and the weather and the rolling of the sea and the number of planes ready for the dawn strike and the location of those storms that always hovered near his ships. He had posted the night watches and he could do no more.

Land

It was the greatest liberty port in the world. It had more variety than Marseilles, more beauty than Valparaiso. Its prices were cheaper than New York's, its drinks better than Lisbon's. And there were far more pretty girls than in Tahiti.

It was Yokosuka, known through all the fleets of the world as Yu-*koss*-ka, and almost every man who had been there once had a girl waiting for him when he got back the second time. For in the cities near the port were millions of pretty girls who loved American sailors and their hilarious ways and their big pay checks. It was a great liberty port.

Now as the *Savo* moved cautiously in toward her dock hundreds of these girls waited for their sailors and thousands were on hand for sailors they had not yet seen. Grim-faced guards kept the invaders away from the ship, but the girls did gather outside the gates, and among them on this windy, wintry day was one especially handsome girl of twenty dressed in plaid skirt from Los Angeles, trim coat from Sears Roebuck, and jaunty cap from San Francisco. She wore her jet hair in braids and kept a laugh ready in the corners of her wide, black eyes. Her complexion was of soft gold and seemed to blush as some of the other girls caught a glimpse of the *Savo* and pretended they had seen her sailor.

"There's green hat!" they cried in Japanese.

"You don't worry about green hat," she replied, pressing against the fence.

A comic among the girls put her right hand high above her head and swaggered as she had seen Mike Forney swagger on earlier leaves, and excitement grew as the *Savo* approached her berth. But this morning the girls would have to stand in the cold a long time, for there was a sharp wind off the sea and the lumbering bulk of the carrier presented so much freeboard for the wind to blow against that tugs with limited maneuvering space could not hold her from crashing into the quay, and emergency measures were clearly necessary. Accordingly the bull horn wailed the bad news, "F4U and AD pilots prepare for windmill."

Every propeller pilot cringed with disgust but none showed such outrage as one of the jet men. Stocky, florid faced, with a cigar jutting from his teeth, this forty-year-old Annapolis man whipped his bullet head and underslung jaw toward the bridge to see what stupid fool had ordered another windmill. As "Cag," commander of the air group, he was in charge of all planes and felt sickened as he watched the propeller jobs wheel into position. He was about to storm off the flight deck and raise a real row when Brubaker, standing with him, caught his arm and said, "Take it easy, Cag. You don't have to pay for the burned-out engines."

"It's murder," the Cag groaned as his valuable prop planes were lashed down to the edge of the deck which threatened to crash against the quay. Their noses were pointed into the wind and their unhappy pilots sat in the cockpits and waited.

"Start engines," yowled the bull horn. Sixteen valuable engines revolved and sixteen sets of propeller blades tried to pull the big carrier away from the quay, but the effort was not sufficient, and the *Savo* appeared certain to crash.

"Engines full speed," moaned the bull horn and the noise on deck became great as the props clawed into the air and magically held the great ship secure against the wind.

This caused no satisfaction among the propeller pilots, for since their planes were stationary on deck, with no wind rushing through to cool them, each engine was burning itself seriously and one plane mechanic rushed up to the Cag with tears in his eyes cursing and crying, "They're wrecking the planes! Look!"

One of the low-slung F4U's had begun to throw smoke and the Cag ran over to study it. He chomped his cigar in anger and said grimly, "They're killing these planes."

"Somebody's got to stop this," the mechanic said.

"I'm going to," Cag replied quietly and started for the admiral's plot, but before he could get there Brubaker hauled him down and the two men watched the propeller planes gradually ease up and allow the *Savo* to inch into her berth as gently as a fragile egg being laid into a basket by an old farm wife.

"Cut engines," rasped the bull horn and the Cag said bitterly, "Burn those engines up now and next trip over Korea the pilot bails out. This lousy captain thinks he has a new toy to play with."

"Save it for the hotel," Brubaker said. "Take it up with the admiral there." So the Cag turned away and as he did so Brubaker looked down from the carrier deck onto the quay and there stood Nancy and the two girls, dressed in winter coats and huddling to-

gether to protect one another from the wind. A great
lump came into his throat and for a moment he could
not wave or call, so that Mike Forney, who was marching up and down, impatient to burst ashore, asked,
"That your family, sir?"

"Yes."

"It's worth bein' saved for them, sir." The way Mike
said *sir* made Brubaker look to see if the cocky Irishman
were kidding him, but Forney was staring raptly at
Nancy and the two girls. "Hey, Mrs. Brubaker!" he
roared. "Here's your hero."

Jumping up and down on her toes Nancy called ex-
citedly to her daughters, "There's Daddy!" And they
all threw him kisses.

Mike, watching with approval, said, "Right beyond
that fence, sir, I got the same kind of reception waiting
for me."

"You married?" Brubaker asked in astonishment.
Somehow he had never thought of Mike as a family
man.

"Not yet, but I may be. This shore leave."

"Some girl who came out with the Occupation?"

"Japanese girl," Mike said, adjusting his green hat
at a night-club angle, but a messenger from the ship's
executive officer arrived to inform Forney that the
uniform of the day called for something more traditional and the insulted Irishman went below.

Immediately Brubaker wished that Mike had stayed,
for the pain of seeing his women on the quay below
was too great. They had come too far, they loved him
too much and they reminded him too soon of icy Korea's waters clutching at him, trying to drag him down.

For the first time in his life he became desperately afraid and wanted to leave the *Savo* right then, for he saw leading from the deck of the carrier, right above the bodies of his wife and daughters, four bridges stretching far out to sea and they were the bridges of Toko-ri and he was breathlessly afraid of them.

"Nancy," he whispered. "You should have stayed home."

But as soon as the ship's lines were secured, he dashed down the gangplank to embrace his wife and as he did so his youngest daughter caught him by the leg and began to babble furiously and from the way he bent down and listened to the excited little girl—as if he actually wanted to know what she had to say—every married man on the deck of the *Savo* towering above knew that Brubaker really loved his kids.

What the child said was, "I made a long airplane ride and now I know what you do on the ship." But Brubaker remembered the icy water and thought, "Thank God you don't know. And thank God your mummy doesn't, either." Then he laughed and caught the little girl in his arms and kissed her a lot and she said, "I like to fly airplanes like you, Daddy."

For Mike Forney reunions were somewhat less complicated, at first. Attended by silent Nestor Gamidge, he strode to the gates of Yokosuka Naval Base, threw the marine on guard a nifty salute and stepped outside to freedom. He was a cocky figure, his fists jammed into his pea coat jacket, his uniform a trifle tight, and it took him only a moment to find the girls. He stopped dead, thrust his big paw in Gamidge's chest and cried, "Look at her, Nestor! Best-dressed girl in Japan!"

Then he gave a bellow, rushed forward and caught
Kimiko in his arms and kissed her lovely little cap right
off her head.

"Hey, Kimiko! Fleet's in!"

To his astonishment she pushed him away, sedately
picked up her cap and said, "Not so fast, big boy. We
got to talk." And she led him to a bar and started patiently to explain the radically new situation, the one
which was to cause the two riots.

For the officers of the *Savo* the Tokyo brass had
reserved rest and recuperation rooms at the Fuji-san,
a meandering Japanese hotel whose exquisite one-
storied rooms and gardens hung on a mountain top
which commanded a superb view of Fujiyama. In the
old days this had been Japan's leading hotel but for
the first six years after the war it served Americans
only. Now, in the transition period between occupation and sovereignty, it had become a symbol of the
strange and satisfying relationship between Japan and
America: the choice rooms were still reserved for
Americans but Japanese were welcome to use the hotel
as before; so its spacious gardens, bent with pine and
cherry, held both Japanese families who were enjoying
luxury after long years of austerity and American military men savoring the same luxury after long months
in Korea.

No one enjoyed the Fuji-san more than Admiral
Tarrant. He arrived on the second day of liberty,
changed into civilian clothes, gathered about him his
younger staff officers and forgot the rigors of Task
Force 77. Other admirals, when they reached Japan,
were whisked into Tokyo for press conferences where

they sat on the edges of their chairs trying to say exactly the right and innocuous thing. They must not, for example, admit that they were fighting Russians, nor must they even indicate that any of our men were being killed. In this special war there were special rules to keep the people back in America from becoming worried.

Admiral Tarrant was not the man for such interviews. The Navy tried it once and he had said bluntly, "We're fighting Russian guns, Russian radar, Russian planes and Russian submarines. And a hell of a lot of our men are being killed by this Russian equipment, manned by Russian experts." General Ridgway's headquarters in Tokyo had blown a gasket and the entire interview was made top secret and the Navy was advised that whereas Tarrant might be terrific as a task force commander, "Send him to some good hotel when he gets ashore . . . and keep him there."

Now he lounged in the bar and watched a group of pilots pestering Beer Barrel. Ten minutes after the *Savo* docked, the landing-signal officer had grabbed for the bar stool and he had sat there for almost twenty-nine hours, lapping up the wonderful Japanese beer. "Look at him!" one Banshee pilot cried. "He's goin' crazy. Doesn't know whether to claim Texas has the biggest midgets in the world or the smallest."

Four jet men, themselves pretty well hung over, formed a solemn circle about Beer Barrel and began to chant the carrier pilot's version of the Twenty-third Psalm:

> *The Beer Barrel is my shepherd*
> *I shall not crash.*

He maketh me to land on flat runways: he bringeth
me in off the rough waters.

He restoreth my confidence.

Yea, though I come stalling into the groove at sixty
knots, I shall fear no evil: for he is with me; his
arm and his paddle, they comfort me.

He prepareth a deck before me in the presence of
mine enemies; he attacheth my hook to the wire;
my deck space runneth over.

Admiral Tarrant laughed at the nonsense. Since his big operation two years ago he drank only coffee, but he often growled, "Just because I'm a reformed drunk no reason why I should deny pleasure to others." He poured himself some inky black coffee and looked into the gardens, where he saw Harry Brubaker's wonderfully lovely wife and her two daughters and they reminded him of what wars were all about. "You don't fight to protect warships or old men. Like the book says, you fight to save your civilization. And so often it seems that civilization is composed mainly of the things women and children want."

Then the admiral grew glum, for Mrs. Brubaker had told him at lunch, "If the government dared to ask women like me, this stupid war would end tomorrow." There lay the confusion. These bright, lovely women, whose husbands had to do the fighting, wanted to end the war on any terms; but these same women, whose children would have to live through servitude or despair should America ever be occupied, would be the precise ones who would goad their men into revitalization and freedom. So Admiral Tarrant never argued with women because in their own deep way they were invariably right. No more war . . . but no humiliation. He hoped to see the day when this difficult program could be attained.

But a more present problem was at hand, for the Cag stormed across the garden, his cigar jutting belligerently ahead like a mine sweeper. The tough airman was known throughout the Navy as a fireball and this time Tarrant, himself an airman, knew the Cag was right. The *Savo's* use of windmill had been intemperate, a perversion of aircraft engines, but a deeper concern was involved, so the admiral prepared to squelch the likeable hothead.

For the Navy high command had secretly asked Tarrant to send in a concurrent report upon this demon flier when his Korean duty ended. It was hinted that a bright and brash young man was needed for rapid promotion to a command of real authority and Tarrant guessed that the Cag was being weighed as an eventual task force commander. "It's a big job," the admiral mused.

He could recall that day in 1945 when Admiral Halsey commanded a supreme force built of five components each twice as large as present Task Force 77. It was so vast it blackened the sea with more than twenty carriers. It stretched for miles and ultimately it sank the entire Japanese fleet. One brain had commanded that incredible force and it behooved the United States to have other men ready for the job, should such a task force ever again be needed.

Long ago Tarrant had begun to argue that some new weapon—rockets, perhaps, or pilotless planes of vast speed—would inevitably constitute the task force of the future. He had seen so much change, indeed had spurred it on, that he could not rely perpetually on ships or airplanes or any one device. But until America was secure behind the protection of some new agency that could move about the earth with security and apply pressure wherever the enemy chose to assault us, it would be wise to have young officers trained to command a sea burdened with ships and speckled with the shadows of a thousand planes.

Perhaps the Cag was such a man. A lot of Navy people thought so but no one knew for sure whether he had those two ultimate requirements for vast command: had he a resolute spirit and had he due regard for human life?

The Cag jammed his cigar through the door and asked, "May I speak with you, sir?"

Tarrant liked the younger man's brusque approach. "Sit down. Whisky?"

"Please."

"What's wrong?"

The Cag sailed right in. Chomping his cigar he snorted, "These lazy carrier captains. They're burning up our engines."

Tarrant thought he'd better let the fireball have it right between the eyes. Staring coldly he asked, "You think you could handle a carrier better?"

This stunned the Cag and he fumbled for a moment. Then, fortunately, the bar boy arrived with his drink and he grabbed for it. "You not having one, sir?" he asked.

"You know the doctor made me lay off," the admiral explained coldly.

Such treatment threw the Cag off balance, for he knew Tarrant's power in the Navy. The old man may have queered his own promotion but he was still known as the incorruptible and his judgment on the promotions of others was prized.

In the embarrassing silence Tarrant asked grimly, "What's your major complaint against the carrier captains?"

The veins stood out on the Cag's bullet head, but he stamped his cigar out and said firmly, "They shouldn't burn up our propeller planes."

"How would you berth a big ship against the wind?"

"In the old days I would have waited. But whatever I did I wouldn't run a lashed-down engine at top speed."

Admiral Tarrant stared impersonally at Fujiyama, the wonderful mountain, and although he wanted to agree with Cag, he pondered precisely what question would most completely throw this young hothead off balance. Finally he settled on: "So you'd have a group of complaining F4U pilots dictate naval procedure?"

Again the Cag was staggered. "Sir, I . . ." He fumbled for words and then blurted out with startling force, "Sir, an engine has only so many good hours. If you burn them up on deck. . . ." He fumbled again and ended weakly, "Why can't they use half-power?"

The admiral turned slowly away from Fujiyama and asked bleakly, "Do you consider an F4U engine more valuable than a carrier?"

The Cag retreated. "What I was trying to say. . . ."

"Another whisky?"

The Cag needed something to restore his confidence but reasoned that if the old man was in an evil mood he'd better not accept two drinks, so he said lamely, "Thank you, sir, but I have a reservation for one of the sulphur baths."

"They're fun," the admiral said mournfully, and when the Cag awkwardly excused himself, the old man sagged into a real depression, for he found it ugly to watch a promising young commander back away from what he knew was right. "Well," Tarrant grumbled, "he's popular. He'll be able to wangle a desk job. But he's no good for command. And I'll have to say so when we get home." Grieved, he decided to leave the bar.

But before he could get away, young Brubaker and his pretty wife approached and it was apparent she had been crying. "She wants to talk to you," Brubaker said with the air of a young husband who hopes somebody else can say the magic word which he has been unable to find.

"My husband tells me you can explain why this war is necessary," she said. "I sure wish somebody would."

"It isn't necessary," Tarrant said. Then, seeing the Brubakers' surprise he added, "You two have something to drink?"

"May we join you?" Nancy asked.

"Doctor won't let me." Then, seeing the young people frown, he added humorously, "I have no vices, no ambitions, no family and no home."

"That's what I mean," Nancy said. "I can understand why you get excited about war. But we do have a home and family."

"I'm not excited about war," the admiral contradicted. "And I don't think it's necessary. That is, it wouldn't be in a sensible world. But for the present it is inevitable." He poured himself some coffee and waited.

"If it's inevitable, why should the burden fall on just a few of us?" Nancy pressed.

"I don't know. You take the other night when your husband. . . ." Before he could tell of the ditching he saw Brubaker make an agonized sign indicating that Nancy knew nothing of the crash and the admiral thought, "Like the rest of America, she's being protected."

He salvaged the sentence by concluding, "Your husband bombed a bridge. Because he's one of the best pilots in the Navy he knocked out two spans. He didn't have to do it. He could have veered away from the bridge and no one would ever have known. But some men don't veer away. They hammer on in, even though the weight of war has fallen unfairly on them. I always think of such men as the voluntary men."

Nancy fought back her tears and asked, "So until the last bridge is knocked out a few men have to do the fighting? The voluntary men."

"That's right. The world has always depended upon the voluntary men."

Before Nancy could reply, the bar boy hurried up and asked, "Is Lieutenant Brubaker here?" The boy led Harry to a back door of the hotel where Nestor Gamidge stood, bloody and scarred.

"I'm sure glad to see you, Lieutenant," he gasped. His blues were ripped and his face was heavily bruised.

"What's up?"

"Mike's been in a terrible fight, sir."

"Where?"

"Tokyo. I came out in a cab."

"What happened?"

"He's in jail."

"A public riot?"

"Yep. His girl's marryin' a bo'sun from the *Essex*."

"You mean his . . . Japanese girl?"

"Yes, and if you don't come in he'll be locked up permanent."

Tokyo was sixty miles away and to rescue Forney in person would consume many hours of leave that he might otherwise spend with his family, so Brubaker said, "I'll phone the M.P.'s."

"Callin' won't help, sir. Mike clobbered two M.P.'s as well as the gang from the *Essex*."

"You two take on the whole town?"

"Yes, sir."

Brubaker had to grin at the vision of these two tough kids on the loose and made up his mind abruptly. "I'll help."

He hurried back to where Nancy and the admiral sat and said quickly, "Admiral Tarrant, will you please see that Nancy gets dinner? There's been trouble in Tokyo and I . . ."

"Oh, no!" Nancy protested.

"Admiral, it's Mike Forney."

"Drunken brawl?"

"Girl threw him over."

Nancy pleaded, "On our second night, why do you have to get mixed up with drunken sailors?"

Brubaker kissed his wife and said tenderly, "Darling, if Mike were in China I'd have to help."

"But, Harry. . . ." It was no use. Already he was running down the long hallway.

When Nancy realized that her husband actually was on his way to Tokyo, she looked beseechingly at Admiral Tarrant and pleaded, "Who's this Mike Forney he thinks more of than his own children?" Her eyes filled with tears and she fumbled for a handkerchief.

The admiral studied her closely and asked, "If you were freezing to death in the sea and a man brought his helicopter right over your head and rescued you, wouldn't you help that man if he got into trouble?"

Nancy stopped crying and asked, "Did Harry crash at sea?"

"Yes."

She looked down at her white knuckles and unclasped her hands. Very quietly she said, "You know your husband's at war. You know he's brave. But somehow you can't believe that he'll fall into the sea." Her voice trembled.

When she regained control Admiral Tarrant asked, "Has Harry told you about the bridges? At Toko-ri?"

"No. He never talks about the war."

"You must ask him about those bridges."

Weakly she asked, "Is he involved with the bridges?"

"Yes. When we go back to sea, your husband must bomb those bridges."

In a whisper she asked, "Why do you tell me this?"

He replied, "In 1942 I had a daughter as sweet as you. She was my daughter-in-law, really. Then my son was killed at Midway trying to torpedo a Jap carrier. She never recovered. For a while she tried to make love with every man in uniform. Thought he might die one day. Then she grew to loathe herself and attempted suicide. What she's doing now or where she is I don't know, but once she was my daughter."

Nancy Brubaker could hardly force herself to speak but in an ashen voice she asked, "You think that . . . well, if things went wrong at the bridges . . . I'd be like. . . ."

"Perhaps. If we refuse to acknowledge what we're

involved in, terrible consequences sometimes follow."

A strange man was telling her that war meant the death of people and that if she were not prepared, her courage might fall apart and instinctively she knew this to be true. "I understand what you mean," she said hoarsely.

"Let's get your little girls and we'll have dinner," Tarrant said.

But Nancy was too agitated to see her daughters just then. She pointed to the end of the bar where Beer Barrel lay at last sprawled upon his arms, his face pressed against the polished wood. "Will he fly against the bridges, too?" she asked.

When the admiral turned to survey the mammoth Texan, his lean Maine face broke into a relaxed smile. "That one?" he said reflectively. "He flies against his bridges every day."

When Brubaker and Gamidge reached Tokyo, night had already fallen and there was slush upon the wintry streets that lined the black moat of the emperor's palace. At the provost marshal's office a major asked sourly, "Why you interested in a troublemaker like Forney?"

"He's from my ship."

"Not any more."

"Major," Brubaker asked directly, "couldn't you please let me handle this?"

"A mad Irishman? Who wrecks a dance hall?"

"But this man has saved the lives of four pilots."

"Look, Lieutenant! I got nineteen monsters in the bird cage. Everyone of them was a hero in Korea. But in Tokyo they're monsters."

Patiently Brubaker said, "Mike's a helicopter pilot. The other night Mike and this sailor. . . ."

The major got a good look at Nestor and shouted to a sergeant, "Is this the runt who slugged you?"

"Listen, Major!" Harry pleaded. "The other night I ditched my plane at sea. These two men saved my life. This runt, as you called him, jumped into the ocean."

The major was completely unimpressed. Staring at Nestor, he said scornfully, "I suppose the ocean tore his clothes. Did he get his face all chopped up jumping into a wave?"

"All right, there was a brawl."

"A brawl! A brawl is when maybe six guys throw punches. These two monsters took on all of Tokyo."

It was apparent to Brubaker that pleading along normal lines would get nowhere, so he asked bluntly, "You married, Major?"

"Yep."

"Tonight's the second night in eight months that I've seen my wife and kids. I left them at Fuji-san to get Mike out of jail. That's what I think of these two men."

The major stared at the docket listing Mike's behavior. "You willin' to cough up $80 for the damage he did?"

"I'd pay $800."

"He's yours, but you ain't gettin' no prize."

A guard produced Mike Forney, his face a nauseating blue in contrast to the green scarf. "She's marryin' an ape from the *Essex*," he said pitifully.

"I suppose you tried to stop her."

"I would of stopped the ape, but he had helpers."

When they reached the narrow streets where hundreds of Japanese civilians hurried past, Mike begged, "Talk with her, please, Lieutenant. She might listen to you."

He led Brubaker to one of the weirdest dance halls in the world. A war profiteer had cornered a bunch of steel girders and had built a Chinese junk in the middle of Tokyo. He called it the Pirates' Den and installed an open elevator which endlessly traveled from the first floor to the fifth bearing an eleven-piece jazz band whose blazing noise supplied five different dance floors. The strangest adornment of the place was a mock airplane, piloted by an almost nude girl who flew from floor to floor delivering cold beer.

The steel ship was so ugly, so noisy and so crammed with chattering girls that Brubaker wondered how anyone had known a riot was under way and then he met Kimiko, Mike's one-time love. She was the first Japanese girl he had ever spoken to and he was unprepared for her dazzling beauty. Her teeth were remarkably white and her smile was warm. He understood at once why Mike wanted her, and when she rose to extend her hand and he saw her slim perfect figure in a princess evening dress which Mike had ordered from New York, he concluded that she warranted a riot.

"I very sorry, Lieutenant," she explained softly, "but while Mike at sea I lose my heart to *Essex* man. *Essex* not at sea."

"But Mike's a fine man," Brubaker argued. "No girl could do better than Mike."

Kimiko smiled in a way to make Brubaker dizzy and plaintively insisted, "I know Mike good man. But I lose my heart."

Things started to go black for Mike again and he shouted, "Not in my dress, you don't lose it!" And he clawed at the dress which represented more than two months' pay.

Kimiko began to scream and the owner of the Pirates' Den blew a shrill whistle and prudent Nestor Gamidge said, "We better start runnin' now."

"Not without this dress!" Mike bellowed.

Nestor handled that by clouting Mike a withering blow to the chin, under which the tough Irishman crumpled. Then Nestor grabbed him by the arms and grunted, "Lieutenant, sir. Ask the girls to push."

In this way they worked Mike out a back door before the M.P.'s could get to him, but in the alley Nestor saw that Mike still clutched part of Kimiko's dress. He pried this loose from the stiff hand and returned it to Kimiko, saying, "You can sew it back on." Upon returning to Brubaker he reported, "Japanese girls are sure pretty." But when Mike woke up, sitting in one of the gutters west of the Ginza, he said mournfully, "Without Kimiko I want to die."

Gently they took him to the enlisted men's quarters, where Gamidge put the rocky Irishman to bed. When this was done, the little Kentuckian laboriously scratched a note and tucked it into the lieutenant's fist: "We owe you $80. Mike and Nestor." Then Brubaker started the long trip back to Fuji-san, where his wife waited.

It was nearly three in the morning when he reached the Fuji-san, but Nancy was awake and when he climbed into bed she clutched him to her and whispered, "I'm ashamed of the way I behaved. Admiral Tarrant told me about Mike Forney."

"I wish he hadn't. But don't worry. Nobody ever crashes twice."

There was a long silence and she kissed him as if to use up all the kisses of a lifetime. Then she controlled her voice to make it sound casual and asked, "What are the bridges at Toko-ri?" She felt him grow tense.

"Where'd you hear about them?"

"The admiral." There was no comment from the darkness so she added, "He had good reason, Harry. His daughter-in-law had no conception of war and went to shreds. He said if I had the courage to come all the way out here I ought to have the courage to know. Harry, what are the bridges?"

And suddenly, in the dark room, he wanted to share with his wife his exact feelings about the bridges. "I haven't really seen them," he whispered in hurried syllables. "But I've studied pictures. There are four bridges, two for railroads, two for trucks, and they're vital. Big hills protect them and lots of guns. Every hill has lots of Russian guns."

"Are Russians fighting in Korea?"

"Yes. They do all the radar work. We have only two approaches to the bridges. The valley has one opening to the east, another to the west. When we bomb the bridges we must dive in one end and climb out the other." He hesitated and added quickly, "At Toko-ri there is more flak than anywhere in Germany last time. Because the communists know where you have to come in from. And where you have to go out. So they sit and wait for you."

They whispered until dawn, a man and wife in a strange land talking of a war so terrible that for them it equaled any in history. Not the wars of Caesar nor the invasions of Napoleon nor the river bank at Vicksburg nor the sands of Iwo were worse than the Korean war if your husband had to bomb the bridges, and toward morning Nancy could control her courage no longer and began to cry. In her despondency she whispered, "What eats my heart away is that back home there is no war. Harry, do you remember where we were when we decided to get married?"

"Sure I remember. Cheyenne."

"Well, when I was explaining to the girls about the birds and the bees, Jackie looked up at me with that quizzical grin of hers and asked, 'Where did all this stuff start?' and I said, 'All right, smarty, I'll take you up and show you.' And I took them to the Frontier Days where you proposed and I almost screamed with agony because everything was exactly the way it was in 1946. Nobody gave a damn about Korea. In all America nobody gives a damn."

When the morning sun was bright and the girls had risen, Harry Brubaker and his wife still had no explanation of why they had been chosen to bear the burden of the war. Heartsick, they led their daughters down to one of the hotel's private sulphur baths, where they locked the door, undressed and plunged into the bubbling pool. The girls loved it and splashed nakedly back and forth, teasing shy Nancy because she wouldn't take off all her clothes, so she slipped out of her underthings and joined them.

They were cavorting in this manner when the locked door opened and a Japanese man entered. He bowed low to both Nancy and Harry, smiled at the girls and started to undress. "Hey!" Harry cried. "We reserved this!" But the man understood little English and bowed to accept Harry's greeting. When he was quite undressed he opened the door and admitted his wife and two teen-age daughters, who laid aside their kimonos. Soon the Japanese family stood naked by the pool and dipped their toes in. Harry, blushing madly, tried to protest again but the man said with painstaking care, "Number one! Good morning!" and each of his pretty daughters smiled and said musically, "Good morning, sir!"

"*Ohio gozaimasu!*" shouted the Brubaker girls, using a phrase they had acquired from their nurse. This pleased the Japanese family and everyone laughed gaily and then the man bowed again. Ceremoniously, father first, the family entered the pool.

By now Harry and Nancy were more or less numb with astonishment, but the pleasant warmth of the room, the quiet beauty of the surroundings and the charm of the Japanese family were too persuasive to resist. Harry, trying not to stare at the pretty girls, smiled at the Japanese man, who swam leisurely over, pointed to one of the Brubaker girls and asked, "Belong you?"

Harry nodded, whereupon the man called his own daughters who came over to be introduced. "Teiko, Takako," the man said. They smiled and held out their hands and somehow the bitterness of the long night's talking died away. The two families intermingled and the soft waters of the bath united them. In 1944 Harry had hated the Japanese and had fought valiantly against them, destroying their ships and bombing their troops, but the years had passed, the hatreds had dissolved and on this wintry morning he caught some sense in the twisted and conflicting things men are required to do.

Then he sort of cracked his neck, for he saw Nancy. His shy wife had paddled to the other side of the pool and was talking with the Japanese man. "We better hurry or we'll miss breakfast," Harry said, and for the rest of his stay they became like the spectators at the Cheyenne Frontier Days and they enjoyed themselves and never spoke of Korea.

Then shore leave ended in one of those improbable incidents which made everyone proud he served aboard a good ship like the *Savo*. Admiral Tarrant went aboard at noon and toward four Beer Barrel staggered up the gangplank with his two golf bags. Brubaker had obtained permission for Nancy to see his quarters but when she found how astonishingly small the room was and how her husband slept with his face jammed under two steam pipes she said she felt penned in and would rather stay on deck.

In the meantime hundreds of sailors and their Japanese girls had crowded into Yokosuka and in the lead were Mike Forney and Nestor Gamidge, accompanied by seven girls from the dance halls of Tokyo, Yokohama and Yokosuka. "I never knew there were so many girls," Nestor said to one of the plane captains. "Best thing ever happened to Mike was losing Kimiko to that ape from the *Essex*."

Mike agreed. When he had kissed his girls good-by he swung onto the quay, elbows out, and pointed to the *Savo:* "Greatest flattop in the fleet." Then he stopped dead for he saw that the *Essex* was alongside and there stood beautiful Kimiko, wearing the expensive plaid he

had bought her. She was kissing her ape from the *Essex*
and things went black. Clenching his fists, Mike lunged
toward the lovers but little Nestor grabbed him.

Mike stopped, slapped himself on the head and muttered, "Sure, what's one girl?" With grandiloquent
charm he approached Kimiko, kissed her hand and said
loudly, "The flower of Japan." Then he grabbed the *Essex* man warmly and proclaimed, "The flower of the
fleet. The best man won. Bless you, my children."

Then everything fell apart. For some loud mouth in
the *Essex* yelled derisively, "And we could lick you
bums in everything else, too."

Mike whirled about, saw no one, then looked back at
golden Kimiko and she was beautiful in that special way
and she was his girl. Blood surged into his throat and he
lunged at the *Essex* man standing with her and slugged
him furiously, shouting, "You lousy ape!"

Six *Essex* men leaped to defend their shipmate and
stumpy Nestor Gamidge rallied *Savo* men and soon
M.P. whistles were screeching like sparrows in spring
and there was a growing melee with men in blue dropping all over the place. Mike, seeing himself about to be
deluged by *Essex* reinforcements, grabbed a chunk of
wood and let the ape have it across the ear, laying him
flat. At this Kimiko started to scream in Japanese and
Mike grabbed her hat and tried to pull off the pretty
plaid jacket, bellowing, "Go ahead and marry him. But
not in my clothes." Three *Essex* men, gallant to the end,
knocked him silly.

The captain of the *Savo* witnessed this disgraceful
riot and determined on the spot to get rid of Mike
Forney, but Admiral Tarrant, surveying the brawl from
flag bridge, thought, "I'd hate to see the day when

men were afraid to mix it up for pretty girls." He called for his glasses and studied Kimiko, who knelt over her *Essex* man and all the sailors aboard the *Savo* and the officers too were a little more proud of their ship.

Sky

⚓

THE sun had to be well up or the photographs wouldn't be any good, so it was nearly 0945 when Harry Brubaker's jet catapulted violently across the prow of the *Savo* and far into the sky toward Korea. Ahead of him streaked a single Banshee with an extraordinary nose containing nine broad windows through which heavy cameras would record the bridges of Toko-ri.

While the *Savo* was in Yokosuka, other carriers were supposed to photograph the target but they had failed. When Cag bent his bullet head over their muddy films he growled, "What's the matter? They afraid to go down low? We'll show 'em how to take pictures," and he assigned himself the dangerous mission, choosing Brubaker to fly protective cover.

Now, as the two Banshees streaked toward higher altitudes, Brubaker concerned himself with trivial details: "Lay off those even altitudes. Use 25,300. Makes it just that much tougher for the anti-aircraft crews. And remember that when Cag goes down for the pictures, keep 3,000 feet above him."

Then, in the perpetually mysterious way, when he had climbed into the higher atmosphere, he experienced the singing beauty of a jet as it sped almost silently through the vast upper reaches of the world. Sea and sky fell away and he was aloft in the soaring realm of the human spirit.

It was terrible and supreme to be there, whistling into the morning brilliance, streaking ahead so fast that the overwhelming scream of his engines never quite caught up. In this moment of exhilaration he peered into the limitless reaches of the upper void and felt the surging sensation that overtakes every jet pilot: "I'm out front." Through the silent beauty of this cold February morning he soared through the blue-black upper sky and thought, "I'm out front."

Then, as his eyes swept the empty sky in casual patterns, he uttered a stunned cry, "My God! There it is!" But when he looked directly at what he had seen it vanished, so he returned to scanning and from the powerful corner of his eye he saw it again, tremendous and miraculously lovely, one of the supreme sights of creation: Fujiyama in morning sunlight towering above the islands of Japan. The cone was perfect, crowned in dazzling white, and the sides fell away like the soft ending of a sigh, and somewhere on the nether slope Nancy and the girls were waiting.

He now looked at the majestic volcano with his full eye, but again it was the omniscient corner which startled him, for it detected the mountains of Korea. Dead ahead they lay, bold and blunt and ugly. Tortured and convoluted, they twisted up at the two fleeting jets, the terrible mountains of Korea. They were the mountains of pain, the hills of death. They were the scars of the world's violent birth, the aftermath of upheavals and multitudes of storms. There was no sense to them and they ran in crazy directions. Their crests formed no significant pattern, their valleys led nowhere, and running through them there were no discernible watersheds or spacious plains. Hidden among them, somewhere to the west, cowered the bridges of Toko-ri, gun-rimmed and waiting.

Brubaker knew the guns would be waiting, for as the Banshees crossed the coastline, a signal battery in Wonsan fired and he could follow the course of other gun bursts across Korea, for the communists announced impending danger exactly as the Cheyennes of Colorado had done two hundred years before.

Now the day's hard work began. As soon as the Banshees came in range of communist guns, Cag began to descend in swift jinking dips and dives to confuse ground gunners, never staying on either course or altitude for longer than fifteen seconds. This threw a special responsibility on Brubaker who stayed aloft, weaving back and forth lest some stray MIG try to pounce upon the preoccupied photographic plane. So imperceptible was Cag's silvery slim Banshee as it skimmed across the mountain tops that Brubaker was taxed to keep his eye upon it.

At Yangdok a flurry of ground fire exploded at almost the right altitude to catch the photographic plane, so the jets increased speed to 560, jinking violently. Below them they spotted the ruins of a less important bridge, four spans rusting in the river. Farther on a communist working party strove to rebuild a major bridge, but this morning Cag ignored them, certain that later flights would halt the work. For now on the horizon rose the peaks that guarded Toko-ri.

Each was pock-marked with many circular red depressions in the snow. These were the gun emplacements and in swift estimate Brubaker decided there must be more than sixty. Lower were gaunt walled nests for the huge five-inch guns, a single shell from which could pulverize a plane before it fell to earth. And deep within the hills, hiding along the river, were the four bridges. On this first fleeting glance he noticed that the two historic bridges were on tall stone pillars and decidedly vulnerable, but that the two emergency alternates were extraordinarily low, scarcely clearing the water.

But most significant of all was one solemn fact: to get to the bridges you really did have to fly in one end of a valley, traverse it and fly out the other end. Brubaker swallowed and thought, "They got you lined up going and coming. And when you pull out for rendezvous you're a dead duck." Then he laughed to relieve his tension and whispered, "No wonder they saved this one till last."

At that instant Cag started his bold run into the western entrance to the valley. Pushing his nose down into a 40° dive, he screamed along the shimmering river, held courageously to the hairline railroad tracks, and roared upon the bridges at 580 miles an hour. During each inch of this run more than two hundred communist guns fired at the streaking Banshee, but it howled straight on, its cameras grinding, making no concession to the fire. Cag had one mission only, to bring back photographs, and he ignored everything else. Five-inch guns, three-inchers, machine guns and even carbines blazed at his wailing jet, but at last he pulled away from the mortal pit and with a sickening upward twist sped off to the north.

For a moment Brubaker lost the sleek Banshee as it fled to the hills for rendezvous. In some anxiety he cast his eyes swiftly left and right and thus caught a fleeting glimpse of the plane in the corner of his eye. Quickly rotating his vision in that area he gradually pinpointed the photographic plane, twisting and turning toward the safer hills. He had the sensation of spying upon an animal retreating to some sheltered valley after a wounding fight.

"Drop down and look me over," Cag called. "My tail section OK?"

Brubaker passed under the long-nosed jet and studied the fuselage minutely, for although both planes were doing more than 400 miles, in relation to each other they were nearly motionless. "Nothing visible," he reported.

"Back we go," Cag said.

The photographic jet heeled over in a tight turn, jinked to a lower altitude and went into a paralyzing dive. Out of the sun it streaked with blazing speed, but the communist gunners were waiting and in monomaniac fury they poured their fire upon the wraithlike Banshee as it screamed upon them. It seemed positively impossible that Cag could writhe his way through such fire but he bore on, clicking his shutters at the doomed bridges.

From aloft Brubaker followed this incredible mission and experienced a resolute desire to be there with his commander, but the instant this thought came to mind it was dispelled by the vision he had seen at Yokosuka: four bridges reaching out into space far above the heads of his wife and daughters, and he grew afraid; for he knew that tomorrow as the sun came up he would be pushing his own overloaded Banshee down, down upon the real bridges. It was then that the great fear came upon him, the one he would not be able to dispel.

Then he heard Cag cry, "Well, home we go."

Ecstatically the two jets zoomed to 26,000. Far below them the savage, cheated mountains of Korea began to assume a beautiful countenance. Gone were the tortured profiles and the senseless confusion, for with the bridges of Toko-ri behind him, Brubaker saw Korea with a kindlier eye. To the north sprawling reservoirs glistened like great brooches, holding the hills together. To the south snow hung upon the ridge lines and made the valleys shimmering wonderlands of beauty, while beyond the upcoming range of mountains lay the vast blue sea, bearing somewhere upon its bosom the task force, that fair circle of home, with Beer Barrel waiting on the after deck.

Even Cag was impressed and called, "Real estate sure looks better on the way home."

But when they reached home there was dismal news. "You heard the hot scoop?" Harry's plane captain asked as soon as Brubaker was out of the cockpit.

"We ordered home?"

"Forney and Gamidge are being sent to the barge."

"The barge?" This was a scow stationed near the Korean coast, and helicopter men with that duty lived miserably and engaged in one dangerous land mission after another.

A destroyer moved in and the last the *Savo* saw of Mike Forney was when he climbed into the bo'sun's chair, green top hat, green scarf and Irishman's pipe. "I'll send you the eighty bucks, sir," he yelled, giving the word *sir* its old infuriating touch.

Brubaker didn't care if the captain was watching. He grabbed the disgraced man's hand and said, "Take care of yourself, Mike. Pilots need you."

"I go for rough duty," Mike yelled, clutching his hat as the lines started to draw him over to the destroyer. "Because I really hate communists."

The chair dipped perilously toward the sea but Mike kept his legs clear. Instinctively the pilots cheered but the Irishman yelled derisively, "You apes go into the drink, not me!"

The new helicopter pilot was an officer, a college kid and no doubt competent, but the jet men and propeller crews knew that flying off the Savo would be a little tougher now.

The fear that was reborn when Brubaker watched Cag dive into the valley at Toko-ri grew all that day, augmented by the gloom of Mike Forney's dismissal and the briefing. After dinner, in the crowded ready room, the intelligence officer had passed around marked copies of the photographs made that morning and said, "Take-off at 0900. By then the sun will have driven ground fog out of the valley. Keep well south of the guns at Majon-ni. Cag, you tell them about the approach."

Cag, cigar in mouth, said briefly, "On paper it looks like a lot of flak concentrated here." He jabbed at the map with his right forefinger. "But it's not accurate. We'll go in low. We'll go in three times. And we'll go in from the east each time. When we're through, there won't be any more bridges."

There were some questions and then Cag handed them the cold dope. He held his cigar in his left hand and said, "Marty, you take your four men in at 1000 feet

to suppress flak. I'll follow with my four at 1200. Brubaker, you mop up."

Tightly Brubaker gripped the arms of his chair and
fought back his fear. He couldn't fly this mission. He
couldn't take his jet inside that blazing rim of hills.
His old bitterness at having been called back into service sneaked up into his throat and corroded his courage.
Frantically, as if afraid he might break down before his
peers, he rose and hurried out.

Stumbling down the narrow passageways of the carrier, he banged against stanchions and bruised his shin
upon the damnable hatches. Seeking out his own room
he slammed the door shut and climbed up into his
bed under the steam pipes. In uncontrolled panic, there
in the dark room, he cast about for some way to avoid
the strike against the bridges.

"I'll go see the doc. I'll just walk in and announce,
'I've lost my nerve.' " Impulsively he climbed down and
started for the door. Then he stopped and laughed
nervously at himself.

For the Navy had worked out the perfect way to
handle situations like this. Suppose you went in and
said you were too jittery to fly, the doc simply said,
"OK. Don't fly." It was so easy that a man thought a
hundred thousand times before he used that dodge. He
stood alone, sweating, in his dark room and recalled the
Cag's flight into the valley, and almost without
knowing it he uttered the tricky words that bind a
man to duty, those simple words that send men in
jet planes against overwhelmingly protected bridges:
"If Cag can fly that flak, so can I." That was what kept
the Navy system working. You could weasel out any
time, but within the essence of your conscience lived

the memory of other men no less afraid than you who were willing to tackle the dirty jobs. So you stuck.

But then a late flight returned and he thought ungraciously, "What mission did they draw? Rail cuts. Up where there are no guns. Why don't they get the bridges? Why does it have to be me?"

He felt ashamed of himself and turned on the light but was appalled by his own gray and ashen face in the mirror. "Get hold of yourself!" he commanded. Methodically, as if attention to some one job would restore his courage, he sat down to write a letter to his wife, but after he had written only a few lines he drew back in disgust. "You stinker!" he whispered at his picture in the mirror. "Scaring Nancy by letting her know you expect to be killed at the bridges."

He began a new letter and with great composure told Nancy how much he loved the children and of how he longed for the days of peace when they could all go camping again in the Rockies back of Denver. He ended with a paragraph in which he described in detail the suit she had worn that day on the quay at Yokosuka. "It looked very expensive," he wrote, "and I was amazed when you said you made it yourself."

But when he crawled back into bed things were worse than before, and like a stabbing agony in the darkness he cried, "Why does it have to be me?" He remembered the men he had known in Colorado. Some hated their wives but they stayed home. Others hated their jobs, but they stayed on those jobs. Some of them, he recalled, had always wanted to travel, some had loved airplanes, others were always picking a fight and some good Catholics like Mike Forney hated communism so much they could taste it. Others were poor and needed Navy pay. But all of them stayed home.

Through the long night Brubaker wrestled with his fear. Toward morning he was taken with frenzy and leaped from bed, rushing down the passageway to report his loss of nerve, but he never reached the doctor. A shattering sound halted him and in the gloomy darkness he whispered, "They're launching the dawn planes. It won't be long now." Then the catapult fired again and he remembered something Forney had once said and he stumbled down the ladder to the port catapult room, breaking in among the crew and crying, "Where did Mike Forney stand?"

"Here."

"Is that the pistol he told me about?"

"Yep."

Before Brubaker could ask more questions the engine fired and from its nest forward eleven tons of gleaming metal roared back with appalling force to stop a few inches from his face. Involuntarily he stumbled backward. The enlisted men laughed.

"Forney stood stock still," they said.

Mike had explained that he came to the catapult room whenever his nerves were getting tight and the explosion of that enormous piston right into his face cured him: "If a guy can take that, he can take anything," Mike had said, but before Brubaker got set the monstrous machine fired again and that tremendous gleaming force sprang at him. He fell back.

"Takes a real idiot to stay put," a crewman shouted.

"You ever tried it?" Brubaker asked.

"I ain't no idiot."

Brubaker rooted himself to a position from which he could not be budged, and like a frightened bullfighter he mumbled to himself, "This time I keep my feet here." While he watched, the mighty piston leaped at him, then stopped with a powerful uuuuush less than four inches from his face.

The catapult crew applauded and said, "Pretty soon now you'll be as crazy as Forney."

"Is that bad?" Brubaker asked. Briskly he returned through the darkened ship and climbed into bed. "Well," he assured himself, "at least I'm not yellow." But immediately he was more afraid: "Because you know the catapult's got to stop. But the guns at Toko-ri never do."

So when the messenger called at 0700 he found Brubaker awake and sweating, staring at the steam pipes. When he reported to the wardroom bleary-eyed, Cag asked, "What were you doing in the catapult room last night?"

There was no use kidding anybody so he replied, "I was jittery."

"Does sticking your face in a piston cure that?"

"Yes."

Cag knew he should have left it at that but this mission was too important so he asked, "You want to ground yourself? Because today we've got to do a first-rate professional job."

"That's what I'm here for."

"Good. I put you in the follow-through spot because I know that if my gang miss the bridges, you'll get 'em."

"I'm going to."

At 0730 the pilots moved into the cold ready room

where the worst part of the flight took place. Twelve reasonably trim lithe young athletes began to pile onto themselves such a mass of encumbrances that soon they waddled like pigs, completely muscle bound and sweating from every pore. Sometimes even the bravest pilots felt their nerves shiver when they faced the degrading job of dressing for a winter flight.

Brubaker started in shorts. First he climbed into long-handled woolen underwear, then into a skin-tight g-suit, which applied pressure on vital parts of his body so that when he pulled out of steep dives the enormous drag of gravity, the g's, would not suck all the blood from his head. He covered the g-suit with inch-thick quilted underwear, two pairs of short bulky socks and a third which reached his knees. Then came the rough part, for even though the watertight rubber poopy suit had already saved his life once, getting into it was always murder.

Since the neck band had to be tight to keep out freezing water and since no zippers were allowed, he had to get into the poopy suit in a special way. A long slash ran from the left shoulder across the chest and down to the right hip and he climbed in through this hole, pushing his feet down into the massive boots and his head up through the impossibly tight neck band. Then he grabbed the two flaps of extra rubber along the slash and rolled them together into a bulky, watertight seal which fattened him like a watermelon. And as soon as he closed this final seal he began to sweat like a pig and every minute he wore the poopy suit he was smelly and wet and uncomfortable. From time to time he pulled the neck band out and blew fresh air inside to get some relief. That's why the ready room was kept so cold, to keep the pilots from sweating, but all the same they sweated.

After the poopy suit came the survival vest, the pistol, the bulky Mae West, the hip knife, three cumbersome pairs of gloves, golden crash helmet, oxygen connection, harness straps and heavy goggles. Weighed down like some primeval monster, he waddled to the escalator which lifted him to the flight deck—another trick to keep down sweat—where an enlisted man handed him the board for clamping onto his knee with navigation data, codes, plots and all kinds of miscellaneous papers.

Even when he climbed into his jet there was more gear, so complicated that his plane captain had to crouch behind him and adjust safety belt, shoulder harness, ejection gear, microphone cord and oxygen supply. Harry Brubaker, who was about to soar into space with a freedom no previous men in history had known, was loaded down with such intolerable burdens that at times he felt he must suffocate; just as many citizens of his world, faced with a chance at freedoms never before dreamed of, felt so oppressed by modern problems and requirements that they were sure they must collapse.

As Brubaker adjusted himself to the cockpit he was hemmed in on left and right by more than seventy-five switches and controls. Directly facing him were sixteen instruments and thirteen more switches. He thought, "If there were one more thing to do. . . ." He never finished the sentence for the mighty catapult fired and he was shot into space, where the suffocating paraphernalia and the maze of switches seemed to fall away and he roared into the upper blue, tied down only by his cancerous fear of the bridges at Toko-ri.

But today he would not see those bridges, for at Wonsan the radio crackled and he heard Cag's disappointed voice, "Weather scout reports target closed in. Ground fog. Stand by for alternate instructions."

When Brubaker heard this life-saving news he shouted, "A reprieve! I knew I wasn't meant to tackle the bridges today." He started to sing the chorus of *Cielito Lindo* but stopped in embarrassment when he saw that in his surging joy he had unconsciously lifted his Banshee 400 feet higher than the formation.

But ground fog did not save him, for in the next minute a miracle of modern war occurred. Cag received a radio message from Admiral Tarrant, and instantly the twelve jets stopped in midflight, almost as if they were a flock of pheasant searching for a Colorado grain field. Abruptly they turned south, heading for the mountainous battle front, where in the trenches a new emergency had arisen.

At dawn that morning a battalion of South Korean infantry had been hit by a murderous concentration of communist power and it became apparent that the Koreans would be annihilated unless air support could be provided. So a United States Army liaison officer serving at the front phoned a Korean general, who called the United States Army command in Seoul, who got hold of an air force general, who said he had no planes but would try to get some from a marine general, who suggested that Admiral Tarrant, far out to sea, might have some to spare. The inquiry arrived in flag plot just as the early-morning weather plane was reporting: "Toko-ri closed in but good. Takusan ground fog. Takusan no see."

Tarrant, who normally would not see such a message, made a note to chew out a pilot who would use Japanese in a battle report, and replied, "One flight of twelve heavily armed jets available. Already airborne."

Seoul immediately ordered, "Proceed Roundelay. Operate as he directs."

So by means of field telephone, radio, ship-to-shore communication and ship-to-plane, American jets were diverted to rescue South Korean foot soldiers. As the planes swept south Cag called ahead, "Roundelay, twelve jets reporting for orders. We're loaded."

From the bright morning sky came a whispery voice: "This is Roundelay. I'm flying an SNJ."

Each jet pilot was astonished that in today's swift war the out-of-date old SNJ would still be used. It had been ancient before they took basic training, but no one had quite the shock that Harry Brubaker experienced. "An SNJ?" he repeated incredulously and he was back in 1935, a gangling boy stretched out upon the floor, quietly and supremely happy, for he had mailed the box tops and the company had kept its promise. Here was the highly colored put-together of America's latest plane. "It was an SNJ," he recalled.

Then suddenly from behind a mountain, there was the real SNJ, a rickety, two-bladed propeller job with a high greenhouse, a useless spare seat and six smoke rockets slung precariously under its wings. A slap-happy air force captain was wheeling it slowly around and Harry thought, "What's an SNJ doing here?" Then he learned.

"This is Roundelay. Get the big guns first."

"Can't see 'em," Cag said.

"Follow me."

And to the amazement of the jet pilots Roundelay trundled his slow plane down almost to the treetops and delivered a smoke rocket against the target. "See it now?" he called.

"Will do!" Cag cried, and he led his twelve screaming jets into a howling dive, right onto the gun and it fired no more.

"Strictly wonderful," Roundelay called. "D'you see the other two?"

"Negative."

"Watch this smoke." And the buglike SNJ hopped almost at ground level up a narrow valley to deliver another smoke rocket against another gun. Then, when it seemed the midget plane must follow the rocket against the rocks, the pilot twisted free, skipped over a ridge and ducked down upon a third gun.

"Will do!" Cag reported, and when his swift jets had silenced the guns, Roundelay called cheerily, "You must come back often."

The jets had zoomed so high they could not keep track of the tiny plane, but then sunlight glinted on the ridiculous greenhouse and they heard Roundelay call, "I think I see Red troops beginning a new attack. Follow me." And once more he hurried off like a busy old woman going to market.

Brubaker's division was aloft and he watched Cag's four jets roar low into a column of communists assaulting a hill. With appalling accuracy the Banshees spread their hundred-pound bombs, each wound with high-tension steel wire that shattered into small pieces with machine-gun fury. The communist advance wavered.

"Next division," Roundelay called. "Keep hitting them while they're confused."

"Will do," Brubaker replied, but as he prepared for his dive, the SNJ wheeled suddenly and Roundelay called, "Do you see what I see?"

Below, in obedience to some order of incredible stupidity, more than one hundred communists had moved out of a woods and onto a frozen road, and as Brubaker's jets came screaming at them they did an even more unbelievable thing. They fell to their knees in the middle of the road, clasped their arms about their heads and made no effort to escape inevitable death. The tactic so astonished Brubaker that he gasped, "They're sitting ducks!" And some ancient boyhood training in the mountains back of Denver restrained him.

But when he had zoomed high into the heavens he heard the unemotional voice of Roundelay: "Clobber those guys. That's their standard trick. Throwing you off balance."

So the jets wheeled and came screaming back down the road. Not a communist moved. Not one hit the ditch. They huddled and waited. "Here it comes," Brubaker whispered grimly, and his finger pressed the trigger. Keeping his eye upon the kneeling troops, he watched his bullets spray a path among them. "You wanted trouble," he said weakly.

Roundelay now spotted another column of attacking communists and called in Cag's division. Brubaker, with sickening detachment, watched the merciless jets and thought, "Those people in Denver who ridicule air force reports of enemy dead ought to see this." And he remembered Admiral Tarrant's words: "If we keep enough planes over them enough hours somebody's got to get hurt. And when they hurt bad enough, they'll quit."

"How's your fuel?" Roundelay asked.

"Can do one more pass," Cag replied, and the jet pilots, who approached the speed of sound, watched as the slow little doodlebug SNJ hopped about in search of fat targets. Brubaker, pulling out of his last bombing run, sped past the prop plane and for an instant of suspended time the two men looked casually at each other. Harry saw that the air force man was very thin and wore a moustache but he saw no more, for a five-inch communist gun, hidden until then, fired one lucky shot and blew the frail little SNJ completely to ribbons.

In terrible fury Brubaker launched his jet at the gun and tried to root it from its cave. He carried his fire almost into the muzzle of the enemy gun. Then, although his fuel was getting tight, he turned and made another run, pushing his jet to a deadly speed. He saw the gun, saw the wounded crew and the shell casings. On he came, firing until his own guns were silent, and the communists fell away. Then he zoomed aloft to overtake the homeward jets, but except for his wingman the planes were far away.

"You ought to tell me when you're going to run wild," the wingman protested.

"I really clobbered that one," Brubaker said grimly, but as the two Banshees soared away from the ravaged battleground with its wrecked artillery and dead bodies huddled along frozen roads, the enemy gun that Brubaker thought he had destroyed resumed firing.

Mute with outrage, Brubaker wanted to dive upon it once more but he heard his wingman say, "Their side has guts, too."

Finally, when the roar of battle was past and the jets were far in the wintry sky Brubaker called, "How's your fuel?"

"Thousand five."

His own gauge read just under a thousand and he thought, "I hope Beer Barrel is bringing us in." Then he heard his wingman cry, "There's Cag, up ahead."

The two jets increased speed to rejoin the flight and all pilots began the difficult job of trying to spot the task force. Drifting clouds mottled the sea and made the ships almost invisible, but they had to be within a small area, for to the east hung the permanent snow line and to the north a new storm boxed in the fleet, but no one could see the ships.

It was ridiculous. Twelve highly-trained pilots couldn't find a task force of nineteen ships, including carriers, cruisers and a battleship. For some perverse reason Brubaker took delight in this limitation of human beings and thought, "You never master this business." Then Cag called, "There's home!" and where absolutely nothing had been visible a moment before the jet pilots saw the nineteen ships. And Brubaker, seeing them as big as barns on an open meadow, laughed.

But his relief didn't last because when the jets descended he saw that the carrier deck was pitching rather formidably, and this meant many wave-offs because the landing officer would have to wait until the carrier stabilized itself between lurches, so that you might approach in perfect altitude but find the deck in a momentary trough and have to go round again.

That took fuel. Because when you got a wave-off you had to pour it on. And there went your fuel.

Then he had a happy thought: "They probably haven't turned into the wind. The deck'll be better when they do."

But as he watched, a flight of jets took off from the *Hornet* and that proved the carriers were already into the wind, so he looked at the heaving *Savo*, stern leaping high in the air, bow down and said, "There's your deck and you'll like it." Then, although he never prayed, he mumbled, "Beer Barrel, be out there today!" And as if in answer to this plea Cag announced, "Beer Barrel's bringing us in on a pitching deck. Anybody short on fuel?"

Brubaker reported, "1591 reporting over ship with 800."

He listened to Cag forward this news to the *Savo* and then call, "We'll double up. No trouble getting aboard."

So instead of the normal interval which would enable one jet to land each 26 seconds, the twelve Banshees formed a tight little circle yielding 15-second intervals so that whenever the deck stabilized there would be some jet diving right for it. But this also meant that one out of every two planes would have to take automatic wave-offs. "Hope I'm one of the lucky ones," Brubaker said.

He was. On his outward leg the *Savo* pitched so badly that no landing plane got aboard, but by the time Harry's downward leg started, the big ship was shuddering into stabilized position. "It'll hold that position for at least a minute," Brubaker assured himself. "Time to get three of us aboard." Nervously he ticked off the jets ahead of him in the circle. "Seven of them.

Just right. First two will have to pass because the deck won't be steady enough, but three, five and seven'll make it. Boy, I'm seven!"

Then he saw Beer Barrel's paddles bringing number three in and the deck crew had the hook disengaged in two and a half seconds and the deck was steady and clear. "What an outfit when the going's tough," Brubaker said admiringly.

Then hell broke loose. The pilot in jet number five did what Beer Barrel had warned his men never to do. As his Banshee neared the cut-off point the deck lurched and the pilot tried to compensate. Instead of flying Beer Barrel he flew the deck and missed every wire. In great panic he managed to pancake into the barriers but he ripped them both away and the crucial barricade as well.

Brubaker, screaming over the wreckage, saw instantly that it would be many minutes before the deck could be cleared and he cried feverishly to himself, "I don't want to go into the sea again."

His fear was unreasonable. He could see the helicopters waiting to rescue him. He saw the alert destroyers, always quick to lift a downed pilot from the waves. But he also saw the gray sea and he'd been down there once. "The second time you crack up. You sink and they never find you." Instinctively he felt to see if his three gloves were watertight at the wrist. That's where the sea crept in and froze you. Then he pulled his hand away in horror and whispered, "Beer Barrel, don't let me go into the drink."

Then he got hold of himself and heard Cag's quiet voice say, "All nylon torn away. At least ten minutes to repair it. Is that critical for 1591?"

Brubaker breathed deeply to drive down any quiver in his voice and reported evenly, "I'm down to 600."

Cag said to the ship, "1591 low on fuel. Must land on first pass after barrier is fixed."

The radio said, "*Hornet's* deck temporarily fouled. But would landing there in eight minutes be of help?"

Promptly Brubaker said, "I'd waste just as much gas getting in the circle. I'll stick here." What he did not say was that without Beer Barrel's help he might lose his nerve completely.

With mounting fear he noticed that the crashed plane still fouled up the landing space and the broken barriers were not being promptly repaired. What made this especially infuriating was that all this time the carrier remained in stabilized position and all the jets could have been landed. Then he saw something that froze him. The towering black crane called Tilly was being moved into position alongside the wrecked Banshee, right where the missing nylon barricade should have been. Then a quiet, reassuring voice spoke to him, offering a choice. "1591," the impersonal voice said, "*Hornet's* deck still not ready. Impossible to erect barricade in time for you to land but we must protect planes parked forward. Have therefore moved Tilly into position to stop you positively in case you miss wire. Do you wish to attempt deck landing or do you wish to ditch? Advise."

He stared down at the monstrous crane looming up from the middle of the deck. "That'll stop me. Oh boy, will that stop me!" It was a brutal thing to do, to move Tilly out there, but he appreciated why it had been done. Behind the crane were parked $40,000,000 worth of aircraft and they must be protected and he

felt no resentment at the maneuver. But before reply-
ing he reasoned carefully, "The last guy missed the
wires because the deck pitched. I can too," and he
was about to elect ditching but a compelling instinct
told him that his only hope for safety lay with Beer
Barrel.

"I'm coming in," he said.

He made his first turn and prayed, "Beer Barrel,
bring me in. I don't care if the deck is going crazy, bring
me in."

On the down-wind leg he dropped to correct altitude and avoided looking at the pitching deck. He kept
his eyes on the screen that shielded Beer Barrel from the
wind but for a moment he became quite sick, for the
stern was bouncing about like a derelict rowboat.

"Bring me in, Beer Barrel."

Then as he whipped into the final turn he saw that
terrible thing, the crane Tilly filling the end of the landing space and he would have turned aside had he not
also seen Beer Barrel. The big man stood on one foot,
his paddles up . . . still good . . . still coming . . .
oh, Beer Barrel, keep me coming. . . .

Then mercifully the cut sign, the firm hook catching
securely, the run of singing wire, the tremendous pull
upon his shoulders, and his eyes looking up at the monstrous crane into which he did not crash.

From the flag bridge Admiral Tarrant followed the
emergency landing and when he saw Brubaker lunge
onto the deck safely he sent an aide to bring the pilot
to him as soon as intelligence had checked battle reports. Some minutes later the young man appeared
relaxed and smiling in freshly pressed khaki and said,
"Somebody told me there were eight hundred ways to

get back aboard a carrier. Any one of them's good, if you make it."

Tarrant laughed, jabbed a cup of coffee into the pilot's hands and asked casually, "What were you doing in the catapult room last night?"

Brubaker sat down carefully, sipped his coffee and said, "I lost my nerve last night."

"You looked pretty steady out there just now."

It was very important now that Brubaker say just the right thing, for he knew that something big was eating the admiral but he couldn't guess what, so he looked up over the rim of his cup and said, "Best sedative in the world is Beer Barrel and those paddles."

The admiral remained standing, somewhat annoyed at Brubaker's having presumed to sit. Nevertheless, the bonds of sympathy which bound him to the younger man were at work. He didn't want Brubaker to participate in the attack on the bridges, so in an offhand manner he asked, "Son, do you want me to ground you . . . for tomorrow's flight against Toko-ri?"

Brubaker thought, "If he'd wanted me to stay down he wouldn't have asked. He'd have told me. This way he hopes I won't accept." But of his own will and regardless of the admiral he decided to say no and replied evenly, "If anybody goes, I go."

Admiral Tarrant was at once aware that he had posed his question the wrong way and said, "I think you're jittery, son. I think you ought to stay down."

Again Brubaker thought, "The old man's wrestling with himself. He wants to ground me but he's afraid it would look like favoritism. So he's trying to trick me into asking. That way everything would be OK." But again he said, "I want to fly against the bridges."

Certain, and in some ways pleased, that the young man would refuse the order, Tarrant said, "Harry, I've been watching you. There's nothing shameful in a man's reaching the end of his rope for the time being. You know I consider you our finest pilot . . . after the squadron leaders. But I can't let you fly tomorrow."

And Brubaker said quietly, "Sir, if you'd offered me this chance last night I'd have jumped to accept it. Or half an hour ago when I stared at that big black Tilly. But I think you know how it is, sir. Any time you get back safe, that day's trembling is over. Right now I haven't a nerve. Look." He held out his coffee saucer and it remained rigid.

"You're sure it's passed?"

"Positive. Remember when you told my wife about the voluntary men who save the world? I've seen two of these men. It shakes you to the roots of your heart to see such men in action."

"Who'd you see?" Tarrant asked, the sparring over.

"Yesterday I saw Cag take his photographic plane. . . ."

"Cag?"

"Yes, sir. I saw a man so brave. . . . Admiral, he went in so low that he simply had to get knocked down. Then he went in again . . . lower."

"Cag?" Admiral Tarrant repeated, amazed.

"And this morning. . . . Did anyone tell you about the air force spotter in the SNJ?"

"No."

Brubaker's voice almost broke but he stammered, "He was killed by a gun I might have knocked out . . . if I'd really been on the ball." There was a long silence in which Tarrant poured more coffee. Finally Brubaker said, "Sometimes you look honor right in the face. In the face of another man. It's terrifying." His voice trailed away and he added in a whisper, "So I have no choice. I have to go out tomorrow. If he could fly an SNJ, I can fly a jet." He laughed nervously and thrust his saucer out again. It remained immovable, like the end of a solid stone arm. "No nerves now," he said.

It was 1145 next morning when Cag, his jets poised aloft for their first run against the bridges, cried, "Attack, attack, attack!"

With deadly precision, and ignoring the mortal curtain of communist fire, four Banshees assigned to flak-suppression flung themselves upon the heaviest guns at more than 500 miles an hour. Rendezvousing to the north, they swept back in ghostly blue streaks and raked the principal emplacements a second time, but as they reached the middle of this passage communist fire struck number three plane and with a violence few men have witnessed it smashed into a hill and exploded in an instantaneous orange flash.

Before the eight pilots aloft could realize what had happened Cag called quietly, "Prepare to attack," and the four jets in his division peeled off for swift assault upon the bridges. They descended at an angle steeper than 50° and for the entire final run of two miles no pilot swerved or dodged until his first huge bomb sped free.

From aloft Brubaker saw that Cag had got two of the bridges. Now he must finish the job. He brought his division down in a screaming dive, aware that when he straightened out the pull of gravity upon him would suck the blood away from his head and drag his lips into grotesque positions, but the fascination of those looming bridges of Toko-ri lured him on. Lower and lower he came. When he finally pickled his bomb and pulled away he absorbed so many g's that a heaviness came upon his legs and his face was drawn drowsily down upon his chin. But he knew nothing of this for he experienced only surging elation. He had bombed the bridges.

Then he heard the dismal voice: "No damage to main bridge."

And you had to believe that voice, for it was Roy's, last man through. Tomorrow stateside newspapers might exaggerate the damage. You could kid the intelligence officer. And you could lie like a schoolboy to pilots from another squadron, but last man through told the truth. No damage.

"I'm sure Brubaker got a span," Cag argued.

"Negative," Roy replied flatly.

"How about the truck bridges?"

"Clobbered, clobbered, clobbered."

Cag called, "Stand by for run number two," and eleven jets orbited for position. The three flak-suppression Banshees stampeded for the gun-rimmed valley and as they roared in the leader confirmed Roy's report: "No damage to the main bridge." But the last of the flak jets reported, "We really have the ground fire slowed down."

Then, to the surprise of the communists, Cag brought his men in over the same check points as before and cheated some of the communist gunners, who had been gambling that he would use the other entrance to their valley. Through gray bomb smoke and bursts of flak, through spattering lead and their own fears, the first four pilots bore in upon the bridges. Roaring straight down the railroad track like demon trains they pickled their heavy freight upon the bridge and pulled away with sickening g's upon them, their mouths gaping wide like idiots, their eyes dulled with war and the pull of gravity.

As Brubaker led his men upon the bridges he saw a magnificent sight. Three spans were down and a fourth was crumbling. The two truck bridges were demolished and the alternate railroad span was in the mud. In triumph he called, "This is Brubaker. All bridges down. Divert to the dump." And with blood perilously withdrawn from his head he swung his Banshee away from the bridges, over a slight rise of ground, and down upon the sprawling military dumps. Strafing, bombing, twisting, igniting, he screamed on, his three teammates following. Somebody's bomb struck ammunition. Consecutive explosions, each keeping the next alive, raced through the stores.

This time Roy, last man through, said, "We hit something big."

Cag, aloft, called, "All planes, all planes. Work over the dump."

Brubaker, now higher than the others, watched the dazzling procession of Banshees. Swooping low, they spun their fragmentation bombs earthward and retired into the lonely distance. Returning, they dodged hills and spread deathly fire. Over snowy ridges they formed for new runs and wherever they moved there was silent beauty and the glint of sunlight on the bronzed helmet of some man riding beneath the plexiglas canopy. It was a fearsome thing to watch jets assume control of this valley where the bridges had been, and it was gloomy, for no matter where any of the pilots looked they could see the scarred hillside against which one of their team had plunged to death a few minutes before.

His ammunition nearly spent, Brubaker nosed down for a final run upon the spattered dumps, but Cag called, "Stay clear of the ammo dumps. We have them popping there." So he twisted his jet to the south, away from the ammo but before he could launch his dive, two jets streaked across his target and jettisoned their bombs so that again he had to pull away. He was tempted to drop his last bomb where he thought he saw a gun emplacement but promptly he discarded this idea as unworthy, for it occurred to him, quite clearly in this instant of decision, that even one bomb more might mean significant interdiction of supplies to the front: fewer bullets for communist gunners, fewer blankets for their trenches, less food. He recalled Admiral Tarrant's words: "If we keep the pressure high enough something's got to explode over there."

So in an effort to add that extra degree of pressure which might help to beat back aggression, he turned away from his easy target and picked out a supply dump. He activated his nose guns and watched their heavy bullets rip into valued cargo and set it afire. Then he resolutely pickled his last bomb but as he pulled out of his dive, with heavy g's upon his face, he heard a pinking-thud.

"I've been hit!" he cried and as the jet sped upward chaos took over. He lost control of his mind and of the thundering Banshee and in panic thought only of Wonsan harbor. He felt the irresistible lure of the sea where friendly craft might rescue him and violently he wrenched his nose toward the east and fled homeward like a sea-stricken thing. But as soon as he had made this desperate turn he became aware that panic was flying the plane, not he, and he called quietly, "Joe, Joe. Just took a hit. So far I'm all right."

From the dark sky aloft came the reassuring whisper, "Harry, this is Joe. I have you in sight."

"Joe, drop down and look me over."

Now an ugly vibration identified itself as coming from the port engine but for one fragile second of time it seemed as if the frightening sound might abate. Then, with shattering echoes, the entire engine seemed to fall apart and Brubaker whispered to himself, "I'm not going to get this crate out of Korea."

A communist bullet no bigger than a man's thumb, fired at random by some ground defender of the dump, had blundered haphazardly into the turbine blades, which were then whirring at nearly 13,000 revolutions a minute. So delicately was the jet engine balanced that the loss of only two blade tips had thrown the entire mechanism out of balance, and the grinding noise Brubaker heard was the turbine throwing off dozens of knifelike blades which slashed into the fuselage or out through the dark sky. Like the society which had conceived the engine, the turbine was of such advanced construction that even trivial disruption of one fundamental part endangered the entire structure.

He had, of course, immediately cut fuel to the damaged engine and increased revolutions on the other and as soon as the clatter of the damaged turbines subsided he cut off its air supply and eliminated the destructive vibrations altogether. Then, in fresh silence, he checked the twenty principal indicators on his panel and found things to be in pretty good shape. "I might even make it back to the ship," he said hopefully. But promptly he discarded this for a more practical objective: "Anyway, I'll be able to reach the sea."

He laughed at himself and said, "Look at me! Yesterday I pushed the panic button because I might have to go into the sea. Today I reached for it because I might miss the water."

As he reasoned with himself Joe came lazily out from beneath his wing and waved. "Everything all right now?" Joe asked.

"All under control," he answered.

"Fuel OK?"

"Fine. More than 2,000 pounds."

"Keep checking it," Joe said quietly. "You may be losing a little."

Then the sick panic returned and no more that day would it leave. Impeded by heavy gear he tried to look aft but couldn't. Straining himself he saw fleetingly from the corner of his eye a thin wisp of white vapor trailing in the black sky. Knocking his goggles away he tried to look again and his peripheral vision spied the dusty vapor, no thicker than a pencil.

"Joe," he called quietly. "That looks like a fuel leak."

"Don't your gauges show it?"

"Don't seem to."

"You'll make the sea all right," Joe said, and both men surrendered any idea of the ship.

"I'll make the sea," Harry said.

"I'll trail you," Joe called.

In a few minutes he said, "You're losing fuel pretty fast, Harry."

There was no longer any use to kid himself. "Yeah. Now the instruments show it."

Joe drew his slim blue jet quite close to Harry's and the two men looked at one another as clearly as if they had been across a table in some bar. "I still think you'll make the sea," Joe said.

But Harry knew that merely reaching the sea wasn't enough. "How far out must we go in Wonsan harbor to miss the communist mines?" he asked.

Joe ruffled through some papers clipped to his knee and replied, "You ought to go two miles. But you'll make it, Harry."

The turbine blade that had sliced into the fuel line now broke loose and allowed a heavy spurt of gasoline to erupt so that Joe could clearly see it. "You're losing gas pretty fast now," he said.

There was a sad drop on the fuel gauge and Harry said, "Guess that does it."

To prevent explosion, he immediately killed his good engine and felt the Banshee stutter in midair, as if caught by some enormous hand. Then, at 250 miles an hour, he started the long and agonizing glide which carried him ever nearer to the sea and always lower toward the mountains.

Quickly Joe cut his own speed and said, "We better call the word."

With crisp voice Brubaker announced the strange word which by general consent across the world has come to mean disaster. In Malaya, in China, over Europe or in the jungle airports of the Amazon this word betokens final catastrophe: "Mayday, Mayday."

It was heard by communist monitors and by the officers in Task Force 77. Aloft, Cag heard it and turned his jets back to keep watch upon their stricken member. And aboard the scow the newly reported helicopter team of Mike Forney and Nestor Gamidge heard it.

"Mayday, Mayday."

Silently, through the upper reaches of the sky, the two men flew side by side. They had never been particularly friendly, for their interests and ages varied, nor had they talked much, but now in the dark violet sky with sunlight gleaming beneath them on the hills of Korea they began their last urgent conversation, their faces bright in plexiglas and their voices speaking clear through the vast emptiness of the space.

"We'll make the sea," Joe said reassuringly.

"I'm sure going to try."

They drifted down to the sunny spaces of the sky, into the region of small cloud and laughing shadow and Joe asked, "Now when we reach the sea will you parachute or ditch?"

"I ditched once, I'll do it again."

"I never asked you, how does the Banshee take the water?"

"Fine, if you keep the tail down."

"Remember to jettison your canopy, Harry."

"I don't aim to be penned in."

"Six more minutes will put us there."

So they fought to the sea. As if caught in the grip of some atavistic urge that called them back to the safety of the sea after the millions of years during which men had risen from this element, these two pilots nursed their jets away from inhospitable land and out toward the open sea. They were low now and could spot communist villages and from time to time they saw bursts of communist guns, so they fought to reach the sea.

But they did not make it. For looming ahead of them rose the hills in back of Wonsan harbor. Between the jets and the sea stood these ugly hills and there was no way to pass them. Instinctively Harry shoved the throttle forward to zoom higher—only a couple of hundred feet, even fifty might do—but relentlessly the stricken Banshee settled lower.

From the adjoining plane Joe pointed to the obstructing hills and Harry said, "I see them. I won't make it."

Joe asked, "Now, Harry, are you going to jump or crash land!"

"Crash," Harry said promptly. Back in the States he had decided to stick with his plane no matter what happened. Besides, communists shot at parachutes, whereas the speed of a crash often took them by surprise and permitted rescue operations.

"Keep your wheels up," Joe said.

"Will do."

"Be sure to hit every item on the check-off list."

"Will do."

"Harry, make sure those shoulder straps are really tight."

"Already they're choking me."

"Good boy. Now, Harry, remember what happened to Lou. Unhook your oxygen mask and radio before you hit."

"Will do."

"Knife? Gun?"

Harry nodded. Although he was soon going to hit some piece of Korean ground at a speed of 130 miles, his plane bursting out of control at impact, in this quiet preparatory moment he could smile out of his canopy and converse with Joe as if they were longtime friends reviewing a basketball game.

"Pretty soon now," he said.

"I'll move ahead and try to find a good field," Joe said. Before he pulled away he pointed aloft and said, "Cag's upstairs."

Soon he called, "This field looks fair."

"Isn't that a ditch running down the middle?"

"Only shadows."

"You think I can stop short of the trees?"

"Easy, Harry. Easy."

"Well then, that's our field."

"Listen, Harry. When you do land, no matter what happens, get out fast."

"You bet. I don't like exploding gas."

"Good boy. Remember, fellow. Fast. Fast."

Desperately Brubaker wanted to make one run along the field to check things for himself, but the remorseless glide kept dragging him down and he heard Joe's patient voice calling, "Harry, you better jettison that canopy right now."

"I forgot."

Like a schoolteacher with a child Joe said, "That was first on the check-off list. Did you hit those items, Harry?"

"I got them all," Harry said.

"Field look OK?"

"You pick 'em real good, son."

Those were the last words Harry said to his wingman, for the ground was rushing up too fast and there was much work to do. Dropping his right wing to make the turn onto the field, he selected what looked like the clearest strip and lowered his flaps. Then, kicking off a little altitude by means of a side slip, he headed for the earth. Tensed almost to the shattering point, he held the great Banshee steady, tail down, heard a ripping sound, saw his right wing drop suddenly and tear away, watched a line of trees rush up at him and felt the final tragic collapse of everything. The impact almost tore the harness through his left shoulder socket but without this bracing he would surely have been killed. For an instant he thought the pain might make him faint, but the rich sweet smell of gasoline reached him and with swift planned motions he ripped himself loose from the smoking plane. But when he started to climb down he realized that his oxygen supply tube and his radio were still connected, just as Joe had warned. Laughing at himself he said, "Some guys you can't tell anything." With a powerful lurch he broke the cords and leaped upon Korean soil.

He was in a rice field three miles from a village. Beyond lay other rice fields and many curious U-shaped houses of the Korean countryside, their roofs covered with snow. To the north were mountains, to the south a row of trees, while from the east came a hint of salt air telling him that the sea was not far distant. But even as he surveyed his field he started running clumsily from the plane and before he had run far it burst into flame and exploded with numerous small blasts which sent billows of smoke into the air, informing communists in the village that another American plane had crashed. "They'll be after me soon," he thought and ran faster.

Within a few steps he was soaked with sweat inside his poopy suit and his breath hurt as it fought its way into his lungs. But still he ran, his big boots sticking in snowy mud, his intolerable gear holding him back. Finally he had to rest and sat upon a mound of earth forming the bank of a wide ditch that ran along the western edge of the field, but when one foot went into the center of the ditch he drew back in disgust for the smell he stirred up told him this was used for storing sewage until it was placed upon the rice fields. The stench was great and he started to leave but across the field he saw two communist soldiers approach the burning jet with rifles. So he did not leave the ditch but hid behind the mound of earth and reached for the revolver which he had once fired nine times in practice. He inspected its unfamiliar construction and remembered that it contained six bullets, to which he could add the twelve sewed onto his holster straps. "None to waste," he said.

Then one of the soldiers shouted that he had discovered the American's trail in the snow. The two men stopped, pointed almost directly to where he hid and started for him, their rifles ready.

At first he thought he would try to run down the ditch and hide in the line of trees but he realized the soldiers would intercept him before he could accomplish that. So he decided to stick it out where he was, and he hefted his revolver, for American pilots knew that if they were captured in this part of Korea they were usually shot.

"I'll wait till they reach that spot," he said, indicating a muddy place. "Then I'll let 'em have it." It did not occur to him that he probably wouldn't be able to hit a man ten feet away and that the spot he had selected was ridiculously remote, but fortunately he was not called upon to learn this ugly lesson, for as the two soldiers approached the point at which he was determined to fire, Joe's Banshee whirled out of the noonday sun and blasted the communists. Then, with a wailing cry, it screamed to rendezvous with Cag for the flight back to the *Savo*.

From his filthy ditch, Harry watched the mysterious and lovely jets stream out to sea and cried, "I'd sure like to be going with you." They were supreme in the sky, these rare, beautiful things, slim-lined, nose gently dipping, silver canopy shining in the sun. Once he had been part of those jets and now, huddling to earth, he was thankful that he had known the sweeping flight, the penetration of upper space, the roaring dive with g's making his face heavy like a lion's, and final exultant soaring back to unlimited reaches of the sky. Then, as they disappeared completely, he pictured them entering the landing circle and he thought, "It would be fun, heading in toward Beer Barrel right now." Then he dismissed the jets.

He was determined to find a better refuge before new communists arrived, for the smell in this ditch was becoming too strong to tolerate, but when he did start to run toward the trees he saw four people standing there. Quickly he brandished his revolver at them, but they must have known he could not shoot them from so far for they stood impassively watching.

They were the family from the nearest farm, a mother, father and two children, dressed in discarded uniforms and brandishing rakes. He stopped to see if they intended attacking him, but they remained still and he saw them not as Koreans but as the Japanese family that had intruded upon his sulphur bath that

morning in the Fuji-san and an unbearable longing
for his own wife and children possessed him and it was
then—there in bright sunlight in the rice field—that he
knew he would not see his family again.

He was driven from this brief reflection by the arrival of more soldiers. From the very trees to which he
was heading appeared eleven guards, shouting in Korean, so he hastily dived back to his stinking ditch
where they could not hit him. They launched a me-
thodical encircling attack but before they could bring
him under fire four F4U's appeared overhead, called in
by Cag to protect the downed pilot until rescue operations could begin.

Using Brubaker as their focus point, the slow propeller planes established a four-leaf clover in which each
flew a big figure eight with such perfect timing as to
have one plane coming in over Brubaker at all times,
with alternate planes commanding different sectors
of land so that no enemy dare approach.

The very first run enabled the F4U men to spot the
eleven communists, and with sharp fire they tied the
soldiers down. In the respite Brubaker thought, "With
such cover a helicopter might make it," and he began
to hope. Then, thinking to find a better spot from
which to dash to the copter if it should arrive, he
started to move out, but the Korean family saw him
and thought he was moving toward them, so they withdrew. The F4U man responsible for this sector spied the
Koreans, saw their tattered uniforms and roared upon
them, his guns ablaze.

"No!" Brubaker screamed.

"No! No! No!" He waved his arms, jumped wildly to
divert the F4U.

But the pilot could not see him. Focusing his sights grimly at what he knew to be the enemy, he brought his fiery guns a few yards from the faces of the Korean family. For one ghastly moment he thought two of the soldiers might have been children, but by then he was far away, roaring back into the four-leaf clover.

Sick, Harry Brubaker stood in the ditch and thought of his own daughters, and his heavy body was cold with much sweat.

He was standing thus when the helicopter appeared. It had lumbered in from the scow, dodging ground fire and flying so low that a revolver bullet could have destroyed it. Smack in the middle of the rice field it landed and Mike Forney got out. He wore his green top hat, a new Baron von Richthofen scarf of Japanese silk and a carbine. Behind him stumbled sad-faced Nestor Gamidge, also with a carbine. Leaving Gamidge at the copter, Forney ran across the rice field shouting, "Relax, Harry! Everything's under control."

Brubaker shouted, "Better dodge and duck."

"Why, is there a war goin' on?"

"Look!" He pointed toward the trees and as he did so a volley of machine-gun fire spattered the helicopter. Gamidge fell to the ground but rolled over several times and indicated that he was all right, but above his head the helicopter burst into flames.

Forney jumped into the ditch and turned back to watch the fire in silence. No other copter would come onto this field. With flames of noon in their eyes the two men in the ditch looked at each other, unable to speak. Then slowly Mike pulled his right foot up.

"Harry," he asked. "Is this what I think it is?"

"Yep."

Scornfully he said, "You sure picked a wonderful place to fight a war." Then he shrugged his shoulders and growled, "We might as well get Nestor in here. Three of us can stand those apes off for days."

He hefted his carbine nonchalantly and started across the rice field to convoy Gamidge but when the sallow-faced Kentuckian stood up, communist bullets chopped him in the chest and he fell. Mike, still wearing his green hat, blasted the line of trees in pathetic fury, for he must have known his carbine could not carry so far. Then he ran forward to where Nestor lay but soon he crawled back to the stinking ditch and tried not to look at Harry.

"Is he dead?"

"Yep."

In silence the two men tried to build protection for their faces, but when they reached into the ditch for stones, an evil smell arose, so that Forney stared back at the ditch and muttered, "I could have picked a better . . ." Then he said bitterly, "They were goin' to give Nestor a medal."

"Why'd you bring the copter in here, Mike?"

"I take care of my men, sir."

"How is it aboard the scow?" Brubaker phrased the question so as to imply that Forney would be returning there when this day was over.

"It's fair, but carrier duty spoils you."

"I liked the *Savo*," Brubaker said, and when referring to himself he used the completed tense, surrendering hope.

Forney caught this and said, "You know what kills me right now? Thinking of Kimiko going to bed with that ape from the *Essex*."

"That would be tough," Brubaker agreed.

The two men looked up at the F4U's and Forney asked, "How much longer will they be able to stay?"

"Not long," Harry replied.

"Well, we got nothin' to worry about. The jets'll be back."

Harry said, "This morning I had a chance to watch jets in action. They're terrific."

"Look at those apes," Mike said, pointing to where communists were starting to move in. From time to time accurate rifle fire pinked the top of the mound and Brubaker thought ruefully of people back in Denver who visualized communists as peasants with pitchforks who overran positions in mass attacks.

"Those guys know what they're doing," he said.

"But they don't know what they're gonna meet!" Mike laughed. Then he suddenly looked at Harry and said, "Why didn't you tell me you didn't have a carbine." And before Brubaker could stop him, he dashed across the rice field, grabbed Nestor Gamidge's carbine and stripped the dead man of ammunition. Two F4U's, seeing what Mike was doing, roared low and held the communists off while the Irishman dodged and ducked his way back to the ditch.

"Boy, now they'll know something hit 'em!" he cried as he jammed the weapon into Harry's hands.

Realization that Mike intended to battle it out here made Harry shiver and he asked, "You think there's any chance they'd allow us to surrender?"

"Those apes?" Mike asked.

The two Americans piled the last rocks before their faces and Harry asked, "Why do you hate them so much?"

"Simple. One Sunday morning in the cathedral I heard the cardinal explain it all," Mike said. A bullet zinged into the mud behind them and Mike grabbed Brubaker's arm. "You understand, sir, I came out here to save you. I don't want to die. There was a fightin' chance or I wouldn't have come. But now we're here, let's go down really swingin'."

He watched one of the communists creep forward for a better shot. "Don't fire too soon at these apes," he whispered. He kept his hand on Harry's arm for at least two minutes. Then, just as the enemy soldier got into position Mike blasted him right in the face. When Mike looked back he saw that Brubaker was busy with his hip knife, slashing away in his poopy suit.

"What are you doin'?" the Irishman exploded.

"Letting some air in."

"Have you gone nuts, sir?"

"Ever since I climbed into my first poopy suit I've been weighed down. I've been sweating and unable to breathe. Like a zombie. Today I want to feel like a human being." He stripped away large chunks of his burdensome gear and stood reasonably free. "I feel better already," he said.

Mike was sure the lieutenant had gone off his rocker but there wasn't anything he could do about it so he laughed and said, "I'm the same way. I couldn't fight these apes without my green hat."

"Why do you wear that?" Harry asked.

"I want people to know I'm around."

"That's what you told the captain. But what's the real dope?"

Mike stopped, looked frankly at Brubaker and said, "When I was a kid we lived. . . ." He stopped abruptly and asked, "Tell me the truth, sir, wasn't that captain a pathetic ape?"

"The way he used windmill all the time."

"In about three minutes now," Mike said, pointing to the trees.

The communists moved slowly and with deliberate plan. Four of them came in from the south, three from the mountain quarter. "I'm gonna keep my eye on those four out there," Mike said.

Some minutes passed and there was a flurry of fire from the three soldiers in the mountain quarter but Forney yelled, "Forget them!" and he was right for the other four lunged forward and tried to overrun the ditch. Calmly Mike and Harry waited until the communists were close upon them. Then they started to fire rapidly. The communists fired back but Mike yelled, "They're crumblin'," and he chopped them down.

"That'll take care of the boys," he shouted. "Now bring on the men." But as he turned to congratulate Brubaker an unseen communist who had sneaked in from the sea quarter hurled two grenades into the ditch. One of them Mike managed to throw back but as he lifted the second it exploded and tore him apart. His body, motivated by the driving forces that had occupied his mind, stumbled forward toward the unseen enemy and pitched into the snow.

Now the sky was empty and the helicopter stood burned out in the rice field and in the ditch there was no one beside him. Harry Brubaker, a twenty-nine-year-old lawyer from Denver, Colorado, was alone in a spot he had never intended to defend in a war he had not understood. In his home town at that moment the

University of Colorado was playing Denver in their traditional basketball game. The stands were crowded with more than 8,000 people and not one of them gave a damn about Korea. In San Francisco a group of men were finishing dinner and because the Korean war was a vulnerable topic, they laid plans to lambaste it from one end of the country to the other, but none of them really cared about the war or sought to comprehend it. And in New York thousands of Americans were crowding into the night clubs where the food was good and the wine expensive, but hardly anywhere in the city except in a few homes whose men were overseas was there even an echo of Korea.

But Harry Brubaker was in Korea, armed with two carbines. He was no longer afraid nor was he resentful. This was the war he had been handed by his nation and in the noonday sun he had only one thought: he was desperately in love with his wife and kids and he wanted to see them one more time.

The memory of his family was too much to bear and for an instant he pressed his right hand across his eyes and thought, "The girls will be in the garden now. . . ."

He did not complete the picture for the hidden communist who had tossed the grenades had remained close and now with one carefully planned shot sped a bullet directly through the right hand that covered the American's face. In that millionth of a second, while ten slim Banshees roared in from the sea to resume command of the sky, Harry Brubaker understood in some fragmentary way the purpose of his being in Korea. But the brief knowledge served no purpose, for the next instant he plunged face down into the ditch.

Through the long afternoon that followed, Admiral Tarrant haunted his telephone, waiting word of the miracle that would save his son. When Mike Forney left the scow with his helicopter, the admiral had said, "Well, Mike'll get him." Then the leader of the F4U's reported the copter burning.

Now, from the clandestine broadcaster near Wonsan came the facts: "Jet plane crash. Helicopter crash. Three Americans killed by communist troops."

Shaken, the lean, hard-bitten admiral left flag plot and walked gravely to his tiny room, for he knew that he must report these facts to Nancy Brubaker, in Yokosuka. But as he stared at the paper he asked, "How do you explain to a wife that her husband has died for his nation? How do you tell that to a woman with two children?" And he thought of his own wife, sitting somewhere in a dark room knitting a child's garment . . . but it was already more than seven feet long.

The job was too much for him. Later, maybe, he would know what to write. Then he thought of the Cag, who had led this ill-starred mission. He burned with fury and summoned the Cag to him, lashing at the bullet-headed commander as soon as he appeared.

"Why was Brubaker abandoned?"

Cag's eyes were red and tired from too much flying but he controlled his nerves and said, "We kept an air cap over him."

"If one helicopter crashed, why didn't you send another?"

"Sir, it's not my job to dispatch copters. You ask for volunteers. And there are never enough Mike Forneys."

"How was Brubaker hit in the first place?"

"He was working over the dumps."

The admiral pounced on this. "What was he doing at the dumps?"

Patiently Cag explained. "Before we took off we agreed. If we get the bridges, we expend our ammo on the dumps."

Icily, from the empty bitterness of his bosom, the old man asked, "Was that wise?"

Cag had taken enough. He'd stood this angry old tyrant long enough and there was no promotion in the Navy that would make him take any more. "Admiral," he said grimly, "this was a good mission. We did everything just right. I put Brubaker in charge of the third division because I could trust him to fly low and bore in with his bombs. He did just that."

Cag, trembling with anger, rushed on, "Admiral, everybody in the air group knows that you selected Brubaker as your special charge. You do that on every command and we know why you do it. Some kid your own boy's age. So today I led your boy to death. But it was a good mission. We did everything just right. And it was your boy who helped destroy the bridges. Admiral, if my eyes are red it's for that kid. Because he was mine too. And I lost him."

The old man stood there, staring stonily at the shaking commander with the bullet head while Cag shot the works. "I don't care any longer what kind of fitness report you turn in on me because this was a good mission. It was a good mission." Without saluting he stormed from flag country, his fiery steps echoing as he stamped away.

For many hours the admiral remained alone. Then toward morning he heard the anti-submarine patrol go out and as the engines roared he asked, "Why is America lucky enough to have such men? They leave this tiny ship and fly against the enemy. Then they must seek the ship, lost somewhere on the sea. And when they find it, they have to land upon its pitching deck. Where did we get such men?"

He went out to watch the launching of the dawn strike. As streaks of light appeared in the east, pilots came on deck. Bundled like animals awakened from hibernation, they waddled purposefully to their jets. The last to climb aboard was Cag, stocky and round like a snowball. He checked each jet, then studied his own. Finally, as if there were nothing more he could do, he scrambled into his plane and waited. Majestically, the task force turned into the wind, the bull horn jangled and a voice in the gloom cried, "Launch jets."

Admiral Tarrant watched them go, two by two from the lashing catapult, planes of immortal beauty whipping into the air with flame and fury upon them. They did not waste fuel orbiting but screamed to the west, seeking new bridges in Korea.

The Best of the World's Best Books
COMPLETE LIST OF TITLES IN
THE MODERN LIBRARY

A series of handsome, cloth-bound books, formerly available only in expensive editions.

MISCELLANEOUS